ESCAPE FROM
BUBBLEWORLD
SEVEN CURVES
TO SAVE
THE EARTH

Also by Keith Skene

Shadows on the Cave Wall: a New Theory of Evolution
(2009)

Putting Colour into your Curriculum: The Protein Game,
Monkey Business and The CONMAN Simulation (2009)

KEITH SKENE

ESCAPE FROM BUBBLEWORLD
SEVEN CURVES TO SAVE THE EARTH

ARD MACHA PRESS

ARD MACHA PRESS

Published by Ard Macha Press
Ard Macha Press, 5A The Den, Letham, Angus, DD8 2PY, Scotland, UK

Printed and Bound in Great Britain by Printondemand-Worldwide.com

First printing 2011

ISBN 97809562501-2-4

TO MARION

Soul mate, soothsayer and supermum

ABOUT THE AUTHOR

Keith Skene was born in the city of Armagh in 1965. For fifteen years, he has worked as a scientist in the areas of developmental biology and evolutionary ecology and has published widely on plant, animal and ecosystem evolution, his work being translated into four languages. A former AARS Rhodes Scholar, he has carried out fieldwork in the Americas, Asia, Africa, Europe and Australia. He lectured in Natural History at the prestigious College of Life Sciences, University of Dundee in Scotland, for thirteen years, latterly as Convenor of the Board of Environmental and Applied Biology, before leaving to set up the Biosphere Research Institute, an independent think-tank on sustainability and Biosphere function. He still teaches at post-graduate level at the University of Dundee and at the University of St Andrews. Aside from biology, his burning passions are blues guitar and philosophy, which, he claims, inform each other fundamentally. Keith lives in Angus with his wife, young son and foster children.

PREFACE

This book was inspired by a series of repeated events, rather than a single inspirational moment. Time and time again, in seminars, ranging from academic conferences to public lectures, audiences have responded to my message of how we can participate in a sustainable biosphere with a common response, which goes something like this: "*It all sounds great but the world just isn't going to change its ways*". This made me think about why the world "*isn't going to change its ways*". And this book is the consequence of these thoughts.

Ultimately, we find ourselves in a place I call *Bubbleworld*. Its thin walls are transparent, and consist of how we think about things. The walls appear strong but can be broken if we wish to escape. For, ultimately, it is we who voluntarily remain within this bubble. *Bubbleworld* represents a place of isolation, selfishness, distorted thinking and artificial reality. Separated from our original context, as part of a balanced biosphere, we have lost our way and turned to ourselves for solutions.

We trace this isolation back to the Enlightenment, where we turned to human reasoning and technology to solve our problems and we set a course for a utopia, along Progress Road. Industry, economics and experimental science all came under its spell. I argue that the future of our existence does not lie in some technological innovation, in human reasoning nor in some economic miracle, but rather in something as simple as the way we think about things. It's about recognizing that we are the *Vulnerable Ones*, and that sustainability is not about human ecology, conservation biology nor green fuel. Rather the answers lie in the science of the Biosphere, whose relationships pave the way for our true salvation, as participants, rather than as destroyers. Through science, we uncover the broken relationship between humans and the rest of the Biosphere, and learn how we can re-discover our place on the planet. So join me, and let's escape from *Bubbleworld*!

Letham   KRS
August, 2011

ACKNOWLEDGEMENTS

My family are the most inspirational group of people I could ever wish to have shared so much of my life with. As well as Marion and Matthew, and my mother and father, I have been encouraged and strengthened by my cousin, Stephen Rolston, and my uncle, Brian Rolston.

A special mention must also go to Seaton Baxter, Professor of Natural Design at the University of Dundee, and a true polymath, to whom I owe a huge debt of gratitude for his support as I dedicated myself to the process of writing this book, which involved giving up my tenured position at the University of Dundee. It was with him, in February, 2010, that I first suggested the writing of a little publication entitled "*A Little Book of Curves*" which has become this somewhat larger tome! Professor Klement Rejsek and Dr Valerie Vranova, from the Mendel University in Brno, have been hugely influential and my discussions with them, on such a wide range of subjects, planted many seeds in my mind.

Marion, to whom I have dedicated this book, has allowed me to free myself from the salaried world of Academia, in order to focus on writing and studying independently. She has embraced downsizing economically with great enthusiasm! I couldn't have done any of this without her, and she has also been a huge help in copy-editing and defensive editing. The hens (such reliable layers!) deserve a mention here, for providing free breakfast for us every morning! It is fun to live out some of the theory that I write about, although we have some way to go. But it's all about heading in the right direction. After all, before you can stop, you need to decelerate. However that involves everyone who is travelling in the same vehicle, so to Marion, my fellow passenger, I owe so much!

I wish to acknowledge the many readers of my previous work, who encouraged me to write some more. You've only got yourselves to blame! Finally, to all of you who have bought this book, I hope you enjoy it!

A ROUGH GUIDE TO THIS BOOK

A few reviewers mentioned that my first book had not presented evidence for some of its claims. The evidence was there, in the shape of over two hundred papers and books, but I now recognize that I should have signposted it more clearly. To avoid this accusation again, I have carefully cited the evidence throughout this book. All citations refer to the versions viewed by me, so, for example a book may have been first published much earlier than the version cited here.

Using papers mostly from only the world's leading journals (*Nature, Science, Proceedings of the Royal Society of London and Proceedings of the National Academy of Sciences, USA*), all central points are fully supported. To allow you to check on this evidence for yourself, and to expand your knowledge on any of the many themes touched upon, I have cited the relevant sources in the text, and then provided references at the end of each section.

I have also added additional reading for the inquisitive reader. All of these are available from the British Library, but you can access electronic versions of at least the abstracts of the papers through any search engine on the internet. To do this, just type the title of the paper or book as a search. Some search engines have specialized academic search sections, such as *Google Scholar*, which will allow for more specific searches. Local libraries may be able to order books for you if you ask. Finally, university libraries have electronic access to most journals.

There are three specialist appendices, for those interested in more detail, but these are optional extras, which, in places contain some intermediate mathematics.

CONTENTS

SECTION I AN INTRODUCTION

"Everywhere is the wind of heaven; round and above all are boundless sea and sky, infinite space and a great silence. The dweller there is ever listening for he knows not what, feeling unconsciously that he is in the antechamber to something yet more vast which is just beyond his ken."

– Katherine Routledge, *The Mystery of Easter Island*, 1919

Chapter One
Musings on a Rock Face

Evolution can be a very cruel thing, she reflected, as she looked down at the misshapen heap of flesh and bone lying at the bottom of the rocky crag. He'd lost his grip, and lay defeated, exhausted from days of dragging his heavy torso over a terrain completely unsuited to his design. Having said that, there were not, really, any habitats that this odd-looking beast could properly call home. For he represented a mishmash of ideas borrowed from many inspirations, none optimal for its task, and ruled over by a brain that spent more of its time consumed with the past than the future, and with competition and control, rather than with context and community. So many neurons, so little understanding!

Yet the broken body lying far below was a relative of hers. Their families were one, far in the distant past. Of course, all of life could trace its lineage to the sea originally, for it was in the oceans that life had begun, protected from the damaging radiation of the Sun, surrounded in water and bathed in nutrients. From the chaotic world of the amino acids, to the arrival of an ordered coding system, and from the creative power of bacterial gene-swapping syndicates through to the much more conservative domain of the Eukaryotes, the bulk of the journey had been made under water.

Dramatic changes had occurred in this watery realm. Organisms had turned their gaze to the Sun for energy, instead of relying on hydrothermal vents. The splitting of water to drive photosynthesis, releasing oxygen, was another huge event, in hindsight, which ushered in the protective ozone envelope around the Earth, thus opening access to the planet's surface, while catastrophically poisoning many anaerobic organisms at the same time. Oxygen was the classic waste product, the first and greatest life-driven pollution event, and the liberator of a new direction for life all at the same time. One anaerobic prokaryote's toxin is another aerobic prokaryote's oxidative respiration.

Their joint lineage had survived five mass extinctions, and many more minor ones. Together they had acquired a nucleus, requisitioned a notochord, transformed their gills from feeding organs to breathing units and replaced cartilage with calcium. They had evolved a vertebral column and crawled onto land on four limbs. Together they had transitioned from amphibians to early reptiles, and together their ancestors developed the amniotic egg. They had solved the problems of air breathing in different ways, each with lungs, but, of course, the bird lung was structurally and functionally far superior to the mammalian lung.

Eventually they had gone their separate ways, subtly at first, then more dramatically. Yet because their history was shared for so long, functionally they remained very similar. Differences in form can mask a unity of purpose, the common ground lost in a fog of shape-shifting shadows. Both became bipedal. While one went for hairs, another went for feathers, and while one went for beaks, initially with teeth but later toothless, another continued to explore dentition. Yet both of them became warm-blooded, and both were crowned kings and queens of the terrestrial world.

The massive destruction at the end of the Cretaceous period, sixty-five million years ago, provided both of their lines with the opportunity to take centre stage, expanding and diversifying into the liberated ecological space cleared by this vast erasure of other lineages (Feduccia, 2003), particularly those reptiles, both flying and terrestrial. The dramatic, climatic disruption of the Late Eocene and the onset of the *Great Drying* at the end of the

Miocene, bringing with it the expansion of the savannas and the disappearance of shallow coastal seas, had significant impacts upon both of their evolutionary directions (Janis, 1993).

So much shared history, and yet here on the rocks of Moto Nui, a kilometre south west of Rapa Nui (Easter Island), they stare at each other in the bloody end-game for this particular pair of distant relatives. One of her eggs is held in the grasp of his magnificent pentadactyl forelimb, with its ingenious opposable thumb that, together with his swollen cerebral cortex, represent his greatest gifts and his most deeply cutting flaws.

The ability to think in such an isolated way, to ignore all the pleading calls of the Biosphere that urge patience, compromise and non-intervention, and to single-mindedly set out on paths that inevitably lead to destruction, in combination with the hand to translate these thoughts into deeds, is a devastating combination. The hand can rock a cradle, but that same hand can set a spear on its deadly trajectory. This is the hand which strikes a slave, which comforts a child, which fells a forest, which plants a vineyard, which drains a wetland, which sketches a *bauplan*, and which poisons an entire planet.

This hand, so perfect in its engineering, so sensitive and tactile, so capable of consolation and so able to lift up the weary, has been wired into a control chamber, separated from the rest of the building, bridges burnt and all portals firmly shut. Humans have become like a city on a hill, whose decision-making is terminally compromised by its denial of its context, like some cancerous growth, whose success in replication and expansion seems to signify achievement and progress, yet whose existence poses a significant threat to the greater whole. It was no surprise that the kin of this wretched beast would one day claim that genes themselves were selfish.

The only selfish beings on this planet are those who have rejected their part in the scheme of things, who have denied their true identity, and who now suffer under the illusion that selfishness is a foundation stone for life. You cannot be selfish unless you consider yourself as separate from the rest, and this, sadly, is a condition unique to the creature, one of whom lies, bleeding below. Separation leads to selfishness, and selfishness leads to destabilization.

Even as the veil of death approaches, he cradles the fragile shell from the savage impact of the rocks that have ripped and crushed the rest of his body, placing the egg above his own welfare and survival. This unfortunate creature at last finds some peace, the pain numbed by a surge of enkephalins and endorphins, as his internal pharmacy prescribes a final dose of morphine mimics.

He allows himself a smile. The smooth ovoid trophy that he grasps allows him to release himself to the entropic universe, his battle over, his target achieved. He was, after all, the first one to find the egg of a *Manutara* bird on the islet of Moto Nui. And just before he fell, he had yelled across the one thousand metres of shark-infested sea, to the ceremonial site at the village of Orongo, perched high on the edge of the Rana Kao volcano on the main island, where most of the human population had gathered to see who would win the race.

It was the ultimate challenge of strength, agility and, it had to be said, luck, both in terms of evading the great white sharks during the twenty-five minute swim each way and in stumbling on an egg before anyone else. Some said that ancestral spirits would lead you to the egg. He had never really believed this. Of course, he had not voiced this heretical thought to anyone!

No, there was a slice of luck in the whole thing. Indeed the more he thought about it, as he often had, there was a slice of luck about almost everything in life. Mind you, he never had won the egg race. And he wasn't feeling all that lucky in his present state. A dying voice in his head diffidently reminded him of this. Maybe the spirits were needed?

So for the last two weeks, having swum out with all the others searchers to this small remnant of the great volcanic event that, millions of years ago, had created this islet, and to where the birds now had returned on their annual migration, he'd set out each day in an attempt to be the first of his cohort to find that illusive prize, the egg of the Manutara. As he'd searched the rocky surface of this small islet, at first trying to allow the spirits to speak to him and guide him to the treasure, he reverted to a more logical, systematic search, covering the surface in a grid-like way.

And that's how he'd found the little tern, sitting on her egg, in a shallow indent in the rock. Unlike many of the other birds who had nested on the grassy slope, this one had found a spot on the edge of the cliff face. The white ovoid jewel peeped from under the bird. It was neither the spirits nor luck that had taught him to look for the tell tale sign of the soft feathers scattered around the nest. The mother bird would rid herself of the fluffy down feathers on her underside in the area of her body that would be in physical contact with her eggs. It is known as the brood patch, allowing the heat of her blood vessels just under the skin to transfer more efficiently to the eggs.

And when you saw these feathers, you knew an egg was there. His father had told him this family secret, and, indeed, it had been passed down through his lineage for generations. In fact the observation had been first discovered by his great- great-grandfather, and had given his line the edge in many a hunt. The reputation of his family was such that they were always chosen to take part in the annual event.

The screams of the thousands of birds around him slowly faded. They had returned from the land of his ancestors, and affirmed the continuity of his lineage, reborn since that first primeval creation, returning each spring equinox to nest and lay their eggs, part of the greater picture of nature's birth, death and resurrection.

For though he had been born into a place, in time and space, where his race had damaged nature, he knew, deep down, that he was part of a much more all-embracing dance, where identity was not found in him or his species alone, but rather in the entirety of nature, and in the creed of the Cosmos. The invisible hand, not of macro-economics, but of the wider universe, reached into each of its members, and ordered each as they should be. He finally understood his part in all of this, and the part of all of this in him.

Chapter Two
Rapa Nui: Hardships in Paradise

Rapa Nui, or Easter Island, as it has become known in English, thanks to the Dutchman, Jakob Roggeveen, who "*discovered*" it on Easter Sunday, 1722, is primarily associated with its giant stone statues, the Moai. There are around three hundred of these statues at specific sites scattered across the island. A further four hundred still lie in the huge quarry, situated within the crater of the Rano Raraku volcano.

Some one hundred more of these colossal sculptures are deemed to have been discarded or destroyed *en route* along the roads that stretch from the quarry, though many of these are now thought to have been deliberately placed along these paths. The largest Moai measures ten metres in height and weighs in at around seventy-five tonnes (the weight of seven double-decker buses!). The exact significance of the Moai is debated over, and we may never know for sure. However it is thought that they represented ancient chiefs, or patriarchs, and may have acted as a means of communication between the people, their ancestral leaders and the gods.

The construction of the Moai, as confirmed by the most recent carbon dating, began near the beginning of the thirteenth century (Hunt and Lipo, 2006). It appears that most construction ended around 1600 AD (Skjølsvold, 1993; Mann *et al.*, 2008). Some argue that it continued into the nineteenth century, but it is clear that the significance of these statues changed dramatically during the eighteenth century. Roggeveen reported no damage to the Moai in 1722 (Roggeveen, 1908), and this was also the case when the Spaniard, Felipe González de Ahedo, visited in 1770 (González and Haedo, 1908). The Moai had begun to be toppled by 1774, as reported by Captain James Cook (Beaglehole, 1961).

By 1804, the Russian, Yuri Lisyansky, reported that only twenty statues remained upright. The remainder were almost all destroyed by 1825, as reported by Captain Frederick Beechey, onboard HMS Blossom. The toppling of the giant stone figures was done in a very deliberate way, with a stone being placed on the ground, upon which the statue was pushed, leading to the head breaking from the body. This was no random vandalism. These statues were murdered!

Alfred Métraux (Métraux, 1957) and Henry Lavachery (Lavachery, 1939), explorers and anthropologists, believed that statue carving persisted up to the decimation of the human population in the nineteenth century and stopped due to disease, slave raiding and religious conversion. However, given the fact that they had been toppled much earlier, as evidenced by Cook and others, it would indicate that a significant change had taken place in terms of the place of the Moai within the island's culture well before this.

Around this time, conflict increased and the leadership pattern changed. Cook reported the presence of weapons that had not been seen prior to his visit, and, in 1786, La Pérouse noted that there was no longer a chief (La Pérouse, 1997). Prior to this the royal lineage, called the *Miru*, supplied the island's leader, who acted as a religious head, and was possessed with special spiritual powers.

One of the more intriguing and bizarre pieces of evidence of significant upheaval relates to the appearance of stone-built chicken houses! A change in the material used to construct the chicken coops became apparent. Previously, chickens were kept in fairly rudimentary, thatched housing, as had been recorded by Gonzales in 1770. However, after 1786, they now lived in stone structures (Ferdon, 2000). So what led to this upgrade in accommodation? This is thought to represent an increase in the value of the chicken, and the need to secure them against theft (Bahn and Flenley, 1992).

Contemporaneously, there was also a dramatic decline in bones found in middens (rubbish deposits). Some fifty percent of the bones found in waste areas consisted of chicken bones at around 1600. This had dropped to some twenty percent by 1750, and one percent by the early 1800s (Steadman *et al.*, 1994). So the chicken, as a commodity, became an increasingly rare part of the diet. Unless there was a sudden allergy to chicken (unlikely), or widespread alektorophobia (the fear of chickens), this data would suggest that chicken numbers had fallen dramatically, and had became a precious commodity, worth building a proper stone house for.

Little clues like this give a fascinating insight into the context within which the Moai lost their eminence. Value systems were being transformed, and much of it was related to food. Energy availability (food) is the great force of change on our planet. Alter it, and you always see a significant impact upon culture. Countless civilizations across the world bear testament to the impact that a change in available energy has had, as we shall see later. Social structure, religious practice, myths and legends all chart culture transformation when resource availability changes.

In fact, it is estimated that the human population of Rapa Nui peaked between 1350 and 1450, and this was accompanied by a shift from a plant-based diet to a marine-based diet. The marine diet declined around 1650. This is evidenced not only by a decline in fish bones in the middens, but in a sharp decrease in fish hook production (Steadman *et al.*, 1994). Following this, a change in the shellfish being eaten, from the larger, preferred *Cypraea,* to the normally less-valued *Nerita (Ayres, 1985)* has been noted, again from the rubbish deposits. This change points to a population collapse of the *Cypraea,* as any other reason to move to an inferior food source would seem unlikely. So we see a human population down-shifting between energy sources.

This was unlikely to have had anything to do with new dietary fads! Seafood restaurants didn't suddenly catch on, replacing the vegetarian cafes! *Nerita* did not suddenly become the *plat du jour*. Chicken wasn't suddenly off the menu. No, these changes in diet were forced upon the islanders as they impacted negatively upon their environment. The peak in human population led to the need to find increased nutrition, and so they turned to the sea. Further degradation of the energy landscape led to the human population crashing, reflected in the later decline of fish remains.

Ongoing decline of land-based resources, and the degradation of chicken and *Cypraea* populations all reflect continuing destruction, even with a lower population of humans. The chickens, the shellfish and the fish bones chart significant changes in the wellbeing and behaviour of the humans on the island. Putting your chickens in stone buildings hints at panic, a bit like burying carbon dioxide under rocks or driving over antiseptic straw after the outbreak of Mad Cow's Disease (an airborne virus!).

Wood also became scarce. Cook reported that there were no trees taller than three metres (Beaglehorn, 1961), while the French expedition of Du Petit-Thouars, in 1838, reported that the native people asked for wood before anything else (Du Petit-Thouars, 1841). Very few canoes were noted by any of the visiting Europeans, and any that were seen were small and inadequate for pelagic fishing or long-distance travelling. They were, well-and-truly, trapped. Driftwood became treasured, and dying fathers would promise to send a tree from the afterlife for their children. Although much later in the history of the island, when the chef on the ship of the 1914 Katherine Routledge expedition first saw the island, he bemoaned *"I don't know how I am to make a fire on that island, there is no wood"* (Routledge, 1919).

So it would appear that a number of major issues had arisen, focused around food and wood, at the time when the Moai began to be toppled. These issues were mostly energy-related, in terms of food, and thus would be culture-transforming.

As the people of Rapa Nui ceased their worship and carving of the monumental Moai, petroglyphs and wall murals started to appear, showing creatures with the bodies of humans and the heads of birds: the birdmen. There are four hundred and eighty-one of these in the ceremonial village of Orongo alone. These birdmen represented avatars, or earthly manifestations, of *Makemake*. Makemake was a deity unique to Rapa Nui, found nowhere else in Polynesia. He rose to prominence along with his cult, at around the time of the toppling. He was viewed as the creator god, who was born from a skull that had floated across the sea. He created humans and guided sea birds to migrate to Rapa Nui.

The Birdman Cult was based around the appointment of one of the islanders as the Birdman, for a twelve-month period. This was decided by a competition to find the first egg of the year, laid by the migratory terns (*manutara*, or sacred birds) that visited the tiny rocky islet of Motu Nui, one kilometre southwest of the main island, every spring.

Interestingly, the head of the Birdman wasn't that of a tern, but of a frigate bird. However there were no frigate birds on the island at this time. Frigate birds nest in trees, and so it could be that the choice of a frigate bird relates to a distant memory, passed through generations, which associated this bird with a time when there was forest on the island, when things were much better. The frigate bird represented a bygone era, a golden age long lost.

Ironically, the sooty tern would, one day, end up like the frigate bird, a distant memory. In 1983, only one pair of sooty terns nested on Moto Nui, a striking contrast to the thousands of pairs from just 150 years earlier. It is what we do best – eradicate one species then move on to the next. The switch from *Cypraea* to *Nerita* echoes this. In the Southern Ocean, sperm and humpback whale populations were decimated by hunting, and so we turned to blue whales. When these declined, we turned to sie, fin and minke whales.

It is also worth noting that the sooty terns, according to legend, were placed on the little rocky islets off the coast of Rapa Nui by *Makemake*, the creator god, for their protection. This was possibly the first example of conservation biology! This also indicates that it was recognized by the islanders that the main island was not a good place to be if you had feathers and laid eggs!

Chapter Three
Shave Your Head, You Have the Egg!

The Birdman competition was an important event, because the clan from which the winner emerged would have significant privileges, particularly relating to food resources. Competitors were chosen by supernatural visions given to holy people called *ivi-atua*. Only members of the dominant clans at the time could be chosen, and, often, conflict would occur, leading up to the event, in an attempt to unseat the ruling clan and gain entry to the competition. The visions not only revealed each competitor's identity, but also the title they would be given if they won the race. This title would also be given to the following twelve-month period. So a chronology existed, based upon the names and sequence of birdmen.

Once the competitors were chosen they would each select a runner, or *hopu*, to actually do the hard work, and to represent them in the race. The competitors and their runners had already been at the foot of the volcano since the end of the last competition, the previous year, in order to ensure they were controlling the next event. In July, they, along with their supporters and others involved in the competition, would march up to the ceremonial site of Orongo.

Orongo is perched in a precarious position, on a narrow ridge. On the eastern side, there is a steep drop into the crater of the volcano, while on the western side, cliffs plunge, precipitously, into the Pacific Ocean, some three hundred metres below. The site consists of two rows of terraced huts, one above the other, facing out to sea towards three little rocky islets, the largest, most distant, being Moto Nui. The huts and pavements are still covered in drawings and stone carvings, dominated by the strange foetal figures of a creature with a bird's head and torso combined with human limbs, representing the Birdman.

Interestingly, some of these are drawn over the top of pictures of European ships in full sail, one with a sailor dressed in a red shirt. This places at least some of the Birdman drawings to a time after the first Europeans visited the Island, in 1722. It is also noteworthy that the ships are within the same context as the Birdman, both featuring at this sacred site, suggesting that these boats were held in awe.

Once at Orongo, the gathering spent their time chanting, dancing, eating and sleeping. Meanwhile the runners headed out to the tiny islet. This was challenging, to say the least. The runners had to climb down the cliffs, and then swim one kilometre across the sea to the islet of Moto Nui. They used small rafts of reeds, in which they wrapped their provisions to see them through the waiting period for the birds. These rafts are still found on the island today. They were shaped like long, straight bananas, about one and a half metres in length, and were used as floats, held in front of the swimmer. The crossing was extremely dangerous, with sharks accounting for many of the participants, while others perished in the tumultuous seas.

Moto Nui is about twenty thousand square metres in area (twice the size of the Wembley Football Stadium pitch in London), with a raised, gently sloping, grassy plateau. At its highest, it plunges some ten metres down steep cliffs to the ocean. On reaching Moto Nui, the hopu gathered in a cave, awaiting the coming of the Manutara. When the birds arrived, usually in September, the men would emerge to search for an egg.

The first one to find the prize would hold the egg sky-wards, and shout back to the crowd gathered at Orongo. He would call out the spiritual name of his leader, and then say *"Shave your head, you have got the egg"*. Just below Orongo, in a cave known as *Haka-rongo-manu* (literally, *listening for the birds*), a group of men had held a vigil since the hopu had set out on their quest, awaiting news from the islet. The news would then be relayed to the gathered throng in Orongo. The losers would return to the main island, followed by the winner, who would put the egg in a small basket and tie it to his head, before returning to Orongo and climbing up the sea cliff, where he would present the egg to his sponsor.

The winning sponsor was now proclaimed as *tangatu manu*, meaning *learned man of the sacred bird*, for the next twelve months. He literally became the avatar, or earthly representative, of Makemake. Quite a gig! However, his year was not spent in lavish style. Having, as instructed, shaved his head and painted it red, he would retreat to a hut for five months, in strict taboo, separated from his wife and with only a servant for company. He wore a crown of human hair, slept all day, and did not wash. His clan, however, benefitted hugely, gaining the rights, among other things, to the birds and eggs on Moto Nui.

The shift from the royal lineage of the Miru to the yearly rotation of leadership has been suggested to have been a response to increasingly uncertain, desperate times. As lifespan declined, then a lineage would be vulnerable to interruption. This would bring great irresolution and instability. It would be far better to switch to a short-term leadership, which would prevent such problems, or at least, reduce them.

With the Birdman Cult, a leader was certain to emerge each year, as someone would find an egg on Moto Nui eventually! Furthermore, the emphasis of the cult reflected a shift in priorities, from ancestors and lineage, to food and fertility. The egg, with all of its symbolism of rebirth, and with its food value, spoke of changing times. Energy, rather than the human, became central to their value system. The shift away from obsession with themselves and their origins was forced upon them by the recognition that their fate was not in their own hands any longer, but, rather, lay in the energetic context of their existence, the Biosphere.

Another very significant aspect, often overlooked by other studies on Rapa Nui, is that the move away from the ancestral line occurred at the same time as the foreign ships appeared. It seems to me that this must be more than a coincidence. Up until that point, there was unlikely to have been much evidence of human life elsewhere. That was all to change, and the obvious conclusion was that there was a land beyond what they could see, with people and technology completely different than what they knew. This small population, which was unlikely to have seen humans from beyond its horizons in living memory, and, quite possibly, for the five hundred years since the first humans arrived on the island, worshipped the ancestral origins of its people.

The legends spoke of the distant land from where they originally came from, and to where the migratory birds obviously went, but the human lineage was everything. They alone survived on the planet, their lineage connecting them to whatever they had come from. However, now there were others, separate lines of descent, and suddenly the sacred lineage was undermined. Surely this must have significantly weakened the claims of the ruling ancestral line, the Miru, and detracted from the ancestor worship associated with the Moai.

Since the writings of Herbert Wells (better known as H.G.Wells), in such books as *War of the Worlds*, the idea of meeting, for the first time, with an alien race has filled us with trepidation and fascination. The arrival of the Europeans in 1722, on their huge ships, which must have resembled alien spacecraft, and their similar, but much paler appearance, would have been an extraordinary experience for the islanders.

The ships themselves, huge and constructed from massive pieces of that priceless commodity, wood, must have been extraordinary sights. When nine of their people were shot dead by the Dutch, in a moment of panic, the sight and sound of a gun unloading must have been akin to fictional accounts of ray guns. The Dutch language would have been as incomprehensible as any alien tongue. We must not underestimate how big an impact all this would have had on these previously isolated people.

Could it be more than a co-incidence that the destruction of the Moai appears to have begun after European contact? Did the arrival of these *"other"* people symbolize a devastating blow to some strongly held belief? Did *first contact* signal the end of a religious structure that denied this possibility, or, in fact, relied on the absence of other human forms as a core part of their catechism? Was it a moment of revelation, undermining the political masters' authority?

The Birdman Cult was still being practiced as late as 1860. When Katherine Routledge, the English anthropologist, visited the island in 1914, to commence her landmark study, there were people alive who remembered it, and told her of the specific details. Indeed, she was able to collect the names of the previous eighty-six Birdmen (Routledge, 1919).

Her work is still referenced as the key anthropological record of Rapa Nui, and will remain so, as she worked with primary witnesses to the events surrounding the end of the Birdman Cult and the destruction of the native traditions by a combination of western religion, slavery and disease.

The story of Katherine Routledge is worthy of a book in itself, and indeed there is one, by Jo Anne Van Tilburg (2003). Her life was an extraordinary journey, taking her from a wealthy Quaker upbringing in the north-east of England, to South Africa, where she helped examine the fate of women resettled there from England after the Second Boer War.

It was while in South Africa that she met her husband and they went on to live among the Kikuyu people of British East Africa, writing a respected book on this tribe. They then commissioned a sailing boat and sailed to Rapa Nui, a journey that took a year, and exposed difficult relationships between the expedition team. On Rapa Nui, they spent seventeen months undertaking the first proper analysis of the archaeological and anthropological history of the island.

Katherine Routledge was the first female archaeologist to work in Polynesia. While there, she faced up to the might of the German Navy in 1914, which had arrived at the onset of World War I. She helped to convince them to leave! The end of her life was extremely sad, though nonetheless eventful. She would appear to have suffered from schizophrenia and in 1928, threw her husband out of their London home and barricaded herself in the building. To break the siege, her husband eventually had her kidnapped, and she saw out her days in a mental institute, dying in 1935.

Blame for this deterioration was placed on a prophetess, mystic and leader of the 1914 Rapa Nui rebellion, witnessed by Routledge, called Maria Angata Veri Tahi Pengo Hare Kohou (the islanders had wonderful names!). This, in itself, represents a fascinating counterbalance. In one respect the Europeans have pushed their culture upon the "primitive" islanders, seeking to "improve" their lot, and believing that the European culture was much more advanced and progressive than that of the islanders, whereas on the other side, there was a fear of the power of these people.

Chapter Four
Hope from the Birdman?

What, then, is the significance of Rapa Nui for the modern world, facing, as it does, significant challenges ahead? Do the lessons lie in the decimation of the ecology of the island, or is there a deeper understanding to be gained? To examine this, let's return to the Birdman Cult.

One of the interesting things about Rapa Nui is that in this, the most isolated human population on Earth, we find a cult that shares much with religious beliefs from around the world, particularly in its symbolism. We also find that there would appear to have been a shift towards this cult as times became difficult. So I want to examine the meaning of the shared symbolism in all of the other belief structures, and assess if there are common themes.

If we find such a meaning, then what does this tell us about belief, and more importantly, what does it tell us about what we do as a sub-species when things become difficult? As our planet creaks and strains under the suffrage of our reign of irresponsible and devastating abuse, can we learn anything from past civilizations that have also faced the consequences of damage in their ecology?

By examining what happened at times of stress, in terms of these belief structures, I suggest that this will give us an insight into the deeper workings of the human mind, and will point us towards a message of hope. This might seem to go against the more general trend of pessimistic humanism that persists among many ecologists and environmentalists at present. But I feel convinced that the answers to the issues we have created do exist within us, and, as we shall see from history, these answers have, previously, come to the surface when we have been most threatened.

Myths and legends are exactly that, myths and legends. However they represent an expression of human thinking, and are not completely isolated. Indeed, the reason that they establish and spread is because they make sense to lots of different people relative to the contexts that they find themselves within. I like to think of them as fossils of the human condition, rather than fossils of the human body. Ancient tales report a part of the existence of humankind from the past, just like rock fossils do.

And so the myths and legends that adorn human history allow us an insight into the thinking of humans over vast periods of time. They sketch out a part of the journey, not of matter but of mind, and along the way provide important indicators of our response to change and to stability. In the rest of this introductory section, I want to examine the Birdman Cult in more detail, as it is a journey that I feel we need to take, before examining the scientific and anthropological evidence for a new direction in sustainability.

Why take this journey? Well, the underlying hypothesis that I want to propose is that we did not evolve *within* the Biosphere, but are *part* of an evolving Biosphere. In other words, a large part of our identity is the Biosphere, and the essence of what we are is within that context. Only by operating as part of the greater whole can we hope to remain in a sustainable environment.

We originally evolved as part of this system, and deep within us lies, often locked away beneath layers of modern human thought, a positive *Pandora's Box*, with the instruction manual of how to live like a signed-up member of the Biosphere. And, boy, do we need to open it! In the original myth from Ancient Greece, when the jar was opened, evil escaped, and all that was left in the bottom of the jar was hope. In our version of *Pandora's Box*, the only thing that escapes *is* hope!

We have turned our backs on our true identity, which is shared with the greater whole, and instead have separated ourselves from this relationship. The consequence of this is that we have lost touch with the bulk of who we really are. Acting in the interests of ourselves and, at best our sub-species, we have become selfish. In this state of altered reality, where the individual is all, and the complexity of the Biosphere is reduced to a building merely made of blocks, we now destroy that which was a part of us, and of which we were a part.

As John Donne famously wrote, in *Devotions upon Emergent Occasions*, *"Never send to know for whom the bell tolls; it tolls for thee"*. The isolationist approach not only destroys our environment, but destroys our ability to understand what we do.

Reductionist thinking (which declares that a complex system is merely the sum of its parts, and therefore the study of these parts is all that is needed to understand the system as a whole) strips all thinking of its context, thus allowing us to depersonalize the destruction of the Biosphere. We now make decisions for the survival of our own species within the vacuum of selfish isolation.

So far, this is a negative message. However, I want to suggest that when the going gets tough, we have, historically, sought to reconnect to the greater whole, embracing our part in the Biosphere. There appears to be some deep-set switch that allows us to reconnect with our greater identity. This can be seen in the fossils of the mind, those legends and myths, which show how we have changed our value systems at such desperate times. And such changes have brought us back from the brink.

I have spoken to many audiences on a range of solutions for our planetary *malaise*, and a common response is to agree with me, but then shake their heads, saying that there is no hope of the human race taking up these ideas, because they would cost us and lower our standard of living. I agree wholeheartedly with them, but explain that the solutions only appear hopelessly impractical because we are living in an altered state of understanding, twisted and distorted by our selfish separation from our true identity.

By embracing who we really are, then these solutions will become the most natural thing to do. We need to transform our judgement systems. This doesn't mean swapping between capitalism and socialism, or from one religious faith to another. No. What is required is much more basic: to flee from reductionism, and embrace the greater truth about whom we are, as part of a living Biosphere.

And this is why I felt that I needed to write this particular book. The most important thing for the human race to do at present is not to invent a new kind of green power generation. It is not to reduce our carbon footprint. It is not to eat organic food, nor to give up our cars. It is not to recycle more of our tin cans or to save the giant panda. All of these things are good things to do. But what we really need to do is to rediscover our true identity, and having discovered it, to live and breathe it.

The beautiful thing is that the answers really do lie within us, and all that limits us is ourselves. Central to these answers is one word, *relationships*. We need to understand these relationships. Yet relationships are often difficult to comprehend and envisage, especially ones that have been lost, rejected or deeply buried within us.

So we will look at seven relationships that offer hope, and that point to a single solution. Now that's a claim! Each relationship is based on clear scientific evidence, and we will examine the evidence carefully. It has all been published in peer-reviewed journals, that is, the evidence has been checked and assessed by leading academics throughout the world. The vast majority of the work cited is from one of the leading journals in the scientific world: *Nature*, *Science*, *Proceedings and Philosophical Transactions of the Royal Society of London* and the *Proceedings of the National Academy of Science, USA*.

However the evidence has never been put together in this way before, and so the book you are now reading will present to you, for the first time, a new way of understanding our planet, and will apply this understanding in pursuit of one particular goal: finding our place within the world. I hope it acts as a sort of marriage guidance counsellor, aiming to help us heal our broken relationship with the Biosphere, and pointing towards a reconciliation that is essential if we are to continue to co-habit under the same roof!

This book is all about understanding relationships: the relationships of the Biosphere and the relationship between human beings and the rest of life on Earth. Once we do this, the decision making, life-changing, planet-sustaining actions we need to take will become the obvious ones, not the difficult ones. Our relationship with the Biosphere is at present distorted beyond recognition. By straightening this out, we will learn how to live. Otherwise we will effectively continue to destroy ourselves, without even realizing it.

Years of working with teams has taught me one thing: fundamentally, most problems are solved by adjusting our thinking, rather than altering our structural environment. You can repaint the office, restructure the management, re-tile the restrooms, but if the thinking of each employee is not in resonance with your own, then you will see no improvement.

The voyage may appear daunting, but it's a journey I think we need to make. And it can have a happy ending! So let's cast aside any thoughts of our destiny as a black, toasted, desperate future. This is not a book of pessimistic environmentalism. Arthur Schopenhauer painted a grim picture of a crippled man, able to see the light, but being carried by a giant. The giant represented the human will. He postulated that the act of human will would always override reason ultimately (Schopenhauer, 2007).

Peter Zapffe, the Norwegian philosopher, became the first environmental pessimist. In his book, *Om det Tragiske* (*On the Tragic*), published in 1941, he painted the human race as irreversibly separated from nature. Bill McKibben, in his dark book, *Eaarth: Making a Life in a Tough New Planet* (2010), suggests that the planet is irrevocably broken. James Lovelock's thinking has become significantly darker of late, and in his most recent book, released in 2009, *The Vanishing Face of Gaia: A Final Warning: Enjoy It While You Can*, he states that *"There is only a small chance that... we could reverse climate change."*

I will argue that there can be light at the end of the tunnel, and the cripple can break free and move towards it. Not only is a positive outcome conceivable, but the statement of it is essential. If we submit to being carried along by the giant that is our will, as Schopenhauer claims (Schopenhauer, 2007), then there is no point in struggling. We're going to go where the giant wants, so we may as well sit back, turn up the air-conditioning and kill another species or two. What's the point?

Pessimism breeds *ennui*. It is the bedfellow of apathy. By suggesting that there is no hope, we leave the people of the world as slaves to their fate, like the dispossessed in a totalitarian state or the exiled in a foreign land. Of course, if there really is no hope, then it would be equally wrong to offer some fictitious promise and falsely raise expectations.

However, if there is any hope, then the people need to hear about it, in order to at least have the opportunity of breaking free from the powerless state of listlessness, from the vice-like, clammy grasp of that giant, and run towards the light. My position is one of *positive realism*, which I define as recognizing who we are, and then being who we are. Recognition requires an understanding of our place in the grand scheme of things. By being, I mean taking our place, positively, within this scheme. And this book ultimately identifies what this grand scheme is.

So let's make a start. Before launching out into the big seven relationships, we need to return to our island, and reflect on the Birdman Cult.

Chapter Five
The Global Birdman

I want to examine the global significance of the Birdman Cult in order to establish if the components represent more than just a local tale. Rather, do they speak to us of a more general relationship between ourselves and the planet we live on? This broader, comparative approach also seeks to avoid the danger of constructing a pyramid upside down. In other words, I want to avoid building a huge theory on a single island system. Instead, with the pyramid the right way up, we start with a broad, comparative base, and see where that takes us.

In particular, I want to search for the occurrence of the Birdman icon, the bird and the egg in the mythologies of other cultures from around the world, stretching back an amazing seventeen thousand years. By understanding the context of these symbols within their historic settings, I suggest that there is a very significant message for us today. This message is all to do with the relationship between ourselves and the rest of the living planet.

The Birdman Cult represents an example of our response to a changing world, and as such, gives us an insight into who we actually are. It tells a story of a deeply fundamental, but forgotten view of our place in the world. That view was part of what we were when we initially evolved, because we were, originally, extensions of the Biosphere. Not made by it, or from it, or for it, but rather as part of it.

And when disasters come, and crises hit, we often talk of "*hidden depths*" being discovered. These depths, I suggest, represent part of who we really are. And that identity lies at the heart of a meaningful future, individually and as a species. Mythology often allows an expression of these things now mostly lost to the Western World. So before we examine the science of this relationship, let's go looking for some ancient clues to our modern conundrum: how to be part of a sustainable Biosphere.

As we have seen, the birdman of Rapa Nui was the avatar, or representative of Makemake, the creator god. Makemake is a unique deity to this island. This avatar had the head of a frigate bird, itself long extinct from the island, most probably because of over-hunting and the disappearance of suitable trees for nesting. This combination of an animal and a human in union is a common symbol throughout the history of humankind, and the birdman motif is particularly widespread.

Often the head is human and the body is avian. The *Sirens* and *Harpies* of Ancient Greece, and *Sirin* and *Gamayun* from Russian folklore, all have female human heads. *Nike*, *Boreas* and *Eros* are humans with bird wings, while the *Faravahar*, the symbol of Zoroastrianism of ancient Iran, took the form of a winged disc, with a human head in later versions. Angel-like figures from many religions have winged human forms.

The Msangwini rock shelter of Swaziland has winged human forms painted on its walls. A Mesopotamian beast, *Lamassu*, went one stage further, having the head of a human, the wings of a bird and the body of a bull! Quite a combination! However, I want to limit our investigation to birdmen of the same sort as are found at Easter Island, those with a human body and a bird head. We shall find that these birdmen are prevalent in many important mythologies, and, indeed, would appear to be the earliest mythical creatures ever to be recorded by humans.

Chapter Six
When Robot the Dog Went Missing

On Sunday, 8th September, 1940, four young lads in a small village in Western France were oblivious to the great events that were unfolding around them, unaffected by the recently signed Vichy Agreement between France and Germany. They had attended Mass, and now they had the rest of the day free. They grabbed some bread, cheese and a bag of freshly picked apples, and headed out together with Robot, the ever-inquisitive terrier dog. Sixth months earlier, France had been invaded by Germany, and the nation was now divided into three zones, the occupied zone to the North and West, the Free Zone in the South, and the Italian Occupation in the far South-East. Yet on this Sunday morning, life in the Free Zone felt just like it always had done.

However, this particular Sunday was not going to be like any normal day. These young lads were on the edge of making a discovery that would have a huge impact on our understanding of human origins and of the Birdman of Easter Island. They were about to be transported seventeen thousand years back in time.

The story of the discovery of the Lascaux caves and the Birdman of provincial France, over sixty years ago, is Blytonesque to its core, and brings together inquisitive humans separated by millennia. It was to provide the clearest evidence of what Georges Bataille, the French writer, reflecting on Lascaux, called *"the basic desire of all men, of whatever period or region, to be amazed"* (Bataille, 1979).

Marcel Ravidat, Jaques Marsal, Georges Agnel and Simon Coencas had grown up in and around the idyllic, small Aquitaine village of Montignac, built on the banks of the Vézére River, and owing much of its existence to its old bridge, an important crossing point for traders and travellers alike. Many fine medieval, half-timbered merchant houses recalled six hundred years of business.

This idyllic rural setting provided ample space for play and exploration for children. Their creative minds had latched on to rumours of a secret tunnel, connecting the Chateau de Montignac, a thousand year old ruin, with the Manor of Lascaux. From this tunnel, so the story went, a second tunnel led under the river, in which was stored buried treasure. Occasionally they would search the woodlands, pretending to be treasure hunters looking for pirates' treasure.

Robot the dog was always in the middle of things, running hither and thither, sniffing and digging amongst the undergrowth. On this particular Sunday, just at the end of *les grandes vacances* of the summer of 1940, they were walking through the pine woodland on the east bank of the river, above the Manor of Lascaux, when the boys suddenly realized that Robot had disappeared.

One minute the dog was there in front of them, and the next, he was gone. Searching around, they came on a depression in the terrain, where a huge pine tree had fallen and its roots had ripped the earth away. They remembered the terrible storm three years earlier, that had wrecked havoc with natural and man-made structures alike. In the silence of this tranquil Sunday, they heard a faint whimpering coming from the collapsed pit in front of them. Looking more closely, they realized that there was a hole, about the size of a big saucepan lid. Robot had fallen into it!

One of the boys remembered the treasure story, and so they excitedly started to widen the hole, digging with sticks, and then just using their bare hands, a bit like how Robot would do it. Soon the hole was big enough for them to slide through, and so, one at a time, they squeezed through, into a world that had remained hidden for many thousands of years. They were in a shaft and could hear Robot barking from below.

After fifteen metres, they emerged into a cave, and looked around. As their eyes adjusted to the darkness, they couldn't believe what they saw. They were surrounded by huge paintings of monstrous cows, horses and unicorns, frozen in a dance that had begun seventeen thousand years ago, when humans from a different age had drawn them on the cave walls. The dizzying kaleidoscope of prehistoric fauna resembled a modernist style. Yet this was some of the oldest art ever created by early humans.

The boys couldn't see far, so they grabbed Robot, climbed back through the tunnel and emerged into the bright light. They vowed to return and swore to keep it a secret. After all, the buried treasure could be down there! A few days later, they came back, this time with lanterns and a rope, and explored further. No treasure, but what an incredible collection of beautifully painted Palaeolithic art confronted them. They finally resolved to tell their teacher, Monsieur Laval. He was obsessed with cave paintings, a member of the Prehistoric Society of Montignac, and loved nothing more than talking about the ancient times. He was the one to trust with their secret.

At first, Léon Laval wasn't at all keen to go into the forest, let alone climb down a narrow hole, suspecting that the boys, who definitely had a mischievous side, were tricking him. They'd never, it appeared, been interested in this kind of thing. But he decided that their enthusiasm and, indeed, tangible fear, were likely not to be a ruse.

And he was right. He recognized the cave paintings for what they were: some of the greatest pre-historic finds ever to have been made. Soon, he had alerted France's foremost expert, Abbé Henri Breuil, the so called *"Pope of Palaeolithic Prehistory"*. Word quickly spread. Within a few months, the Cubist painter, Pablo Picasso, one of the great innovators of modern art, reflected, on leaving the cave, that *"We have invented nothing"*, such was the quality of the work on display. He cannot have failed to have noted the frequent use of twisted perspective, where faces appear in two different perspectives at the one time, an approach often taken by Picasso to great effect.

Chapter Seven
Lascaux, and the Oldest Birdman of Them All

That these caves belong to a different time completely is brought home by the creatures that populate its walls. It is estimated that the woolly rhinoceros went extinct in this area around nineteen thousand years ago, and so their recoding must have been near the end of this time. The auroch, ancestor of our domestic cattle, is no longer with us, the last one dying in Jaktorów Forest, Poland, in 1627 (Grubb, 2005). Other creatures, such as the ibex, bear and big cats (possibly lions) no longer exist in France.

Yet when the artists worked in these caves, all of these animals must have formed a significant part of the local fauna. Of equal interest were the animals that were not portrayed. Woolly mammoths would have been extinct by this time. They appear in the Chauvet Caves, a relative stone's throw away, which date back thirty-two thousand years, and the disappearance of them as part of the fauna is recorded by their absence in Lascaux.

The legend had said that the tunnel would lead to a second tunnel with treasure, and, in many ways, this was true of Lascaux. The *Rotunda of the Bulls*, with its massive paintings, including the largest known single figure, a five metre-long auroch, narrows into the *Axial Gallery*, which feels like walking inside a giant snake, with its undulating ceiling resembling a serpentine ribcage. The surfaces of the Axial Gallery are festooned with horses, ponies, ibex, and yet more aurochs, and, finally, *the Upside-down Horse* and *the Falling Cow*, titles that would seem more appropriate in the wonderland of Alice!

Turning right after the *Rotunda of the Bulls,* another corridor stretches into the distance. The *Great Black Cow* and the *Crossed*

Bison lie further up there, along with two mating lions. Turning right after entering this corridor, the scene changes again. This is the *Apse*, and it was clearly a very important site to the early humans who gathered here.

Testifying to this was the discovery of a number of ceremonial ornaments, watched over by the *Major Stag* who has stared down in darkness upon the remnants of early human religion for the last seventeen millennia. Its walls and domed ceiling are covered in over one thousand symbols and figures, the most intense artistry in the entire cave system. Clayton Eshleman, poet and cave art expert, describes it as *"Lascaux's "holy of holies," it evokes a primordial star map, as well as a visual pun-filled labyrinth, a kind of Upper Paleolithic Finnegan's Wake"* (Eshleman, 2010).

Yet the *Apse* is not the end of it. Going further on, the cave suddenly drops dramatically, falling four metres. A ladder is needed to descend into its deepest secret, the *Shaft of the Dead Man*. Indeed, fragments of ancient rope have been found, down which an artist may have descended in that bygone age, to draw what is the most mysterious and extraordinary scene in palaeolithic art. Examine it for yourself by searching for *"shaft of the dead man"* in *Google Images*.

On the wall to the left of the bottom of the ladder is a scene that has puzzled experts since its discovery. It contains the only human-like representation in the entire cave. A powerful, muscular auroch with hair erect and two elegantly curving horns stands at the right hand side, head turned towards the viewer and angled as if beginning a charge (there has been much debate as to whether this is a bison or an auroch. Taking into account the twisting horns, I will go with the auroch, as bison have horns that bend at right angles, but do not twist. Given the accuracy of the woolly rhinoceros, I will give the artist the benefit of any doubt regarding the detail he has captured).

A broken spear appears to enter the belly of the auroch, and its intestines hang out from the gaping wound. On the left hand side, a woolly rhinoceros has turned its back to the auroch, its shadowy, powerful profile almost disappearing into the rock, but details of its huge front horn (known to be one metre long from fossils) and shorter secondary horn are clearly visible.

Sandwiched between the two great palaeolithic beasts is a human figure with a bird head, its beak clearly visible. That's right, a birdman! This represents the oldest representation of a birdman, by some considerable distance, on our planet. He is in a state of sexual arousal, but appears to be falling back from the auroch. Below him is a stick with a bird on top of it, facing the rhinoceros. Unlike the man, who is at an angle, the stick is vertical.

We will never know, of course, what the significance of the birdman of Lascaux really is. But what we do know is that it is there, sandwiched between two great beasts of the Palaeolithic, seventeen thousand years ago, and celebrates the union of bird and man in one form, millennia before its later representations.

Given that all of the other creatures in the caves of Lascaux are extremely accurate depictions of animals, the single slender figure of the birdman stands out from the crowd. This is not for its artistic merit, for it is one of the least detailed drawings in the system, but, rather, because it is the only truly mythical beast, half-bird half-man, and the oldest such creature to be found in the history of humankind. Indeed it predates *The Sorcerer*, a part-man, part-stag, from the Chauvet system, by two thousand years.

The Birdman of Lascaux marks the birth of mythology, fiction and fantasy.   Furthermore, it signals that the imagination and creativity that would beautify the otherwise often repellent and destructive tenure of our race on this planet, was present at the bottom of a rocky shaft, deep in a cave system in south-west France, all those years ago.

Chapter Eight
Other Birdmen

The Birdman appears in many other ancient mythologies. Dating back four thousand years ago, in Eagles Reach, one hundred and sixty kilometres south-west of Sydney, Australia, aboriginal birdmen appear on the cave walls. The Aborigines believe that these composite creatures represent ancient ancestors, and are not painted by humans, but rather are created by the ancestral spirit settling on the rock face. In Asia, the Birdman is best known as *Garuda*, of Hindu origin, a half-man, half-eagle, representing the blazing rays of the Sun, and acting as Vishnu's avatar, or representative. In the Sanskrit epic of ancient India, many tales of the Garuda are told, including the moment of its birth. Upon hatching from its egg, the power of the event was such that the gods beseeched that he had mercy on them.

Garuda formed the inspiration for a number of other similar figures throughout Asia. It was adopted by Buddhism, and is found throughout Asia, from the temples of *Angkor Wat* to the national symbol of Indonesia and Thailand. The *Karura* of Japan is of the same origin. It is a huge, fire-breathing creature, again with the face, or beak, of an eagle. In China, the birdman is known as the *Great Peng*, an illuminated king with golden wings. In Mongolia, it is called *Khangarid*.

In Ancient Egypt, *Thoth* was a birdman, the god of knowledge and the enumerator of the stars (a busy job!). As with most deities in Ancient Egypt, interpretation depends on which school of thought you follow. Thoth can be viewed as a separate and important deity, in a polytheistic model, or as a representation of the heart and tongue of the sun god, *Ra*, in a monotheistic model. Whichever way we interpret the deities of Egypt, Thoth was extremely significant. *Horus*, another Ancient Egyptian god, of the king, sky and vengeance, was a birdman, having the appearance of a falcon-headed human.

In the Americas, we find one of the most stunning birdmen, in the Peruvian city of Túcume, an ancient city eight hundred kilometres north of Lima in Peru, in the lower La Leche Valley. It lies at the base of a hill called Cerro de la Raya. A collection of twenty-six pyramids made of adobe (a mixture of clay, sand, water and straw or manure) encircle the hill. One of them, the massive *Huaca Larga*, is the largest adobe structure in the world, with a length of seven hundred metres, a width of two hundred and eighty metres and a height of thirty-five metres (Narváez, 2001). As a result of the building material used, the pyramids have suffered badly from weathering over the thousand-odd years since their construction.

This site was occupied by successive civilizations, ending, as so much of the rich history of South America did, when the Spanish invaded. Evidence of building on the site exists for the Lambayeque (or *Sican*) people of the 11th century. The Lambayeque civilization lasted from around 500 AD to 1375 AD. In its Middle Period, it produced beautiful ceramics and metalwork, particularly funerary masks. It also developed the use of arsenical copper, which is much more resilient than pure copper.

However its engineering prowess was also displayed in a large system of canals, thought to be used for agricultural irrigation, and in the pyramids, such as at Túcume. The flourishing middle period of the Lambayeque is thought to have come to an end due to a drought that lasted thirty years, leading to the destruction of their capital city, Baton Grande. It was in the recovery from this disaster that Túcume was constructed, as the new capital city. And to reflect the concern about another drought, this time the

Lambayeque didn't leave things to chance, building a canal, which stretched for forty-three kilometres, to counteract any future shortage of water.

The rebirth of the civilization after this catastrophic natural disaster is fascinating. The religious emphasis shifted towards more traditional relationships with nature, including the use animals and a birdman. These animalistic deities had existed in more ancient times, but had been lost in the heady days of the middle period. Now, when the going got tough, animal images again began to play important roles in the murals and other art and craft.

This is uncannily like what occurred at Rapa Nui, with the Birdman Cult coming to the fore, following whatever disruption that led to the toppling of the Moai. Even more fascinating is the fact that one of these animal gods was of a particular form, half-human and half-bird. Discovered in one of the most weather-worn of all the pyramids, ravaged by *el Nino* events across the intervening centuries, the *Huaca las Balsas* (literally, *the mound of the rafts*, from *Balsa*, the Spanish word for a floating raft), is a high relief frieze, and contains an amazing scene. A birdman stands on a raft, with a bird beside him! Indeed there are a number of portrayals of birdmen framing the central scene, and often they are holding an egg. Here in one frieze we find all of the central components of the Birdman Cult of Rapa Nui.

Around eight hundred years ago, in Gullickson Glen in Wisconsin, a Native American Indian painting also has a raft, complete with a birdman and bird upon it. This bears an uncanny resemblance to the drawing in Túcume. Tragically, only photographs remain of Gullickson's treasure, as this section of the wall collapsed recently. Nearby, in Tainter Cave, an eleven thousand year old birdman is amongst one hundred charcoal drawings recently found. The

American Indians viewed their universe as being divided into two distinct kingdoms, Earth and Sky, and so the Birdman may well have represented a bridge between these two worlds.

In Mexico, we find another, extremely powerful birdman. *Huitzilopochtli* (meaning left-handed hummingbird), portrayed as a hummingbird, or, more often, a human with hummingbird feathers, was an extremely important, powerful Incan God. His mother was *Coatlicue*, the Mother of all Gods, and his father was a ball of feathers! This unholy alliance brought great shame to her family, and her children plotted to kill the offspring resulting from this shocking conjugation.

However, Huitzilopochtli was no ordinary foetus, and hearing about this evil plan, he sprang from the womb and killed his sister, the key plotter in this dark scheme, and many of his four hundred brothers! Having decapitated his sister, he threw her head in the sky, where it became the moon, while his brothers became the stars. Huitzilopochtli became the sun god, and had a constant, ongoing battle with the forces of chaos. Every fifty two years, he weakened and required human sacrifices to strengthen him, a sinister side to the Incan Birdman. For such a powerful force, it is surprising that his avian parts are those of a hummingbird, the smallest bird on the planet.

Meanwhile in the Caribbean Island of Jamaica, in a cave high on Sots Mountain in the Carpenters Range, a discovery was made of three statues in 1792. All of them were facing east. They were *zemis*, carvings that represented gods or ancestral spirits, which were worshipped. Now housed in the British Museum, one of them was a birdman, with a large, awk-like beak hanging down over its human chest. They belonged to the *Taino* people, who along with the *Carib* people (after whom the *Caribbean* region is named), their sworn enemies, occupied much of what is now the West Indies.

So we see that on every continent on our planet where humans live, the Birdman features prominently in the myths and legends of the people. Some of these are obviously connected, or homologous. For example, the *Garuda* of the Hindu and Buddhist faiths is from a single origin and has spread across Asia. However the Lascaux birdman is unlikely to be directly linked to the Australian birdmen, nor the Russian birdmen to the South American birdmen.

Thor Hyerdahl, the famous (though some might say infamous) ethnographer and explorer, suggested that Rapa Nui had been occupied by two very different sets of people, a primitive group of Polynesians, unable to do much in terms of construction, and a sophisticated group of world-travellers, from South America. It was this latter group, pale-faced and red-haired, who brought the stone carving technology and the Birdman, as well as the sweet potato and the chicken, with them, hence forming a direct link to the South American Birdman.

 Indeed, the emphasis, by Heyerdahl, of an east-to-west migration to Rapa Nui was so strong because it was a component of his greater theory, that red-haired Europeans had been responsible for all the greatest archaeological finds in South America, and the greater Pacific. He went to great lengths in an attempt to demonstrate the plausibility of such a link, famously sailing from South America to the Pacific Islands on a primitive balsa wood raft called the *Kon Tiki*, based on the rafts on the carvings at Túcume (Hyerdahl, 1950).

DNA analysis of the native people on Easter Island shows no evidence of a dual origin. Rather, it points to an ancient

Polynesian origin (west-to-east) alone (González-Pérez *et al.*, 2006), only much later acquiring South American and European DNA (Lie *et al.*, 2007). Indeed this European DNA is most likely to have come from hybrid breeding between Spanish invaders and indigenous South Americans, whose offspring would, later, further hybridize with islanders during the slave trade exchanges, and visits to Rapa Nui. Skeletal evidence also supports the Polynesian origin of the islanders (van Tilburg, 1994).

The superior white race, the Aryans, moving across the planet, and building anything of interest as they went, may sound reasonable to those who believe that the Nordic race was a special lineage (and confusingly aligned with the linguistic Aryan division of the Caucasians). However, given recent history, this theory is viewed as both tarnished and without support to the vast majority of anthropologists.

Instead, it would seem more reasonable to conclude that the Birdman is a global phenomenon, and an analogous one at that. In other words, the Birdman is likely to have entered a number of civilization groupings independently, rather than being passed on between them all by a mysterious white people.

Chapter Nine
The Bird in Human Mythology

So what of the bird whose egg would confer such power upon the sponsor? Birds are the most commonly seen vertebrates on our planet. Wherever you are, it won't be long until you either hear or see one, flying through the air, perched on a branch or singing at daybreak. We build feeding tables for wild birds, buy all sorts of fancy seeds, suet tit-bits and fat balls, and many of us, the author included, even build chicken runs. Each winter I cook up vegetable mash and porridge for my hens daily, tucking them in at night with a hot water bottle!

The great expenses scandal that hit the British Houses of Parliament in 2009 was triggered by one politician charging an ornate floating duck house, valued at one thousand six hundred and forty-five pounds, to his expenses bill! The birdman of Alcatraz is reflected upon fondly because of his care of injured sparrows and his breeding of canaries while in captivity, in spite of the fact that he was a double murderer, with a long history of violent assault.

Birds play important roles ecologically, spreading seed, controlling invertebrate pest populations and pollinating flowers. They provide food, both as meat and as eggs. Their droppings (called *guano*) form very important phosphorus sources. Phosphorus is an extremely limiting nutrient, which is essential for agriculture. Thus, guano is an excellent fertilizer, and humans have even gone to war over it (for example, in the War of the Pacific, involving Chile, Peru and Bolivia between 1879 and 1884).

Birds represent freedom, grace and peace, and most countries in the world have a national bird species as well as a national flower.

They are often seen as messengers, no doubt because of their ability to fly long distances. In literature, they play starring roles, from Edgar Allan Poe's *The Raven*, representing mournful, unending memory, the darkest and most retrogressive of messengers, through to the albatross in Samuel Taylor Coleridge's *The Rime of the Ancient Mariner*.

Birds have been seen as links between the supernatural and the Earth, because they occupy the sky, and in many eastern cultures, they betoken immortality. Birds also have been used to represent the journey of the human soul before birth and after death. For example, even today, the stork is used to explain to children where babies come from (even baby elephants with huge ears, such as *Dumbo*!).

The hooded crow represented *Badb* (pronounced *bibe*), the Irish goddess of war, and harbinger of death (she was the sister of *Macha*, of Ard Macha Press fame!). Many cultures believed that the soul itself became a bird upon death. Ancient Egyptian tombs had narrow shafts from the burial chamber to the outside, allowing the soul to come and go in the form of a bird, while others believed that birds were the soul guides. In Syria these guides were eagles. Celtic and Greek traditions held that the dead could re-appear as birds. These themes, of fertility, continuity, immortality and birth and death are undoubtedly essential elements of the Birdman Cult.

And so it is no surprise to find the bird as a central character in Rapa Nui. For oceanic islands have an even closer relationship with birds than the mainland, given that other vertebrates are usually extremely scarce. The birds represented a provisioning and forgiving creator. Although the islanders had destroyed the terrestrial and arboreal ecosystems, and the food that they provided, these carriers of protein rich eggs arrived each year to alleviate the suffering. What a bounteous god was Makemake!

As we have already seen, these birds at the centre of the Birdman Cult were referred to as Manutara. Manutara actually refers to two different species of bird, the sooty terns (*Onychoprion fuscata*) and the grey-backed (sometimes called spectacled) terns (*Onychoprion lunatus)*, which look very similar, the former having a darker back than the latter. Both are found throughout the tropical oceans. There are thought to be about twenty-two million sooty terns globally, and a similarly large number of grey-backed terns, so they are not thought to be endangered. Why, then are they so significant in terms of the Birdman Cult?

Island legend has it that Makemake gave the three islets off the west coast of the main island, Moto Kau Kau, Motu Iti and Motu Nui, to these birds. And so every spring (September in Rapa Nui, which is in the Southern Hemisphere), the manutara returned to these rocky islets to lay their eggs. Importantly, they flew from *Hiva*, which is the legendary homeland of the human population's ancestors. This has been associated with the Marquesas Islands, which sit some three thousand six hundred kilometres north-west, and are thought to be a likely origin for the first humans who found their way to Rapa Nui. It is of interest that the two largest islands of the Marquesas Islands are called *Hiva Oa* and *Nuku Hiva*.

So the manutara represented a bridge between the ancestors and the present, a reminder of their origins and of the continuation of life. These birds were, in ways, like the dove that returned to Noah in the biblical story of the flood, affirming the existence of the land from whence they came, and representing the ongoing link to the future. The eggs that they laid each year, as we will discuss later, also held an important spiritual and nutritional significance to the islanders.

Migratory birds appeared to be immortal, forever travelling through space and time. This is clearly shown in the most well known of migratory bird myths in the Western World, that of the Phoenix and its prototype, the Benu bird. The Phoenix is a Greek figure, while the Benu bird is Egyptian in origin. Both are self-created, self-regenerated sun birds and both are migratory. The phoenix and the Benu bird are part of a larger body of mythology, stretching across the globe from Asia to Europe.

Benu (or *Bennu*) means *to rise in brilliance* or *to shine*. The cry of the Benu bird was said to have broken the silence of the primeval world, heralding the onset of creation. This reminds us of another important role of birds in mythology, as key players in creation myths. The Benu bird then continued to renew itself, just as the Sun rose anew each day. Its earliest appearance, in the Old Kingdom of Ancient Egypt (third millennium BC), was that of a yellow wagtail (*Motacilla flava*), and symbolized the creator god, *Atum*, the most important deity in Early Egypt and the father of the other gods.

By the Middle Kingdom (first half of the second millennium BC), the Benu bird still maintained its position as a central figure, but was now seen as the soul of Re. The symbol also changed from a yellow wagtail to a grey heron (*Ardea cinera*). The Benu bird was thought to spend much of its life in Phoenicia, migrating back to Heliopolis, the city constructed for the worship of the Sun God, once every millennium. It would build a nest of cinnamon and myrrh. The Sun set it on fire, reducing the nest and the bird to a pile of ashes. Overnight, a worm emerged from the ashes, and grew into a winged bird, which flew away at dawn, renewed to live for another thousand years.

There have been many attempts to relate this myth to real birds. An extinct giant heron (*Ardea bennuides*), thought to have lived five thousand years ago (Hoch, 1979), has been suggested as a possible inspiration. Perhaps more convincing is the greater flamingo (*Phoenicopterus roseus),* still found in East Africa. This large, red, black and pink feathered bird nests on salt plains, and builds a nest of twigs and mud, to raise its eggs above the hot surface.

I have seen these birds on Lake Nakuru in Kenya, and the heat rising from the salt plains distorts the air, so that it appears on fire. It can easily be understood how the story of a bird, burning on its nest, yet producing offspring could be adopted. The greater flamingo has a distribution that takes it as far east as India (it is the state bird of Gujarat), and it is migratory throughout its range. Hence, this makes it a candidate, not just as the inspiration of the Benu bird, but of all the phoenix-like legends that stretch from Sri Lanka to Spain (Ogilvie and Ogilvie, 1986).

The fact that the return of the terns occurred around the spring equinox, was also, doubtless, significant. In many cultures, the return of a migrant bird species each spring was viewed as a symbol of renewal. For example the crane was sacred to the Mother Goddess of Ancient Greece, *Demeter*, the goddess of the harvest, linking the bird, who migrated back to Greece each spring, to her role of renewing the Earth. So these birds held a special meaning because they were migratory, and spring migrants were naturally associated with fertility.

Migration is a globally significant aspect of many ancient mythologies. A natural pattern, it reminds humans of a greater dominion, lost, as humans settled and left their nomadic ways behind. Yet humans themselves have often had to move, and, indeed, the movement of the ancestors of the Rapa Nui islanders represented such a migration, as humans spread throughout the Pacific Islands.

So these migrant birds were a reminder of where they had come from (*Hiva*), and the process of how they had gotten there. Furthermore, the birds' ability to leave the island for long periods, and then return, would have appeared impressive, particularly as large timbers needed for substantial ocean-going canoes had become scarce. These small birds could do so much more than the humans could, flying, catching fish on the wing, travelling huge distances, beyond the horizon, and, undoubtedly, visiting the ancestral land of *Hiva*.

The *nomadic hunter gatherer* (NHG), as humans once were, responded to change in their energetic context, by moving around in pursuit of suitable food, water and temperature. They were part of the bigger picture, and so their behaviour was driven by that bigger picture. Much of our technology today targets our escape from NHG: agriculture, cities, industrial mass production, heating, air-conditioning, clothing, water reservoirs and power generators all aim to move us away from the need to be nomadic, the need to hunt and the need to gather.

Indeed the modern world could be defined by our struggle to break free from our original position. We now want the world to come to us, and have transformed our planet, in a process of terraforming, so that we no longer have to migrate, hunt or gather. Thus the rest of the Biosphere has become subservient to us. Or at least, we think it has.

For it is a disturbing reality that the impact of our destruction of the planet is likely to lead to human migration on a scale never before experienced (Warner *et al.*, 2009). Islands such as the Maldives are likely to disappear beneath a watery grave as global warming bears its unpalatable fruit. By 2050, it is estimated that some two hundred and fifty million *"climate refugees"* will be forced to leave their homelands (Biermann and Boas, 2010).

Migration represents an organism's conversation with its surroundings, and our technological pursuit of escaping from it represents the greater schism that we have worked hard to create, between ourselves and the rest of it. Yet within us, we recognize migration as a reminder of this long lost relationship, and birds become symbolic of this. Hence, their powerful presence decorates myths and legends from around the world. These myths communicate our deep reflection upon the meaning of nature and our place within it.

Chapter Ten
The Cosmogonic Chocolate Egg

As well as playing a central role in the Birdman Cult ritual on Rapa Nui, the egg is one of the most powerful symbols in ancient mythology worldwide. Anyone who has seen a bird hatch from an egg cannot fail to be impressed. The stone-like, lifeless ovoid shows no external sign of what lies within. Yet, from this object emerges a tiny little form, all set for its shot at life! As amazing as the hatching is, the meaning of the egg in mythology is much deeper. It is not so much a matter of birth, as of re-birth. Its significance comes from the idea that the Cosmos itself emerged from an egg. Thus, eggs represent re-birth, the repetition of the primeval act of creation. It is its central role in explanations of the origin of the Universe (Cosmogony) that gives it such powerful symbolism (Eliade, 1996).

Thought to have started in Indonesia or India, the idea of the cosmogonic egg has spread throughout Polynesia, the Middle East, Europe, South and Central America. In other words, this is a global phenomenon. In Hindu belief, the Brahma is seen as laying a golden egg at the onset of each cosmic cycle, leading to the rebirth of the Universe. The Society Islands in the Pacific Ocean tell of the ancestor of all the gods existing within a shell, rotating in space.

Many of the most significant figures in Ancient religions are recorded as emerging from eggs. In Ancient Greece, Apollo came from Leda's egg, the conception of which is powerfully described in W.B. Yeats' classic poem, *Leda and the Swan*, the swan being Zeus himself. Osiris and Brahma were also born form eggs. The egg was sacred to Isis, and so Egyptian priests never ate eggs, nor do modern Brahmans, in fear of destroying the germ of life in them.

In Chinese mythology, the first man emerged from an egg, dropped to the Earth by *T'ien*, which represents heaven, or the personification of heaven. This idea is found throughout Oceania, and reflects on the idea that the origin of man replicates the origin of the Universe. In other words, we are a copy of the greater creation process, and within us remain patterns and rhythms that are universal. So by understanding ourselves, we can understand the Universe.

In a way these ancient beliefs see existence as a series of Russian *babushka* dolls, each one mimicking the others, but smaller or larger. This is a form of reductionist philosophy, and perhaps the earliest form of this, though strangely inverted, almost like Gaian theory, where the whole (the Universe or Gaia) explains all beneath it (the human), rather than the building blocks (genes) explaining all above it. In other words, you can argue that the smallest doll determines the shape of those beyond it or that the largest doll determines the shape of those within it.

However the same problems emerge from both approaches: they assume a direction to construction, and a similarity of components. In my earlier book, *Shadows on the Cave Wall* (Skene, 2009), I have argued that the Biosphere is not a reductionist, bottom-up nor top-down system, but rather each level of organization, from gene to biome, is organized separately. The agent of organization, energy, flows through each level, and converses with it differently. Because the components of each level are different, they respond differently in this conversation. I call this a *transductionist* approach, where energy changes and shapes all else, and is transformed itself, as entropy. Here, the organizing agent works across every level, rather than the organizational power filtering down or up. The final outcome is an incredibly beautiful and complex Biosphere, which works by the interactions of each of these levels, in a form of secondary organization.

Energy organizes each level, and then each level spreads the implications of this organization throughout the other levels. Imagine four friends, each conversing with a great expert. Each person has their own way of understanding, because of their very different backgrounds and experiences, and, therefore, each conversation impacts upon each friend differently. However when the group get back together for a coffee, they share their conversations, and each impacts on the other. The Biosphere is like this: a series of conversations, first with the laws of thermodynamics that rule the Cosmos, and then within the Biosphere itself.

In China, the one month birthday of an infant is celebrated with a red egg and ginger party, the dyed eggs representing the renewal of life. Traditionally, infant mortality was highest during the first month of life, and so this milestone marked confidence that the child would survive.

The association with re-birth also means the egg is closely associated with New Year and spring. St John's trees from Germany, maypoles and New Year trees all have painted egg shells tied to them. In ancient Persia, the New Year celebration was called the Feast of the Red Eggs. *Nowruz*, the most important festival in Iran today, also involves decorated eggs. In Slovakia, Venetia Newall recounts that wedding candlesticks are accompanied with a carved wooden man holding a branch, to which are tied brightly painted eggs (Newall, 1967). The egg here is a token of fertility, another important role.

In an initially counterintuitive symbolism, the egg is also associated with burial rituals. All this celebration of life, yet we see a close association with death. The meaning here is not related to the dead *per se*, but to the hope of resurrection. Clay eggs have been found associated with Swedish and Russian tombs, and have been interpreted as symbols of immortality (Arne, 1914). But it is in the Ancient Greek religious cult of Orphism, that we see the consequences of the egg as a representation of re-incarnation.

Orphism was a religious belief based on the legendary figure of Orpheus. The story of Orpheus is really very tragic, and is thought to be one of the first on the theme of love and death. The rumoured child of Apollo, he was born with a beautiful singing voice and an incredible talent of playing the lyre. It was said that rivers would stop their flow to listen to him! He fell madly in love with a woodland nymph called Eurydice, and soon they were married. She would dance through the meadows with his music in her ears. Perfection!

On her wedding day, depending on which version you read, Eurydice was either dancing in the woodland, or was chased by the lustful god of agriculture, Aristaeus, another son of Apollo. As she danced, or fled, she stepped on a poisonous snake that bit her foot, and she died. She was taken, immediately, to the underworld. Orpheus was, unsurprisingly, devastated. He wrote the saddest music ever heard, which moved the gods to tears, and went to Hades, the cold-hearted guardian of the Underworld.

No-one was allowed to return from the Underworld, but even Hades couldn't help but be moved by the beautiful music of Orpheus. And so Orpheus was allowed to take Eurydice back to the land of the living, provided that, during the passage from the

Underworld, he didn't look behind him until they were both back on Earth.

As he emerged into the daylight, Orpheus turned around instinctively, forgetting that Eurydice was a few steps behind and therefore, as yet, still in the Underworld. She instantly was pulled back down, and would never return. Gone forever, Orpheus spent the rest of his life mourning Eurydice, and scorning all other women's advances. Eventually a group of women from his town became so fed up with the constant rejection that they killed him, throwing his head in the river, where it continued to sing until it reached the sea!

The Orphic Cult that grew up around this character had a very specific rule. Its adherents were forbidden from eating eggs. This dietary restriction was in place to help ensure deliverance from the relentless cycle of re-incarnation, which was a key aim of Orphism. Since eggs represented re-birth, then by not eating them, Orphic followers believed that they would escape the endless cycle. So the egg was viewed by the Orphics as not only representing re-incarnation, but somehow being involved in it as an active ingredient.

Already well established as a symbol of nature's rebirth in spring, the adoption of Easter eggs in Christian celebrations of Easter, representing the resurrection of Christ, led, eventually to the chocolate Easter egg. One final and very enlightening point to make about the egg is that our story, and that of humankind, appears to have come full circle, or, rather, can be likened to a figure of eight, where two circles meet. As Admiral Jakob Roggeveen woke on Easter Sunday, 5th April, 1722, and saw the outline of Rapa Nui before him, it was only natural that he should name it Easter Island.

In the Northern Hemisphere, Easter coincided with the spring equinox, marking the rebirth of life, and celebrated in many cultures by rituals involving eggs. Roggeveen only stayed for one week, and was not to know that exactly six months later, when spring would come to the Southern Hemisphere, this very island would have its own egg-based ritual, which itself celebrated rebirth, ancestry and origins. The connection between eggs and the spring equinox was shared across hemispheres and across opposite sides of the planet, and brought together both on mainland Europe and on this tiny oceanic island in the middle of the Pacific Ocean.

So the egg unifies celebrations, at opposite points in the year, but at the same seasonal moment on either hemisphere, showing that humans across the world relate to such symbolism in similar ways, no matter how different the belief structures appear. From the maypole of Germanic paganism, to the resurrection of Christ, and from the Hindu festival of Holi to the creation myths of the Society Islands, a common thread is found. And on Easter islands, these disparate threads meet.

The Dutch sailors and the Rapa Nui islanders would have found no apparent common ground, and yet within their belief structures, the egg stood to represent what these humans could not have seen. This is significant in another way. In this book I want to take you on a search for other common ground that all humans share, not based on myth and legend, but rather on our relationships with such things as ecology, physics and evolution. More fundamentally, these relationships point to our place within the Biosphere, unrecognized by many of us, yet clearly visible if we look in the right places, and with open minds.

Chapter Eleven
Summing up the Birdman Cult

The Birdman Cult, then, brings together three powerful components: the Birdman, the bird and the egg. The Birdman replaced the Ancestor Cult, with its giant stone statues, the Moai, symbolizing deified ancestors. Now nature, ancestors and deities came together, with the creator god, Makemake, represented by its avatar, the Birdman, the migratory sacred birds, shuttling back and forth between Hiva, the ancestral land, and their island, and the eggs, laid around the Spring Equinox, celebrating re-birth, and continuity with the ancestors. So many powerful and ancient themes that we see in mythology from around the world, stretching from the caves of Lascaux to the Easter eggs of Christendom.

Whatever the reason, be it first contact or diminished resources, or both, there was a significant shift in the community structure on Rapa Nui in the eighteenth century. Tribalism increased, with the island becoming divided. Indeed this tribalism, which led to the Birdman Cult becoming the dominant ritual from the eighteenth century onwards, would have clearly targeted each tribe's symbols, including the Moai that represented their ancestors.

Thus the toppling of the statues can be seen as an indicator of increasing tribal tension. This, accompanied by the introduction of a competition each spring equinox between tribes, points towards increasing tribalism as a common theme to both the demise of the Moai and the concomitant rise of the Birdman Cult.

However, Rapa Nui is an island of controversy. The rebuff, by Benjamin Peiser, in a paper entitled *From Genocide to Ecocide: the*

Rape of Rapa Nui (Peiser, 2005), upon Jared Diamond's book, *Collapse* (Diamond, 2005), is a case and point. Diamond argued that over-exploitation of natural resources resulted in the demise of civilization, as marked by the end of construction of the Moai. If the forests were destroyed, then there could be no way to move these huge stone structures, and there would be no wood to construct boats for fishing or escape. Soil erosion would increase due to the lack of trees, and the natives would be left to starve, turning to cannibalism and warfare.

Peiser, on the other hand, argues that it was the arrival of the Europeans, and South Americans, bringing with them a host of diseases against which the native population had no immunity, which led to the demise of the islanders, and that up until that point, the native people were models of sustainable living. W.S. Thomson, an early researcher on Easter Island, commented that there were abundant supplies of fish, crayfish, sea mammals, turtles and molluscs available, most of which could be accessed without boats (Thomson, 1891). These, along with an abundance of rats and seabirds and their eggs, provided a reasonable larder. Thus starvation would, Peiser says, be unlikely. Diamond comments that *"We cling to belief in a Rousseau-esque fantasy that the past was a Golden Age of environmentalism, when people lived in harmony with Nature"* (Diamond 1991)

Whatever the case, certain facts remain. By the time Europeans arrived there, there was no sign of the lush forests that pollen evidence in sediment indicated was their originally (Flenley, 1993). The Easter Island palm tree, formerly a significant species, entered extinction. The Moai had begun to be toppled by 1774, as reported by Captain James Cook, and were almost all destroyed by 1825, as reported by HMS Blossom, well before the major disease epidemics. The tree-nesting birds had disappeared.

What then is the lesson of Rapa Nui? Does it serve as a warning to all of us about the abuse of our natural resources? Is it true that, as Flenley, one of the leading palynologists who has worked on Rapa Nui, said, *"Ecological sustainability may be an impossible dream. Easter Island still seems to be a plausible model for Earth Island"* (Bahn and Flenley, 1992)? Or is the lesson deeper than this?

I would argue that by focusing on the resources, disease and slavery, we are missing the real meaning of it all. The questions should not be about what we have done wrong and what we need to *do*. We have done far too much already, and need to lay down our tools for a while and reflect on who we *are*. Doing should stem from being. It is the act of being that we need to understand. What is it to be human?

This struggle to identify who we are amid changing times and increasing worries about our ability to persist on the planet is clearly reflected in the harrowing story of Rapa Nui. What is apparent is that there was a shift from self-obsessed ancestor worship, to a development of a synergy of human and animal, reflecting a move towards animism. What does this tell us?

We find that in many cultures, when conditions worsen, belief systems often revert to more basic animistic approaches. We saw the great droughts of South and Central America, one thousand years ago, leading to belief systems more centrally focussed on nature, and the appearance of the Birdman. Gods became represented by a fusion of animal and human, reflecting a breaking down of the human-centric ancestral worship. A parallel shift occurred in Easter Island. It is, surely, no co-incidence that today, as significant global issues threaten to submerge us (some would say literally), people are becoming more involved with eco-centric movements, not necessarily formalized into deities such as the Birdman, but embracing the totality of nature. What may be surprising to many is that this has happened before.

The seed of a thought that I wish to plant at this point is that we are, ultimately, *the outcomes of the totality of nature*, and so when faced with imminent doom, there is the awakening of a recognition of this. Our relationship with the rest of nature has been damaged by our isolation from this totality, through brain and brawn, and only by understanding this relationship can we hope to exist comfortably within it. So what is this relationship?

Well that is what the rest of this book hopes to explore. This book is all about relationships: our relationship with every other living thing on the planet, and the relationship between life and its material context. It is a story about forgetful squirrels, weedless gardens, sex and death. Fundamentally it is about seven relationships, which, if we understand them, can help save the planet.

Relationships are often difficult things to visualize. They are not static. They may exist between space and time, or between two completely different entities. But we have one amazing trick that allows us to see them: curves, or graphs. Hence the sub-title of this book: *Seven Curves to Save the Earth*.

Before examining the first of these curves, I wanted to say a few words about graphs, and what they can be used for. If you are happy with interpreting graphs, then please feel free to skip this chapter. It is a very basic introduction to the use of lines in interpreting relationships. So either read on, or we'll see you in Chapter Thirteen!

Chapter Twelve
A Brief Word on Graphs

Graphs are abstract. In other word, they don't exist in the real world. They allow you to be in many places at the same time, and they can be used to look into the future. A graph can come into existence in one of two ways. Firstly, you can measure things and plot the results on a graph. For example you could measure the temperature and altitude as you go up a mountain. You could then plot the temperature against the altitude to see how temperature changed as you went higher or lower. This would allow you to produce a mathematical equation that best describes this change. Secondly, you can use a mathematical equation to start with and visualize it using a graph. Here you start with a theoretical situation, and use the graph to examine what happens across a range of values.

Let's take the example of how temperature changes with altitude. Firstly, you need to think about how you will collect the data. You can use readings from a global positioning satellite to determine your altitude, so that is simple enough. You can bring a thermometer with you too. However it will take you a number of hours to climb a high mountain, and so the temperature you experience at each place will be at a different time of day, meaning that the Sun will not be in the same location. You may want to set up a series of weather stations, sited every one hundred metres up the mountain, so that you can record the temperature at each site simultaneously.

Also, how far above the ground do you measure? The bottom of the mountain may be covered in forest, whose shade will alter the sunlight reaching the ground, whereas higher up there may only be shrubs or scree.

So the height above the ground will matter. There may be snow or ice at the summit. The surface may radiate heat to a greater or lesser extent, depending on what it is made of (dark basalt rock or light sandstone, for example). Closer to the ground, the temperature will be more influenced by the reflective and radiated heat, whereas higher up, it will be less so. Finally, if the bottom of the mountain contains a village or town, this will significantly alter the temperature. Built environments increase the temperature, because they radiate and reflect heat from their surfaces. They also struggle to lose heat by evaporative cooling. When we are hot, we sweat. The energy used to change water from a liquid into a gas comes from us, cooling us down.

Plants continually "*sweat*" and this not only moves water from the soil into the air, which is important in preventing flooding and erosion, but it also cools the surface, as heat energy is dissipated by the huge evaporation occurring. Built up areas are usually devoid of significant vegetation, and so lack this natural cooling. The heat can stay trapped in a city.

These built-up areas are called *urban heat islands*. Machinery in these areas generates heat, and as time has gone on, cities have generated more and more heat as technology has increased. Cooling vents have become essential features of many buildings, particularly those with large computer servers. Thus, cities would be expected to become warmer over time, and so an historical temperature record would appear to show the equivalent of global warming, but really it was just the impact of an ever greater generation of heat by technology. This increase in temperature over historical time is called the *Urban Heat Island Effect*.

This effect was at the centre of a huge dispute concerning the reliability of climate change data recently. In a study reported in Nature in 1990, by two scientists, Phillip Jones, based at the

University of East Anglia, and Wei-Chyung Wang, based at the State University of New York, in collaboration with a number of other scientists (Jones *et al.*, 1990), data was recorded from 84 weather stations in China, half in the countryside, and half in the cities. The idea was to examine if the Urban Heat Island Effect really was a significant issue.

They concluded that the Urban Heat Island Effect was minimal, and that climate change data really was reflecting an increase in temperature. However it has since emerged that forty-nine of the eighty-four stations had no record relating to their locations, and, in fact, over the forty years of their data collection, many of the stations had been moved (Keenan 2007).

Thus, it has been alleged, the temperature readings cannot be used as evidence of climate change, as the measuring stations hadn't stayed in the same place. It is like using a bucket to measure rainfall and moving it into a car wash. Suddenly you are measuring a completely different source of water. So where you put the buckets is important, and if you move them, then that can change everything. Unless the weather stations are kept in place, we cannot determine if urbanization has impacted on temperature measurement.

The way that you measure things is, therefore, very important. A graph is only as good as its data. When you look at a graph, you need to check how the data was collected. In the case of the Chinese weather stations, this became the centre of a media frenzy, even leading to a parliamentary Select Committee report. Graphs can lead to significant repercussions!

Let's get back to a real graph. The graph below (Figure I.1) represents the change in temperature with altitude. Measurements were taken at one metre above the surface, in areas cleared of vegetation, away from any buildings, using electronic temperature readers (which weren't moved during the data collection period!). This meant that temperatures at each altitude could be made at exactly the same time each day, and without interference of surface or vegetation anomalies. Basically, good science!

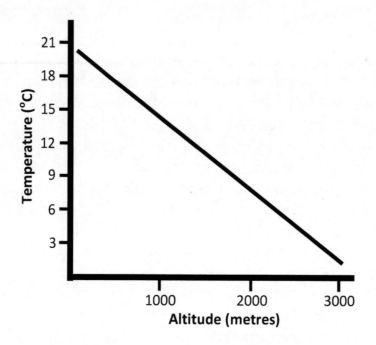

Figure I.1 Temperature change with increasing altitude, when sea-level temperature equals twenty degrees centigrade.

This graph is extremely useful. We can work out how much colder the top of the mountain is from the bottom. So when we climb, we can bring appropriate warm layers at the top. You can actually "see" the change in temperature with altitude. It also can be used to examine plant and animal distributions, to see if temperature plays a big role in restricting where certain species can live.

From this graph, we can generate some questions, and that is another really important aspect of this whole journey. Often, asking the right questions can be the most difficult thing, especially when it involves something as "invisible" as relationships. We'll be using curves to expose some very deeply held but damaging ideas that lie at the centre of our culture. And when such ideas are so deeply engrained, either by education, culture or peer pressure, it can be very hard to look beyond them.

Yet abstract visualization of relationships can provide a way through the invisible ceilings and walls that surround us. They can help us break free and gain a completely new perspective, allowing us to escape from long-held beliefs, or, as Francis Bacon called them (Bacon, 2010), the idols of the tribe (common to all humans), the idols of the cave (biases specific to each person's context), the idols of the marketplace (the misuse of language) and the idols of the theatre (the abuse of authority). We shall see, in this book, that all four idols are involved in preventing us from addressing many of the problems that we have brought upon ourselves.

So what questions come to mind from this first little graph? We could ask why temperature decreases with increasing altitude. The answer to this is that air pressure decreases with increasing altitude. Temperature is the result of molecules banging into each other, and so the fewer molecules there are, the lower the temperature. Thus, thermodynamics lies at the heart of this curve. Would global warming mean species will move up mountains? This does happen, though soil and water conditions need to allow this.

Would building construction and design need to differ at higher altitudes? The answer, again, is yes, due to greater freeze-thaw cycling leading to damaging ice dams. These large ice structures can damage roofs and cause injury if they fall. If pressure decreases, will it take longer to boil an egg high up a mountain? Yes. And will my pancakes over-rise and deflate? Unfortunately, yes! The reduced air pressure means the little bubbles that are important in allowing the baking to rise, grow much bigger than at sea level, and can actually burst, leading to a collapse of the structure of your cake in the middle. If you add a bit more flour, you can avoid the collapse. The extra flour basically reinforces the structure, stopping the collapse. Bread making suffers similarly at altitude, so less yeast may be a way ahead, decreasing the gas production, and thus helping to reduce the bubbles again.

So once you have a curve, all sorts of thoughts come out from it. The curve acts not only as a way of visualizing the relationship between two or more things, but stimulates thinking on issues far beyond this relationship. We can be in many places and times on a curve, and can see all of these places and times at once. Curves can be the ultimate in time machines, and allow us to escape the moment that we live in, or see this moment as part of a greater continuity. As we move along the curve, we experience something otherwise closed to us. That's the beauty of a curve. And it's why this book is going to use these curves to help us examine some fundamental relationships on our planet.

As a final preparation for what lies ahead, I have written an appendix (Appendix I) which gives a very simple introduction to some of the mathematics behind the main curves in this book. It's an optional extra, so take a look if you are interested, but it isn't essential reading for the book. In it, we explore the numbers behind changing shapes in a curve, and what they tell us about the relationship. So nip off to Appendix I for a bit if you want, or keep reading!

Now it's time to move to our first curve. It is one that lies at the centre of debate at present – the number of humans on our planet. Are there too many of us and will this expansion ultimately lead to the collapse in our population, accompanied by the collapse of human civilization and the Biosphere itself? Let's take a look at sex, death, and the invisible ceiling.

REFERENCES

Arne, T.J. (1914) *La Suède et l'Orient: etudes archéologiques sur les relations de la Suède et l'Orient pendant l'âge des Vikings.* K. W. Appelbergs Boktryckeri, Uppsala.

Ayres, W.S. (1985) Easter Island subsistence. *Journal de la Societe des Oceanistes* 80: 103-24.

Bacon, F. (2010) *Novum Organum.* Forgotten Books, Charleston, South Carolina.

Bahn, P. and Flenley. J. (1992) *Easter Island, Earth Island.* Thames and Hudson, London.

Bataille, G. (1979) *Oeuvres Completes IX: Volume 9: Lascaux, ou La naissance de l'art - Manet - La littérature et le mal – Annexes.* First Edition. Gallimard, Paris.

Beaglehole, J.C. (ed.) (1961) *The Journals of Captain James Cook on his Voyages of Discovery. Vol. II. The Voyages of the Resolution and Adventure 1772-1775.* Hakluyt Society, extra series XXXV. Cambridge University Press: Cambridge.

Biermann, F. and Boas, I. (2010) Preparing for a warmer world: towards a global governance system to protect climate refugees. *Global Environmental Politics* 10: 60-88.

Diamond, J. (1991) *The Rise and Fall of the Third Chimpanzee: How Our Animal Heritage Affects the Way We Live.* Radius, London.

Diamond. J. (2005) *Collapse: How Societies Choose to Fail or Survive.* Viking Press, New York.

Du Petit-Thouars, A.A. (1841) *Voyage autour du monde sur la frégate La Vénus.* Gide, édit., 5, rue des Petits-Augustins, Paris.

Eliade, M. (1996) *Patterns in Comparative Religion.* University of Nebraska Press, Lincoln.

Eshelman, C. (2010) http://www.cerisepress.com/02/05/lascaux-lost-caul/5 Last accessed 10/6/2011.

Feduccia, A. (2003) Big bang for Tertiary birds? *Trends in Ecology and Evolution* 18: 172–176.

Ferdon, E.N. Jr. (2000) Stone chicken coops on Easter Island. *Rapa Nui Journal* 14(3):77-79.

Flenley, J.R. (1993) The palaeoecology of Easter Island, and its ecological disaster. In: Fischer, S.W. (ed.) *Easter Island: Essays in Honour of William Malloy.* Oxbow, Oxford. Pp. 27-45.

Flenley, J.R. King, S.M., Teller, S.M., Prentice, M.F., Jackson, J. and Chew, C. (1991) The Late Quaternary vegetational and climate history of Easter Island. *Journal of Quaternary Science* 6: 85-115.

Gonzalez, Y. and Haedo, D.F. (1908) The Voyage of Captain Don Filipe Gonzalez to Easter Island in 1770-71. Trans. By Corney, B.G.. Hakluyt Society. 2nd Series, Volume 13, London.

González-Pérez, E., Esteban, E., Via, M., García-Moro, C., Hernández, M. and P. Moral, P. (2006) Genetic change in the Polynesian population of

Easter Island: evidence from *Alu* insertion polymorphisms. *Annals of Human Genetics* 70, 829–840.

Grubb, P. (2005) Artiodactyla. In: Wilson, D.E. and Reeder, D.M. (eds), *Mammal Species of the World. A Taxonomic and Geographic Reference (3rd ed)*, pp. 637-722. Johns Hopkins University Press, Baltimore, USA.

Hoch, E. (1979) Reflections on prehistoric life at Umm an-Nar (Trucial Oman), based on faunal remains from the third millennium B.C. In: Taddei, M. (ed.), *South Asian Archaeology IV - Naples 1977*. Instituto Universitario Orientale - Seminario di Studi Asiatici, Naples. pp. 589-638.

Hunt, T.L. and Lipo, C.P. (2006) Late colonization of Easter Island. Science 311: 1603-1606.

Hyerdahl, T. (1950) *Kon-Tiki*. Rand McNally & Company, Skokie, Illinois.

Janis, C . (1993) Tertiary mammal evolution in the context of changing climates, vegetation, and tectonic events. *Annual Review of Ecology and Systematics* 24: 467–50.

Jones, P.D., Groisman, P.Y., Coughlan, M., Plummer, N., Wang, W.-C. And Karl, T.R. (1990) Assessment of urbanization effects in time series of surface air temperature over land. *Nature* 347: 169-172.

Keenan, D.J. (2007) The fraud allegation against some climatic research of Wei-Chyung Wang. *Energy & Environment* 18: 985-995.

Lee, G. (1992) *Rock Art of Easter Island: Symbols of Power and Prayers to the Gods*. Institute of Archaeology, University of California, Los Angeles.

Lovelock, J. (2009) *The Vanishing Face of Gaia: A Final Warning: Enjoy It While You Can.* Allen Lane, London.

Mann, D., Edwards, J., Chase, J., Beck, W., Reanier, R., Mass, M., Finney, B. and Loret, J. (2008) Drought, vegetation change and human history on Rapa Nui (Isla de Pascua, Easter Island). *Quaternary Research* 69: 16-28.

McKibben, B. (2010) *Eaarth: Making a Life on a Tough New Planet.* Henry Holt and Company, New York.

Lavachery, H. (1939) *Les Pétroglyphes de l'île de Pâques*. 2 volumes. De Sikkel, Antwerp.

La Pérouse, J.-F. de (1997) *Voyage Autour du Monde sur l'Astrolabe et la Boussole (1785-1788).* La Découverte, Paris.

Lie, B.A., Dupuy, B.M., Spurkland, A., Fernández-Viña, M.A., Hagelberg, E. and Thorsby, E. (2007) Molecular genetic studies of natives on Easter Island: evidence of an early European and Amerindian contribution to the Polynesian gene pool. *Tissue Antigens* 69: 10–18

Métraux, A. (1957) *Easter Island: A Stone-Age Civilization of the Pacific.* André Deutsch, London.

Narváez, A. (2001) *The Site Museum of Tucame: Visitors Guide.* Talleres Gráficos, Chiclayo.

Newall, V. (1967) Some notes on the Egg Tree. *Folklore* 78: 39-45.

Ogilvie, M.A. & Ogilvie, C. (1986) *Flamingos.* Alan Sutton Publishers, Gloucester, UK.

Peiser, B.J. (2005) From genocide to ecocide: the rape of Rapa Nui. *Energy and Environment* 16: 513-539.

Roggeveen, J. (1908) *Extracts from the official log of Mynheer J. Roggeveen (1721-22).* Hakluyt Society. 2nd Series, Volume 13. London.

Routledge, K.S. (1919) *The Mystery of Easter Island.* Sifton, Praed and Company, London.

Schopenhauer, A. (2007) *Studies in Pessimism*. Cosimo Inc., New York.

Skene, K.R. (2009) *Shadows on the Cave Wall: a New Theory of Evolution.* Ard Macha Press, Letham, Angus.

Skjølsvold, A. (1993) The Dating of Rapanui Monolithic Sculpture. *Easter Island Studies*. S.R. Fischer (ed.). Oxbow Monograph 32, Oxford.

Steadman, D.W., Casanova, P.V. and Ferrando, C.C. (1994) Stratigraphy, chronology, and cultural context of an early faunal assemblage from Easter Island. *Asian Perspectives* 33: 79–96.

Thomson, W.S. (1891) Te Pito te henua, or Easter Island. *Report of the U.S. National Museum for the Year Ending June 30, 1889*: 447–552. Smithsonian Institute, Washington.

Van Tilburg, J.A. (1994) *Easter Island: Archaeology, Ecology and Culture.* Smithsonian Institution Press, Washington D.C.

Van Tilburg J.A. (2003) *Among Stone Giants: The Life of Katherine Routledge and Her Remarkable Expedition to Easter Island*. Scribners, New York.

Warner, K., C. Ehrhart, A. de Sherbinin, S.B. Adamo, T. Chai-Onn. 2009. *In search of Shelter: Mapping the effects of climate change on human migration and displacement.* Bonn, Germany: United Nations University, CARE, and CIESIN-Columbia University.

Zapffe, P.W. (1941) *Om det Tragiske.* Gyldendal, Oslo.

General reference works:
Davis Drake, A. (1992) *Easter Island. The Ceremonial Center of Orongo.* Cloud Mt Press: Old Bridge, NJ.

Hill, A.V.S. and Serjeantsom, S.W. (eds.) (1989) *The Colonization of the Pacific: A Genetic Trail.* Clarendon Press, Oxford.

Hyerdahl, T. (1952) *Aku-Aku. The Secret of Easter Island*. Allen and Unwin, London.

Von Saher, H. (1994) The complete journal of Captain Cornelis Bouman, master of the ship *Thienhoven* forming part of the fleet of Jacob Roggeveen, from 31 March to 13 April 1722 during their stay around Easter Island. *Rapa Nui Journal* 8: 95-100.

SECTION II
THE POPULATION-TIME CURVE: SEX, DEATH AND THE INVISIBLE CEILING

"Let me take you by the hand and lead you through the streets of London...I will show you something that will make you change your mind." **Ralph McTell, Irish songwriter.**

Our first curve, shown below, represents what is known as a hockey stick curve (Figure II.1). Strictly speaking it is named after an ice hockey stick, not a field hockey stick. It has a long horizontal handle and an upward pointing blade. Two examples of this kind of curve are atmospheric carbon dioxide levels over the last two thousand years and human population since its origin. Basically, for a long period of time little change occurs. This is the handle. Then, abruptly, there is a rapid increase. This represents the blade of the ice hockey stick.

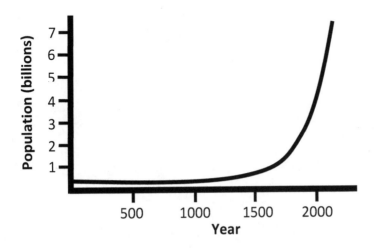

Figure II.1 World population over the last two thousand years.

In this section we will focus on the human population hockey stick. Why does this curve follow this shape, and what does this curve tell us about how we should continue to enjoy living on this blue green jewel we call planet Earth? In the next few chapters, we will explore the history of population monitoring, try to get to grips with some enlightened philosophers, and we will briefly encounter the apple strudel monster. We will look into one of the most important papers ever written in terms of its impact and meet a man who built his house on top of four elephants. Finally, we will ask what the hockey stick curve tells us. We better make a start!

Chapter Thirteen
The Story of a Haberdasher and the Birth of Demography

Demography is the study of human populations – their size, density, growth and other characteristics. On the surface at least, this section is all about the demographic past, present and future of the human race. The history of demography has its modern beginnings with John Graunt, whose life was extraordinarily tragic.

Born in 1620, Graunt was a haberdasher by trade. Haberdashery is an ancient trade, selling *bric-a-brac* such as buttons and fasteners. There have been many famous haberdashers in history, including Harold Truman (the thirty-third American president), Daniel Defoe (author), Charles Taze Russell (the founder of what would become the Jehovah's Witnesses) and, as an apprentice haberdasher, Captain James Cook. In many ways, it is a trade that requires an assiduous eye for detail, and the need to be very organized. Profit margins were narrow and stock-taking could be a laborious process. And so it is not altogether surprising that John Graunt also took an extraordinary interest in the stock-taking of people as well as of buttons.

The London in which Graunt lived was wracked with outbreaks of plague, and so death was a frequent event. He started to study the way that these deaths were recorded. He became fascinated with lists, particularly the weekly *bills of mortality* released by the parishes of London, which recorded the births, baptisms, sex, age and putative causes of death. These bills were introduced in 1592, then discontinued and restarted in 1603, in an attempt to understand when a passage of plague had passed. People could pay for this information, allowing them to decide when it was safe to enter a particular area. The data was gathered by women who he referred to as *"ancient maidens sworn to their office"*. He published his findings in a book, *Natural and Political Observations Made upon the Bills of Mortality* (Graunt, 1662).

His writing was of an extremely accessible style for its time, and he considered possible errors in the data set, by alluding to data collectors suffering from *"the mist off a cup of ale and the bribe of a two groat fee, instead of one"*! His wit is clearly visible at the end of his Preface, where he writes *"I have, like a silly Scholeboy* [sic] *coming to say my lesson to the World (that peevish, and Tetchie Master) brought a bundle of Rods wherewith to be whipt, for every mistake I have committed"*. I think all writers can empathise with Graunt!

He also jokes, in Chapter XI of his *Observations*, that he had delayed carrying out his census because he had been *"frighted by that misunderstood example of David from attempting any computation of the people"*, a biblical reference, to First Chronicles chapter twenty-one, where, ironically, the story is told of a plague that was sent upon Israel, killing seventy thousand people, because King David had carried out a census, ordered by Satan. This reference is clever, because it combines the idea of the census with a reference to the plague as a supernatural punishment. In England at this time, the occurrence of plague was believed to be synchronized with the coronation of a new king. This superstition prevented efforts to address the causes of the problem. Instead, he pointed towards breaking the curse of the census and of the plague, and instead rationally analysing a natural, public health issue.

John Graunt estimated the population of London as three hundred and eighty thousand people, far less than the two million assumed at the time, and he recognized that this population owed its increase not to births, which were more than negated by deaths, but to immigration. In fact, he showed that London acted as a terminal sink for rural areas, people moving to the city and dying there. This he concluded because there were many more burials than christenings in the city, whilst there were many more christenings than burials in the rural parishes.

He estimated some six thousand people were moving from the country to the city each year, and most of them died there. He also demonstrated that more males than females were born in London (the first to demonstrate this universal fact in humans), but due to increased male mortality in childhood, the ratio evened itself out by adulthood. Finally he concluded that cities became increasingly unhealthy as population increased. This is one of the first associations between increasing population and increasing mortality.

Graunt introduced *life tables*. A life table shows the probability of survival at a particular age. He divided the population of London into ten year groupings, worked out the mortality rate of each group, and then used this to calculate the likelihood of death at the end of a year for a person who was alive at the start of the year. His reason for doing this was to estimate the number of men of fighting age that London could provide for an army, but the outcome was to have much greater influence on demography, actuarial science (the calculation of risk for the insurance and finance industries) and ecology, where life tables play a significant part in population ecology.

Graunt had no formal mathematical training, yet his work set in place the beginning of mathematical statistics. He is also credited with being the first epidemiologist, as his analysis was particularly concerned with causes of death, and was inspired by a need to assess the impact of plague on the London population. He further examined the temporal and spatial patterns of the plague, how it started in the port district with bubonic plague, and then, over years, spread as pneumonic plague, changing from a contact infection to an air-borne infection. Finally he discredited the superstition that plague always began in the year of a new king rising to the throne.

The work was greeted with great enthusiasm, as it provided evidence of the significant impact of the plague. Charles II championed Graunt, and ensured his election to the newly formed Royal Society in London, in 1662. Other members disapproved of his election. Gaunt was a mere haberdasher, and hardly fit, they suggested, for such prestigious office.

A final contribution worth mentioning was his advocacy for a welfare state. Graunt argued that although there were many beggars in London, none of them starved to death, so they must be getting fed from the public purse anyway. So if the state, instead, fed them officially, it would be no loss to the state as a whole, and would remove them from the streets. An interesting suggestion! He further argued that these beggars wouldn't make good workers, so forcing them into labour would only weaken the nation's strength in competitive trade with other nations (Hacking, 2006).

John Graunt was a very successful businessman, and held a number of positions of responsibility in the city, including captain and, latterly, major in the London Militia. He was appointed as a governor in the New River Company, one of the main suppliers of water to London. He became a great collector of art. By 1663, Samuel Pepys commented, in his diaries (Pepys, 2010), that Graunt possessed *"indeed the best collection of anything almost that ever I saw, there being the prints of most of the greatest houses, churches and antiquitys [sic] in Italy and France"* (Monday 20th April, 1663 entry). He was foreman of the Wardmote inquest, the inspectorate who checked that all weights and measures used in trade were correct. He also rose to the position of Renter Warden in the Worshipful Company of Drapers, part of the senior governing body of this ancient livery company of the City of London.

However things went very wrong for Graunt, through a combination of bad luck and bad judgement. In 1666, the Great Fire of London destroyed much of the City of London, including the house and business of John Graunt. He had earlier joined the Socinians, a religious sect springing from the Polish Brethern, who denied the trinity and the complete omniscience of God, and were juxtapositioned to the Calvinists. The Socinians and Roman Catholics would both eventually be excluded from recognition in the Act of Tolerance of 1689.

Just before, or shortly after the Fire, according to John Aubrey, the writer and biographer who knew Gaunt (Aubrey and Dick, 1972), he had converted to Roman Catholicism. At this time in English history, there was great tension between catholic and protestant faiths, with Charles II, having been raised in catholic France during the rule of Cromwell, perceived by many as a sympathizer with the catholic cause. As a Catholic, John Graunt came under suspicion for being involved in starting the fire. Indeed, it was rumoured that, as Governor of the New River Company, which was responsible for the supply of water to a section of London, he secretly turned off the water supply, stopping fire fighters from accessing water.

However, given that he wasn't even appointed to his post until twenty days after the fire, this rumour was not only extremely damaging, but wrong. He lost all of his public positions, most likely as a result of his religious affiliations. Destitute, and with no means of income, Graunt was ruined. He lived the rest of his life in extreme poverty, and died, aged fifty-three years, of liver disease (Aubrey and Dick, 1972).

So often, great minds die in poverty. It seems to be the way that it goes. Other greats who met their demise in a state of financial ruin include Machiavelli, the great Italian writer, Phillis Wheatley, the first African-American poet to be published, Franz Schubert, the Austrian composer and Vincent Van Gough, the Dutch painter. Then there was Wolfgang Amadeus Mozart, not to mention James Joyce, the Irish writer, and Spencer Dryden, the late, great drummer from Jefferson Airplane.

The work of John Graunt proved inspirational to Edmond Halley (famous for his research on the comet that bears his name), which he used to develop more detailed life history tables that would form the basis for life insurance calculations. But it was an Anglican country curate, with a hare lip and cleft palate, born on St Valentine's Day, one hundred years after the Great Fire of London, who was to carry the study of populations to a new level. He was to have perhaps the greatest impact globally upon demography and the very theory of evolution itself. His name was Thomas Robert Malthus.

Chapter Fourteen
Thomas Malthus: the Early Years

Of course the tag *"Anglican country curate"* is extremely misleading. We like to paint our heroes as ordinary folk who, muddling about amongst the humdrum messiness of everyday life, somehow manage to stumble upon a great truth. It makes the truth seem all the stronger, that it was actually able to be recognized by some humble chap in amongst all the flotsam and jetsam, like a magical lamp, replete with genie, in a dusty old antique shop. Indeed, it makes the discovery somehow pure, not the outworking of some feverish genius, charged with dark thoughts and intentions, plagued by a need to take over the world.

The picture is presented of Watson and Crick, sitting in the Eagle Pub in Cambridge, figuring out the structure of DNA with a pen and a serviette. No, not some Dr Frankenstein, but rather an innocent young man, or, even better, an innocent holy man, unsoiled by political drive or narcissistic fervour.

Take Gregor Mendel, for example. He is often portrayed as a meddling monk, growing peas in a little friary somewhere in the backlands of Eastern Europe, stumbling on some ratios and writing them down in a little notebook that was subsequently lost. Nothing could be further from the truth. The Augustinian friary at Brno was a seat of learning that gathered together many fine minds, from the fields of mathematics, philosophy, mineralogy, zoology and botany, and was equipped with a herbarium, experimental garden and a huge research library.

And Brno was no dusty little village either, but rather a thriving city, much favoured by the Austrian Empire of the time, since its valiant resistance against the Swedish armed forces, who laid it under siege for months but failed to defeat the city, allowing the Austrian army to re-organize. As a result Brno became a powerful centre in the region. I have the pleasure of teaching a course at the Mendel University of Brno every alternate year, and know how impressive a place the city is, with fine buildings and squares, unsullied by all that Soviet architecture could throw at it. Finally, Mendel didn't hide his scribbling away in the abbey, but, rather, sent it to the forty leading European research universities of his time. His work was rejected by the scientific community, not overlooked.

And so it was with Thomas Malthus. He was not the curious, simple curate that is often portrayed. His was no ordinary upbringing. His father was extremely rich, and he built a mansion in 1759, within an extensive estate consisting of one hundred and seventy-five acres, called *The Rookery*. His father was a Jacobin sympathiser. The Jacobins were a French movement whose adherents did not believe in the right to own property (obviously not something that bothered Malthus Senior!) and played a significant role in the onset of the French Revolution. He entertained some of the leading thinkers of the day. Indeed, he was a close friend of Jean-Jacques Rousseau, the great French philosopher. When Thomas was only 3 months old, both David Hume and Rousseau visited at the same time. So, as I say, this was no ordinary home!

Thomas was educated by two private tutors (the writer, Richard Graves, and the dissenting minister, Gilbert Wakefield), both significant intellectuals of their time, before briefly attending the renowned Warrington Academy. He then completed a degree in Mathematics at the University of Cambridge, becoming a Fellow of Jesus College upon graduation.

It was at this point that his career takes what might appear to be an unexpected turn. Setting aside all of this excellent education, he became a country curate. Certainly it is recorded that he had been extremely self-conscious of his cleft palate and hare lip, and so a small, rural church may have seemed like a good place to hide away. Entering the ministry was a popular vocation for sons who were not firstborn, as it could provide a house and income not possible if inheritance was not on the cards. The position also brought a certain standing in the community.

And so it was that in 1797, he took up his curacy in a small village in Surrey called Albury, where his parents now lived. He moved back to the parental home, a move that was to greatly influence his life's work. It was only a year later that he wrote the first version of what was to become a classic text in demography.

Chapter Fifteen
That Essay and Those Three Dark Enforcers

An Essay on the Principle of Population as it affects the Future Improvement of Society, with Remarks on the Speculations of Mr. Godwin, M. Condorcet, and other Writers (Malthus, 2007) is an extremely bulky title for one of the most contentious and influential tracts of its or any subsequent time. It was published on 7th June, 1798, for the price of six shillings (equivalent to around twenty five pounds sterling in 2011).

Even today, argument rages over its implications and interpretation. Yet for a book that would be forever associated with the name of Thomas Malthus, it seems surprising that the first edition was issued anonymously. Altogether there were six editions, and later versions were much longer and more detailed than the first edition. Before thinking about the context and meaning of Malthus' classic text, let's summarise its content.

Malthus spelled out a simple idea: human populations grew at a faster rate than did food production, so eventually we would face global starvation. He showed that populations increased geometrically (his sister, for example had eleven children), while he suggested that agriculture could only increase yields arithmetically. It was the inevitable intersection of these two laws or tendencies that would, he predicted, trap humans in a future of abject misery. This became known as the *Malthusian trap*. This is pessimistic ecology at its rawest. He further suggested that any attempts to force the soil into greater productivity would lead to diminishing returns from the land.

At the heart of the problem, he suggested, was the tendency for humans to procreate, stating that "*passion between the sexes is an inevitable phenomenon*". He described a cycle, where humans, who he viewed as naturally lazy, continued to procreate, provided their families were well fed. When resources became limiting, they would work harder until, again, there were sufficient resources. At this point, laziness and procreation would again increase, and the cycle, or spiral, would continue.

Populations, according to Malthus, expand into available resource space, just like a gas expands into a given volume. So the more resource you provide, the more a population will increase. It can't help itself. And, like a gas, it is driven to expand. However, with populations, there is a lag in the feedback, so the population will expand beyond that representing available resources.

So, on one side, we have the drive to expand, but on the other, Malthus envisaged three apocalyptic scenarios that act to reduce population: disease, famine and war. As population continued to increase, he predicted an increase in these three dark enforcers.

So was there any way to break the trap and escape? In the second edition of his book, he went as far as to suggest that "*In our towns we should make the streets narrower, crowd more people into the houses, and court the return of the plague*", a dramatic solution indeed! Malthus recognized three processes to achieve an escape. Misery (disease, famine and war) was the natural product of over-population, the modern day revenge of Gaia. Otherwise known as density-dependent feedback (see Appendix I), it was not so much an escape as the natural consequence of the trap.

In addition to the terrifying unholy trinity of disease, famine and war, Malthus recognized vice as a check on population growth. By this he was referring to man-made population controls, and what he envisaged were not exactly things that a curate could approve of! They included infanticide, abortion, and prostitution. Malthus went further, no doubt shocking some of his readership (let alone his congregation), by extending his list of vices to include *"promiscuous intercourse, unnatural passions, violations of the marriage bed, and improper arts to conceal the consequence of irregular connexions* [sic]"!

Finally he argued that there was a third way, moral restraint. Here we again see the cleric in him. What is also interesting is that the solution was the least draconian. Of course, celibacy was an option, but given his belief that the drive to reproduce was a powerful one, he suggested that marrying later (with the obvious implication that there would be no sexual activity before marriage) would be a more reasonable path. There would be less time for reproduction, thus reducing the population growth. So he was saying that you could have your cake and eat it, but that the slice of cake would be served just a little bit later!

The bottom line was that he felt that we needed to take charge of the population issue. Again, from the second edition of his great opus, we find him concluding *"from the laws of nature we could not proportion the food to the population, [so] our next attempt should naturally be to proportion the population to the food"*.

So how come this rural man of the cloth felt driven to write his book? We must understand that he was a young, highly educated person who was not afraid to express his views. Indeed, a year earlier, he had written a short essay opposing Pitt's Poor Law Bill, which suggested financial child support for families with more than two children, entitled *The Crisis, a View of the Present Interesting State of Great Britain, by a Friend to the Constitution*. Although never published, and with no full version existing today, fragments of it have been quoted in print by a number of his contemporaries. Already, he was showing concern for supporting large families.

It would appear that he first stated his ideas in a discussion with his father. Freshly returning home from university, and taking up his new position as a curate, he found himself once again living under the same roof as his parents. As often is the case, a new relationship would probably have developed between his father and Thomas, and this is reflected in his confidence to oppose his father's viewpoint in debate. The clearest indication of a motivation, in terms of the essay, comes at the end of its title: *"with Remarks on the Speculations of Mr. Godwin, M. Condorcet, and other Writers"*. So who were these individuals who merited such mention? As we shall discover in the coming chapters, they offer a significant insight into what drove the young Malthus to write his great work.

Chapter Sixteen
The Marquis of Condorcet: Progress, Parity and Peace in a Dark Place

Growing up at the end of the eighteenth century in England was a very interesting experience in terms of the current affairs of the time. The French Revolution, marking the overthrow of one of the ancient Royal lineages in Europe, sent shock waves through neighbouring countries. No doubt, haunting images of a guillotine rose (and fell) within the nightmares of many an aristocrat. A sense of paranoia developed among the ruling classes, and any sign of support for the revolutionaries was quickly suppressed.

And it was the French Revolution, or rather the writings of a number of men closely associated with it, that became the topic of a conversation between father and son in the village of Albury all those years ago, and led to a book being written that would attract vehement criticism and have significant repercussions in many fields thereafter.

The Marquis of Condorcet, or Marie Jean Antoine Nicolas de Caritat, was an extraordinary polymath. He wrote significant works on integral calculus, probability and the voting system, worked at the Royal Mint of France (the *Hôtel des Monnaies*), wrote on theology, designed a new comprehensive education system for France and was one of the earliest mainstream politicians to call for a republican government in France.

Condorcet led up the committee to design the new constitution of the French Republic. However he felt strongly that King Louis XVI should not be executed. This, and a disagreement over the post-revolution constitution, led to him being charged with conspiring against the Republic, a crime with the death penalty as a likely outcome. Many of his fellow thinkers were executed at this time.

He had to go into hiding, which he did at the home of the widow of the sculptor, Joseph Vernet (not to be confused with Claude-Joseph Vernet, the painter). He realized that he was putting the widow at a terrible risk of death if she was caught, and explained this to her. She bravely replied *"La Convention, Monsieur, a le droit de mettre hors la loi: elle n'a pas le pouvoir de mettre hors de l'humanité; vous resterez."* (literally: "The Convention, Sir, has the right to put you outside the law; it lacks power to put you outside of humanity. You will remain!").

In order to stop him escaping, she basically imprisoned him, and it was during this time of positive incarceration that he penned his most famous work, and the subject of that fireside chat between Malthus Senior and Malthus Junior. His book was entitled *A Sketch for a Historical Picture of the Progress of the Human Mind* (*Esquisse d'un Tableau Historique des Progrès de l'Esprit Humain*) (Condorcet, 1980).

Having finished the essay, he left the safety of the house and was quickly arrested and imprisoned, in Bourg-l'Égalité, dying the following day in mysterious circumstances. Some say a friend gave him poison, others that he was killed by a member of the Revolution, to avoid the potential embarrassment of executing a very well-liked supporter of the cause.

In his masterpiece, Condorcet divided the history of the human race into ten phases, beginning with humans gathered in hordes, then progressing to an agrarian state, the discovery of writing, Ancient Greece up to Plato, Aristotle to the end of the Roman Empire, the Dark Ages, the Crusades through to the advent of printing, from printing to Descartes, from Descartes to the present (i.e. 1779) and, finally, the future.

It was his views on the future that particularly engaged the Malthus family. Condorcet believed that progress would be made in three crucial areas, by the application of rational thinking. These were: the destruction of inequality between nations, the progress of equality within each and every nation and the real improvement of man. He wrote that *"nature has fixed no limits to our hopes"*. To allow this progress to be made would require education of high quality for all. He emphasised that only a very few thinkers had led the dramatic changes of recent history, so how much more could be achieved with a whole nation of thinkers.

Condorcet then addressed improvements in living standards, and asked the question, surely central to the Malthus conversations, as to whether all this improvement would lead to a dramatic increase in population, thus, in the end, destroying the progress that had been made. He instead insisted that this was not likely to happen, because the great progress in science, art and morality would be targeted at man's *happiness*, not merely his *existence*, and so the human race would not allow itself to reach the painful consequences of over-population.

He believed in scientific, artistic and moral progress. He also believed that an institution would arise whose aim was to *"accelerate the progress of this fraternity of nations"* – a prophetic reference to the United Nations? He believed that this organization would help eradicate war – a less than prophetic reference to the achievements of the United Nations.

A little further on, he predicted that a significant technical advance would be made *"uniting a great number of objects in an arranged and systematic order, by which we may be able to perceive at a glance their bearings and connections, seize in an instant their combinations, and form from them the more readily new combinations".*   That, to me anyway, is exactly what computers are! Finally he called for a universal language to reach across the world, and today, surely, the internet has ambitions to fulfil this role.

He sums up his thoughts by stating that "the perfectibility of man is indefinite" and as such, he predicted that human life expectancy would also be greatly increased.

Condorcet was an optimistic humanist. He truly believed that humans could continue to make progress. This must have taken an immense amount of faith, as he hid from the leaders of a revolution that had offered so much in his mind, but now sought his annihilation. What a visionary he was, and what an incredible human being, to be able to write with such convincing optimism, in spite of his appalling situation.

Yet if he could look at the world today, I think Condorcet would have mixed emotions. Universal communication is in place. Computers can analyse data in fractions of seconds, completing calculations that would have been impossible to conceive of at the end of the eighteenth century. And, yes, there is the United Nations. But we have people-trafficking and human slavery, poverty and starvation, war and disease, illiteracy and inequality. All-in-all, there would appear to have been little progress.

Chapter Seventeen
William Godwin: Immortality and the Utopian Man

So what of the *Mr Godwin* that Malthus referred to? One of thirteen children (which would be enough to concern any demographer!) and raised in an extremist form of Calvinism called Sandemanian Calvanism, in Wisbech, Cambridgeshire, William Godwin went on to become the founder of *philosophical anarchism* (the belief that the State has no legitimate right to rule, and that gradual evolution away from this position, rather than revolution against it, is the most positive direction). Having completed an interrupted education with a number of tutors and, finally, theological college, he, like Malthus, became a churchman.

However that was as close as their paths would pass. A member of his congregation encouraged him to read Rousseau, and this had the effect of dramatically altering his views on religion, leading his parishioners to fall out with him. He left for London to pursue a writing career shortly afterwards, one that would lead, some ten years later to his most important work, *Enquiry concerning Political Justice, and its Influence on General Virtue and Happiness,* in 1793 (Godwin, 2009). This was followed up by a popular novel, *Things as They Are, or the Adventures of Caleb Williams* (Godwin, 1970), which reinforced his ideas within a fictional setting, an original approach at that time.

His work very much echoed that of Condorcet, but he did not believe in revolution. Instead, he felt that progressive enlightenment was the best way forward, gradually leading to the transformation of society in terms of politics, economics and sociology. He strongly disapproved of the state control of education and espoused pursuit of wisdom rather than knowledge. He felt that once individuals had their priorities arranged within a true value system, then greed, excess and inequality would disappear. He, like Condorcet, saw technology as playing an important role, and foresaw the day where machines would free humans of work.

His rejection of the political system and of rebellious revolution formed a fundamental belief framework. He had rejected marriage as a state ordinance, but married his partner, the influential feminist, Mary Wollstonecraft, on discovering she was pregnant, which led to many critics lambasting him and his spouse. Tragically, she died just days after giving birth to their child, the future Mary Shelley, who would find fame as the author of *Frankenstein*. Mary would, at the age of seventeen years, elope with Percy Bysshe Shelley, the poet, whose wife then committed suicide, causing great consternation to Godwin.

William Godwin represented *progressive rationalism*, wherein the improvement of the human condition would lead to benevolence, characterizing the perfecting of the human spirit. He saw national governance as a necessary evil which would become unnecessary as human enlightenment progressed. Godwin went further, believing that as the human mind became more perfect, it would dominate over the corporeal existence, enabling us to control illness, an idea in resonance with Condorcet.

He went beyond Condorcet, however, and believed that, eventually, we would become immortal. At this stage, we would no longer have the need to procreate, and thus the population would stabilize, all of us as adults. It is said that his second wife, Mary Jane Clairmont, introduced herself to him from her balcony by saying *"Is it possible that I behold the immortal Godwin"*!

His reputation suffered badly from his over-reaction to Malthus' work (Godwin, 1920), and to some injudicious writing relating to his first wife's sexual habits. He became the target of cruel jokes. The nineteenth century put the French Revolution and its associated ideas of a utopian world behind it, and so Godwin became passé, with the term *Godwinism* used as a form of amusement.

Chapter Eighteen
The Fireside Debate

Malthus' father was an admirer of both Godwin and Condorcet. Sitting beside the fireside after a fine dinner and a glass of port, his aging face glowed both from the dilated blood vessels, from the alcohol and at the pleasure of having his bright son sitting across from him, all further illuminated by the light from the flames. He looked forward to these soirées, where he set forth his argument, as much to enjoy his son's reply as anything else. Young Thomas always seemed to develop a fresh approach to any topic he brought his intellect to bear upon.

So Daniel Malthus put forward the utopian ideal, of humanity being able to work its way towards a perfect future, using a combination of technology, positive rationalism and benevolence. Happiness, rather than mere existence, lay ahead. The future was a place where the interference of government would no longer be required, and where immortal humans, freed from disease, war and famine, would live together in perfect harmony. Equality and contentment would be maintained as self-sustaining values, and the common bond of experience and empathy would hold together this perfect world. All this could be achieved by radically altering the education system, shaking off the symbols of inequality and releasing the controlling grip of the state upon all things.

On the specific issue of population, there would be no need for the cycle of expansion, suffering and contraction, nor the requirement for the controlling forces of death, as humans would understand the need to live within their means in order to ensure happiness. Thomas Malthus disagreed, and proceeded to deconstruct his father's case. And so convincing was his argument, that his father urged him to write it down.

Chapter Nineteen
Where Did He Get That Hat? The Origins of Malthusian Thinking

Malthus' theory did not come out of thin air. They seldom do, at least in my experience. I firmly believe that the origin of an idea tells us more about the idea than the idea itself. Since Malthus' essay has been used as the basis of everything from ecological carrying capacities through to the theory of evolution by natural selection (Darwinian evolution), it is essential that we grasp exactly where it came from. I would suggest that there were five contributory factors.

1. The demographic debate

Following John Graunt's publication in 1662, the subject of demography had drawn increasing interest, in two areas in particular: life expectancy and assessment of the number of soldiers that could be requisitioned in times of need. Edmond Halley developed more advanced methods of assessing life expectancy. Other Europeans, such as Willem Kersseboom (Holland), Johann Süssmilch (Germany), Antoine Deparcieux (France) and Leonhard Euler (Switzerland) all became involved in the *Population Controversy*, which hinged around whether or not the population of England and Wales had decreased or increased since William of Orange took the throne in 1688.

It wasn't that they were trying to implicate the Dutch king as a cause of population change directly, but rather because, in 1688, an estimate of the population of England and Wales had been made based on tax returns (a cunning ploy by a new monarch, ensuring maximum profit from his newly acquired kingdom), thus providing a base line measure. In fact, it was not until 1801 that the first census in England and Wales was carried out, some one hundred years after Iceland (1703) and half a century after Sweden (1749).

The Reverend Dr Richard Price (1723-91) wrote that the population of England and Wales had been falling rapidly since the invasion of William of Orange. He also warned that cities were destroying the food production capacity of the rural areas by drawing populations in from the country, leading to rural depopulation. This was exactly what John Gaunt had demonstrated almost a century earlier.

On the other side of the controversy, the Rev John Howlett claimed that the population was actually increasing and that cities posed no threat. This was an important issue, because demography as a subject was driven by its main use, the calculation of life expectancy within the insurance industry. It was important to predict how long someone might live in order to calculate payments. Otherwise, benefit schemes could become bankrupt, and that just wasn't cricket.

There was a significant move against performing a census. The reason for this was sold as an affront to human liberty, and linked to the overbearing control of the state, a touchy subject given what had happened in France. However, a deeper reason was the concern that England's enemies had much higher populations, and therefore more fighting men available.

There was a worry that if the number of males available for war was as low as some feared, other countries would be encouraged to attack, and the English might be equally discouraged, weakening their resolve to fight back. The use of a census to calculate fighting power had been discussed even in John Graunt's original work. Indeed it was felt strongly in certain quarters that population should grow faster, to supply the soldiers of the future.

So we see that military and economic issues played a significant role in the history of demography, as it has in many subjects. Take science, for example. Brian Martin (1983) writes lucidly on this, demonstrating that not only does science attract huge funding from the military, but that many of the significant scientific advances occur during wars. Nuclear research and computing are two such examples.

David Hume (1711-1776) and Adam Ferguson (1723-1816), two philosophers of the Scottish Enlightenment, both pointed to population growth as an issue. Much earlier, Giovanni Botero (c1544-1617), the Italian polymath, recognized that resources placed a limit on population growth. In his epic work *Delle cause della grandezza delle città* (On *the Causes of the Greatness of Cities),* published in 1588, he showed that a city existed as a balance between reproduction and nutrition, but when nutrition became limiting, the city would die. It was probably the earliest statement of the concept of *carrying capacity.* So the ideas expressed by Malthus had been around in one form or another, for centuries.

One writer who had a particularly powerful impact on Malthus was Robert Wallace (1697-1771), a Scots minister. He wrote an important book, called *Various Prospects of Mankind, Nature and Providence* (Wallace, 1969), in which he initially set out a utopian vision, where all were rich, equality ruled, and the population could rise and rise under a perfect government across the globe. However, he then added *"mankind would increase so prodigiously, that the earth would at last be overstocked, and become unable to support its numerous inhabitants".* Not so utopian after all!

In the end, the issue came down to whether the ever progressive human mind could alter the direction that natural drivers lead to, or whether the drive to reproduce would overpower the rational process. In this respect, Malthus favoured the latter, and so became the first significant environmental pessimist.

Arthur Schopenhauer's cripple carried by the beast that is the human will was foreseen by Malthus. He felt that there was no way to save ourselves, that mankind would not learn quickly enough, and would not be able to stop itself from overpopulation. The beauty of the utopian philosophies of Condorcet and Godwin, embracing the hopes of immortality and the aspirations of technology and reason combining to produce equality and peace, were merely dreams that would never be realized.

Given the high birth and death rates, a quarter of the population of England in 1798 would have consisted of children under ten years of age, and around one half of the population would have been under twenty years of age. So it is not surprising that Malthus was very aware of an apparently increasing population.

Populations increased, and brought with them increasing suffering. Malthus castigated Archdeacon William Paley (1743-1805) for equating a large population with a happy nation. Instead he corrected him by stating *"Increasing population is the most certain possible sign of the happiness and prosperity of the state: but actual population may be only a sign of happiness that is past"*.

In other words, if a population was increasing, then it had not reached its maximum, and so this meant that resources were still adequate to allow expansion and comfort. However, a large population may well represent one that has exceeded its resources, and now will be in great disarray, so total numbers cannot tell us how happy these people are.

2. Philosophical debate

The drive within the philosophers of the Enlightenment, such as Rousseau (though he differed on many topics from the *"mainstream"* thinkers), Condorcet, Godwin and Hume, focused on the liberation of the human mind, and this process was seen as fundamental to the progress of the human condition. Breaking free from the control of the State and Church, it instead built upon the three great pillars of reason, freedom and democracy. Thinking, reasoning individuals were central to a progressive society, and anything that suppressed their development was negative. Education, work and society must all serve as liberators to the potential that lies within each of us.

The drive towards using technology to solve our problems was one of the most significant outcomes of the Enlightenment, and the one, I will later argue, that has done greatest damage to our planet. While celebrated for its positive, and, in many respects, optimistic outlook for the human race, it put forward the human as being capable of thinking and designing their way towards greatness. In doing so, it encouraged humankind to further separate itself from the context from which it had come, and condoned the destruction of all that permitted us to exist in the first place.

Reductionism may lead to solutions, but often not the most sustainable ones. Faith in technology, rather than the celebration of our place within nature, could only lead to disaster.

And Malthus stood against this, pointing out that nature had its power, and that technology would fail. In many ways, I feel that he did not set out to counter the doctrine of the Enlightenment, but when he recognized the outcomes of this philosophy as wrong, he had no choice but to stand against the entire spectacle.

Francis Schaeffer (1912-1984), the controversial philosopher who founded *L'Abri* in Switzerland, where I had the great honour of studying (though, sadly, after his death), famously said that philosophies should be judged at their bottom line. In other words, what does it mean for us in the street?

Malthus exposed the Enlightenment as failing at the bottom line. The immortality, equality and freedom promised by this ideology are as far away now as they ever were, but even more obviously, the human race is just as blind to the destruction and misery it is bequeathing to the rest of the Biosphere.

From a standpoint of sustainability and ecosystem functioning, there is nothing enlightening about the Enlightenment. It merely led to the greater isolation of the human race from the rest of the Biosphere. In an effort to rid society of the oppressive regimes of Church and State, they threw the baby out with the bathwater, focusing on the human as the centre of everything, and pulling down the bridges between ourselves and the greater whole. His *Essay* wasn't just a milestone in demography, but a significant philosophical work. The attempts of Godwin and Condorcet to explain why the human population wouldn't spiral out of control were deeply flawed, as Malthus so convincingly pointed out.

3. Political debate

The French Revolution had a huge impact on England. France was its nearest neighbour and the two countries had shared a long history. The revolutionary events in France rocked the political world of England. Royal heads had been literally separated from their bodies. These were unsettling times anyway. The English Royal family had fled the shores of Britain only one hundred years earlier, supplanted by a Dutch king, and a mere half a century ago (1745), Bonnie Prince Charlie and his army had made it as far as Derby. Revolution, invasion and treason were all high on the minds of the State, and the land crawled with spies and counterintelligence.

It also brought to the forefront of debate the role of the state in society. As we have seen, many philosophers saw the future as dependent on individuals taking responsibility. The state was viewed as suppressing this process and, therefore, blocking progress. However the government and King in England had no intention of relinquishing authority, and as a result, many "free thinkers" were imprisoned at this time.

4. Religious background

What is abundantly clear is that the religious background of Malthus, particularly his vocation as a curate, had a huge impact on his writing. The Enlightenment was as much about freedom from religious persecution as anything else, and most of its advocates were celebrated humanists. It was humanity who could save itself. Indeed the freedom from the control, not just of a state religion, but from God, was important. Our paths were not controlled, our actions not judged, but rather we were free to think and to create our own paths and prospects. Progress lay within us, and our destiny was a heaven on Earth.

Malthus, on the other hand, brought the idea of a judgement day awaiting, the concept that we were all heading towards disaster as a result of the old nature within us. His three great natural restraints, war, famine and disease, were lifted directly from the last book of the Bible, the suitably apocryphal Book of Revelation, wherein we read *"And I looked and behold an ashen horse; and he who sat on it had the name Death; and Hades was following with him. Authority was given to them over the fourth of the earth, to kill with sword and with famine and with pestilence"*.

This horseman of the apocalypse would wreck vengeance on the Earth. Sword, famine and pestilence: the three Malthusian checks. Surely this is more than a co-incidence. In the second edition of the essay, he introduced the solution that we can use, moral restraint. Again, this was a very biblical theme.

Sir William Petty (1623-1687), one of the founding members of the Royal Society and a friend of John Graunt, suggested that the world's population would double six times before the Last Judgement. The Last Judgement would usher in the horsemen of the apocalypse, including the one that rode upon the ashen horse, Death. And so Malthus continued in a religious tradition going back centuries, of the end times, disaster, and of an inevitability that drove the human race towards the Judgement.

5. Population and Economics

Malthus set out an interesting example in his *Essay*. He predicted what would happen if more money was given to poor labourers. They would buy more meat, but because the meat was limited, the price would increase, meaning the poor would, once again, not be able to afford it. Then, due to increased demand for meat, more cattle would be reared, leading to more corn being fed to them, and so the corn would decrease in availability, leading to its price increasing.

The result of all of this would be that the poor would now not only have to go without meat, but without bread as well! This was no light-hearted reference. Increases in bread prices were recognized as having been a significant factor that ignited the French Revolution. Any mention of the French Revolution was enough to pump fear into the average politician or aristocrat at the time. Indeed, Gilbert Wakefield, the childhood tutor of Malthus, who secured his place in Jesus College, Cambridge, fell foul of this fear. Having written a pamphlet defending the Revolution, he was sentenced to two years in Dorchester Goal in 1798, and died shortly after release, from typhus contracted in the prison, aged only forty-five years. And so the use of bread in his argument demonstrates how Malthus was capable of powerful historical reference to make his point.

Chapter Twenty
Adam Smith and the Invisible Hand

Thomas Malthus claimed that a Scottish economist, called Adam Smith, not a London haberdasher, had the greatest influence upon his thinking. However Malthus would disagree with Smith on some fundamental issues. Adam Smith (1723-1790) was described by his contemporaries as a truly absent-minded professor. On one occasion it is said that while preparing a brew, he put bread and butter in the teapot with the hot water, and reported that the tea tasted awful! However in terms of his intellect, he was without equal. François-Marie Aroue, the famous French philosopher, more familiar to us by his nom-de-plume, Voltaire, once said of Smith, *"we have nothing to compare with him, and I am embarrassed for my dear compatriots"* (in Dawson, 1993).

Smith became the father of economics. His work had a huge impact on international trade, and he is accredited with the reform of European commerce. His writings, the greatest of which took him twenty-seven years to complete, have stood as classic examples of the Scottish Enlightenment.

Smith moved in heady circles, counting the leading philosophers of his times as friends and admirers. Yet all of this might not have happened. When he was four years old and visiting his uncle at the village of Strathenry in the Kingdom of Fife in Scotland, he was abducted by a bunch of vagrants. Fortunately, his uncle found out that he was missing and pursued the vagrants, recovering the little boy in the nearby Leslie Woods. It is ironic that the father of free trade was almost enslaved!

Smith's writing produced two significant books. The first, published in 1759, was entitled *The Theory of Moral Sentiments* (Smith, 2010). This book was all about how we make moral judgements. He suggested that we did this by observing the behaviour of others, in turn enlightening ourselves about our own behaviour. This related to the thinking of men such as Condorcet, but, as we have seen, the French thinker approached things differently, saying that we experienced feelings within ourselves, and then recognized these in others.

So, in a way, Smith came at the problem from the opposite direction – the source of moral judgement stemming from others, and not ourselves. In both cases however, the outcome was similar. There was empathy, or sympathy, between humankind. This mutual sympathy was a bond, and led to the modulation of self-interest, and to the preservation of harmony, if allowed to do so.

This bore resonance with Hume, who proposed that judgement came, not from reasoning, but from a natural drive within us, when he wrote: *"Nature, by an absolute and uncontroulable [sic] necessity has determined us to judge as well as to breathe and feel"* (Hume 1955). Just as breathing and feeling are physiological and sensual responses, respectively, so moral judgement is a response to our recognition of how others resemble us.

The others are not acting as mirrors though, but, rather, they are part of us, and we are part of them. Thus social and behavioural cohesion become possible. This is important, because if we are able to experience human solidarity, then this opens the way for humans to progress together towards some form of utopian society.

Smith then took this idea and developed it within the context of economics in his second, most famous book: *An enquiry into the Nature and Causes of the Wealth of Nations* (Smith, 1994). This is usually referred to as, simply, *The Wealth of Nations*. As I mentioned earlier, he wrote this over a period of twenty-seven years! That's a long time, even for a classic in literature.

What makes *The Wealth of Nations* so influential? Well before it, the general economic style was a protectionist approach. The wealth of a nation was judged by how much gold was in the coffers, and so it made no sense to import things, as this meant you had to give some of the yellow stuff away.

It was a priority to keep your assets in your country. Smith demonstrated that free trade between nations was more profitable than closed trade. The nation's wealth should not be measured in gold and silver, but in production and commerce, what is now known as the *Gross National Product*.

The next point he made was that trade should be allowed total freedom to happen, and this became known as the *laizzez-faire* approach (literally leave to make or do). He then explained how this freedom would work. Self-interest was central to his thinking. People were driven by their own desire to survive and provide for their families.

It was this selfish desire that led a man to work long hours, setting up a business and contributing towards the national wealth. He famously wrote *"It is not from benevolence of the butcher, the brewer, or the baker, that we expect our dinner, but from their regard to their own interest."* In other words, these food suppliers are not working for our good, but for their own good.

Previously, Bernard de Mandeville (1670-1733), a Dutch immigrant living in England, had written an extremely controversial book, originally called *The Grumbling Hive* (Mandeville, 2007), where he set out that private vice stimulates society, while private virtue ruins it. In other words, there had to be greed to drive us on to make money, but that money would then be spent supporting a wide range of workers, providing employment. If this greed didn't exist, Mandeville argued, there would be a sharp decline in the nation's wellbeing.

Mandeville went on to suggest that society and virtue were merely constructs of a self-centred greed. It was all about selfishness, a theme that neo-Darwinism would return to, in the shape of the selfish gene, almost four centuries later, with concepts such as *pseudo-altruism*, *kin-selection* and *reciprocal altruism*.

Smith did not agree. Instead, he wrote that virtuous self-interest led to invisible co-operation. There was no need for a human guide. Instead, Smith introduced one of the most interesting and mysterious metaphors in the English literature, and one that we will come back to in the final section of this book: *the invisible hand*.

He wrote *"He intends only his own gain, and he is in this, as in many other cases, led by an invisible hand to promote an end which was no part of his intention. Nor is it always the worse for society that it was no part of his intention. By pursuing his own interest he frequently promotes that of the society more effectually than when he really intends to promote it"* (Smith, 1994).

So here we see him trying to make sense of what appears to be an emergent property in economics, how the activities of lots of small guys end up producing an economic outcome with particular characteristics. The invisible hand is central to his economic theory. It meant that you could really leave trade as free (*laissez-faire!*) and from this freedom would emerge an ordered marketplace.

However, Adam Smith went further, saying that social order would grow best within an open, competitive market place. In this he was bringing his two books together. The invisible hand that produced the best economic outcome for a nation also acted to produce the best social outcome. Social wellbeing was in resonance with economic freedom. And so he tied social order and economic progress together. This was radical. It may have taken twenty-seven years, but we could say that it was worth the wait!

There are tensions in his writing: sympathy and self-interest, monopoly and free trade, to name but two. How could the sympathy that glued us together co-exist with the self-interest that drove our economy? Surely, free competition would eventually lead to survival of the fittest in the form of huge monopolies, thus killing free trade?

The invisible hand was central to resolving these issues. Emerging from our sympathy for one-another, comes a moderating influence that tempered our self-interest. He also believed that the invisible hand would work to keep trade free. This latter belief appears to have been challenged by the economic theory of capitalism, where self-interest would appear to ignore the invisible hand, leading, instead to monopolies and mergers.

We see the familiar theme of the Enlightenment: human progress. If given the freedom and if sensitive to the touch of some influence that reached through them, humanity could build a beautiful world, where all could thrive and enjoy the wealth of the nation. He stressed that the quantity of labour available was important, so an increasing population would lead, with proper investment, to increased production, particularly if division of labour was applied. This would reduce competition, and lead to specialization, one person doing one job, efficiently and effectively, and depending on others for the success of the whole.

This is where Malthus strongly disagreed. Although hugely influenced by Adam Smith (he said that he was the greatest influence upon his thinking), he believed that an increasing population would bring disaster, not economic success, and he pointed to agriculture, rather than economics, as the key issue. If we can't feed ourselves, then what use is economics to us?

Malthus said that investment should be focused on agriculture, not industrial production. He also felt that there would always be poverty, since there would always be greater access to resources by the more powerful individuals. As opposed to man finding a way, guided by some invisible hand, populations would always rise to fill the resource space available, driven by an *invisible urge*, as opposed to an invisible hand, to procreate. Thus, his argument was with the utopian philosophy that garnered the Enlightenment. His was a shot of realism, but it didn't go down well with many thinkers in subsequent years.

Chapter Twenty-One
Malthus in the Dock

His detractors came from an extraordinarily broad church, from the Church itself to the humanist camp, from the architects of Socialism to the movers and shakers of the capitalist and industrialist schools, from communist leaders to conservatives and from creationists to evolutionary biologists, and it wasn't always even civil! His work seems to have really rubbed a lot of people up the wrong way, including some of the most powerful people on the planet at their time. If he had lived under them, he would likely have been parted from his head, literally, or sent to a Gulag in Siberia. Many were for much less!

The Socialists, such as Friedrich Engels and Karl Marx, expressed their fury at what they perceived as his assertion that the poor were a natural outcome of human existence and responsible for their own hardship because of their uncontrolled procreation. They argued instead that Capitalism drove the increase in population, thus suppressing the poor (Marx *et al.*, 1987; Meeks, 1953). Vladimir Lenin, the creator of the Soviet Communist Party and founder of the USSR, echoed these sentiments, claiming that Malthus' essay was *"an attempt to exonerate capitalism and to prove the inevitability of privation"* (Lenin, 1913).

For evolutionary biologists, the subject was a tricky one, because their great icon, Darwin himself, had acknowledged the huge debt he owed to Thomas Malthus, for providing the cornerstone of his theory. However some have tentatively placed their criticisms on the table. John Maynard Smith (1920-2004), one of the most erudite of modern neo-Darwinists, claimed, in 1958, that Malthus had over-estimated the impact of famine as a controller of population (Smith, 1958).

However this view has been undermined recently, by the discovery that a supervolcano, exploding at the present day Lake Toba in Sumatra, some seventy thousand years ago, is thought to have led to a volcanic winter, killing most of the humans, and leading to a genetic bottleneck that had a significant impact on the human race (Jones, 2007; Robock *et al.*, 2009; Williams *et al.*, 2009). The key driver of mortality here would have been the slow-down in plant photosynthesis, leading to starvation.

So famine could well have been responsible for the greatest killing in human history. Certainly famines induced by droughts have over-turned many dynasties, including the Moche and Mayan civilizations, the Anasazi, the Early Egyptian Kingdom, the Late Uruk Mesopotamian society, the Tinanaku Andian civilization, the Akkadian Empire and the Khmer civilization at Angkor (Abbott *et al.*, 1997; *Bar-Matthews et al.*, 1999; Buckley *et al.*, 2010; Cullen *et al.*, 2000; Dalfes *et al.*, 1997; Goring-Morris and Belfer-Cohen, 1997; Hodell *et al*, 2001). Drought means crop failure, and crop failure means famine.

Other critics claim that Malthus completely overlooked the possibility of human technology being able to increase food production. The American economist, Henry George, quoted by Julian Simon (1993), famously quipped *"Both the jayhawk and the man eat chickens; but the more jayhawks, the fewer chickens, while the more men, the more chickens!"* He obviously hadn't heard about the chickens on Rapa Nui.

Such cursory dismissal of Malthus, as an outdated and baseless pessimist, has also recently been heard in the corridors of power in Washington D.C. John Kemp, the then US Secretary of Housing and Urban Development, is reported as saying, in 1992, *"People are not a drain on the resources of the planet"* (Kemp, 1992), while Malcolm Forbes Jnr., a former American presidential candidate, and editor of *Forbes Magazine*, remarked, in an editorial in 1992, when responding to the idea that over-population has created global problems, *"It's all nonsense"* (Forbes, 1992).

Finally, the capitalists and conservatives took great exception to the idea that continued unending industrial progress was not possible. Technology was the great saviour of mankind, as all the thinkers of the Enlightenment had promised, and science would see us through. The ideas of diminishing returns, and demand exceeding supply, were, surely, nonsense. And hasn't that turned out to be true? After all, the population has massively expanded since Malthus, and we're all doing pretty well. We'll reflect on this at the end of this section.

Before that, we need to return to the demographic implications of his work, and to one particular concept that sprang from it, the carrying capacity, one of the most contentious, contested and misunderstood ideas in demography and population ecology as a whole.

Chapter Twenty-Two
Verhulst and the Logistic Curve: From the Cliff Face to the Mountain Plateau

Whatever we think about Robert Maltus' work, two things are clearly correct. Firstly, if a population was not hindered in any way, and so was free to carry on reproducing, that population would quickly increase in size. Imagine a bacterium that divides in two, producing two *"offspring"*. These then divide, to produce 4 offspring. Then 8, then 16, then 32, then 64, then 128, then 256, then 512, then 1024. If division occurred every 24 hours, within one hundred and one days there would be 2^{100} bacteria (i.e. it takes one day to produce two bacteria, so another 100 days of doubling gives us 2^{100}). That is 1 267 650 600 228 229 401 496 703 205 376 bacteria! That's one thousand two hundred and sixty seven million million million billion.

Even for something as small as a bacterium, this represents a huge quantity of bacteria! We know that a single *Escherichia coli* weighs about six hundred billionth of a gram (Ilic *et al.*, 2004), and therefore a billion *E. coli* weigh six hundred grams. So after one hundred days, the mass of bacteria would be seven hundred and sixty million, million, million kilograms. Putting this another way, after 113 days, the bacterial mass would be heavier than our planet!! If we plotted this growth on a graph we would get the curve in Figure II.2. It's called a *geometric curve*. Basically it starts slowly, but with time the population accelerates upwards like a cliff face.

The second point made by Malthus that is irrefutable, is that this doesn't happen. There is not a pile of bacteria the size of the Earth sitting somewhere out there in a giant warehouse. In other words, populations do not grow endlessly. So there must be something slowing down growth. This was his point. Populations eventually run out of resources and stop growing. They level off, due to pressure upon them.

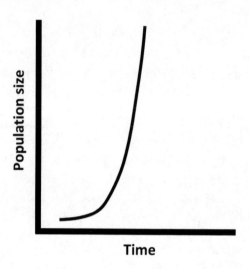

Time

Figure II.2 The geometric curve, representing unrestricted population growth.

Pierre François Verhulst was a Belgian mathematician who read Malthus' paper and decided to try to model how this might happen. As a population grows, each member of it uses the resources available. The more bugs, the more resources get used up. Now since resources are not limitless, eventually, there will be no more food left. Imagine some people trapped in a room. Each day, a lorry arrives and dumps some food in through a chute. At the start, everything is fine.

There's more than enough food falling through the chute each day to feed them. Burgers, cokes, pimento olives stuffed with lemon and those delicious little jam tarts in packets of six! However, if these people start to reproduce, but the lorry continues to deliver the same amount of food, then eventually there will not be enough food to go around. Soon, females and males will not have enough energy to reproduce, and infants are likely to die because they cannot receive adequate nutrition.

The scene becomes very grim, and population numbers grind to a halt as reproduction rates equal death rates. The population reaches an upper limit, defined by the food available, and can't get any bigger. Verhulst realized that to model this, he had to have an increasing pressure on the growth rate, which was based on the number of individuals present. As that number approached the maximum possible, reproduction would slow down to a standstill, and the population would level off at a plateau.

He called this effect density-dependent growth. By this he meant that growth depended on how many people were locked in the room. You can see the mathematics behind this model, if you are interested, in Appendix I of this book, but the bottom line is, we get a different curve, the one shown in Figure II.3. It's called the *logistic curve* (For more details, see Appendix I).

Things start slowly, because initially there are small numbers of organisms. It then enters a rapidly growing phase, a bit like the geometric curve. However, due to increasing use of resources, it starts to slow down, and then levels off. The level it eventually reaches is called the *carrying capacity*. This term simply represents the number of a particular organism that can be supported, or carried, by a given habitat.

Different habitats can support more or less organisms, depending on the resources available. If a field had one apple tree, and another otherwise identical field had six apple trees, then the carrying capacity for apple strudel monsters (a rare, in fact, nonexistent beast, living in the imagination of the author, who only eats apple strudel) will be six times higher in the second field compared to the first one. More apple trees mean more apple strudel monsters! Simple.

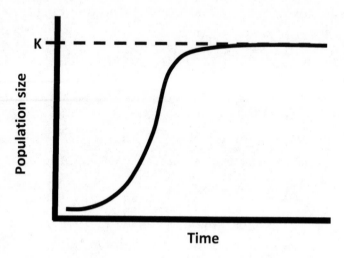

Figure II.3 The logistic curve, showing population growth, initially geometric, but gradually slowing due to density-dependent feedback. **K** represents the carrying capacity, which is the maximum population that a habitat can sustain.

Chapter Twenty-Three
The Trouble with Carrying Capacity...

The steam ship owners were up in arms in 1845. It just wasn't right. Certainly not a level playing field, or whatever the equivalent aquatic metaphor would be. There was definitely a conspiracy. Those canvas lubbers were nothing but low-life thieves! Steam was the future, and the sooner these wind-powered fools woke up to that, the better. You can't halt progress, so the quicker the tax laws were made fairer, the quicker they could move forward to a better future! With steam, it didn't matter where the wind came from. No longer blown around at the whimsy of Mother Nature, steam allowed us to march ahead, man and machine (a very *enlightened* view!).

The dispute was all to do with how tax was calculated on cargo carried by a ship. It was a calculation made, based on the length and breadth of a boat, to estimate the volume of cargo it could hold. Only those two measurements were made. But a steam-driven boat had to contain much more machinery than did a sailing boat, so its actual volume available for cargo was less than the calculation showed. Thus, steam boats were paying for more cargo capacity than they actually had.

And so, on 13th January 1845, the term 'carrying capacity' entered the English language, in a letter from John Calhoun, the Secretary of State in the USA. The volume was calculated separately for each boat, rather than using the overall dimensions. The term quickly spread to rail and canal transport. However it wasn't until 1886 that it was applied to ecology, or, more specifically, agricultural ecology. George Thomson (1848-1933), a New Zealand scientist, and one of the first to recognize the threat of invasive species, calculated the impact of rabbits on the carrying capacity of rangeland. This was significant in a number of ways. It highlighted, unintentionally, one of the great problems with carrying capacity. It doesn't necessarily remain constant through time.

We don't live in a static diorama, a snow globe, where nothing ever changes except for populations. Our activities, and the activities of every other living creature, have impacts upon our habitats, and upon the habitats of every other living creature. And so the carrying capacities of all the creatures on this planet are forever changing. Many decrease, while others increase. Some drop to zero, like that of the tree-nesting frigate birds of Rapa Nui whose trees were all chopped down. No trees, no nests, no birds. The bottom line is that carrying capacity is not a fixed value for a habitat.

The other point to make is that carrying capacities can be deliberately manipulated. If we don't want a particular organism around, then we can either kill it or remove its habitat. In other words, we can reduce the carrying capacity of the habitat. An example of this would be to drain a swamp in order to eradicate a mosquito population.

I remember working in the Arima Valley, in the Northern Range of Trinidad, with a group of students on expedition. Some colleagues from North America, staying in the same accommodation as us, were studying guppies, the favourite fish of the evolutionary biologist, and had set up a series of water basins to keep some specimens. Somehow, the authorities heard about this, and early one morning, a group of officials arrived, ordering their removal. This was because Trinidad was actively eliminating habitats where the dengue fever vector, a mosquito, could reproduce (it has an aquatic larval stage). And these Americans' basins were part of that habitat!

We often seek to increase carrying capacity of a particular species. In the glens of Angus in Eastern Scotland, where I live, pheasant shooting is an important part of the economy in the estates that encompass the glens. Pheasants need mature heather to lay their eggs in, protecting them from the sight of predators, but the young pheasants cannot eat the older heather. They only like eating young shoots, which are much more nutritious, and contain lower levels of defensive chemicals. So gamekeepers burn sections of the heather-covered hills every winter.

The correct intensity of fire leaves the roots intact (a skill that involves ensuring the fire passes through quickly), from which new shoots emerge. They leave neighbouring sections unburnt, forming a sort of patchwork quilt across the countryside. This is perfect for the pheasants – ideal nesting areas of mature heather, bordered by areas of juicy young shoots for the 'children' to eat. The pheasants must think that the humans are their great providers, doing all this work for them – so nice, thoughtful and benevolent – until 1st October each year, when the open season begins and bullets start to fly.

Farming, in a way, is all about the manipulation of carrying capacity. We reduce the capacity of pests and competitors, such as insects and weeds, and increase the capacity for the livestock and crops. But, of course all this manipulation is really part of a much bigger programme – that of maintaining, and increasing our own carrying capacity. For, ultimately, that is what agriculture is all about.

So we see that in our efforts to do this, we deliberately manipulate the carrying capacity of other species for the good of our own species. Of course we aren't the first species to farm. Leaf-cutting ants cut leaves, not to eat, but to create a mulch to grow fungi on. They are farmers *par excellence*, tending their fungal gardens to optimize their growth. Termites and *Ambrosia* beetles do the same. In fact, giant termite mounds, so evocative when you come across them, are now thought to be largely designed to act as air conditioning units for the fungal farms at their bases, drawing air through these fungal gardens and up through the chimney stack.

Among fish, only one species appears to have taken up farming. It is the damselfish (*Stegastes nigricans*), which farms the red alga, *Polysiphonia*, tending it and weeding out other algal species in coral reefs (Hata and Kato, 2006). Meanwhile, some ant species farm livestock, caring for and milking aphids. Aphids feed by injecting a sharp needle into plant transport systems, and sucking out the sugary liquid. It's a vegetarian equivalent of what female mosquitoes do. They often suck too much syrup, and the excess passes through them. Ants can drink this excess liquid. The ants protect and herd the aphids, and some even clip their wings, so that they cannot escape!

However, we have taken farming to a whole new level, transforming much of the planet to form the most dominant ecosystem on the Earth, the agroecosystem. Altering the soil, removing as many other species as we can, pouring on chemicals to kill the unwanted and encourage the wanted, draining huge areas, flooding other areas, removing pristine, ancient habitats and replacing them with high throughput food factories. Industrial agriculture is big business and essential for our huge population.

So our strategy of increasing the carrying capacity comes at a significant cost to many other species. Our pesticides, herbicides and fertilizers hugely impact on the natural world. Killing a pest may sound well and good, but what of the bird that depends on that pest to feed its fledglings? Toxins entering target organisms do not always kill them before they are eaten and, as we have seen from DDT, as so vividly described in *Silent Spring*, by Rachel Carson (Carson, 2002), these toxins can accumulate and pass through the food chain.

The draining of swamps to prevent malaria or dengue fever destroys the habitat of many species. Don't forget that mosquitoes contract malaria from us as much as we contract it from them! They are vectors, not disease agents. It's like blaming the train for a terrorist on board. The terrorist may step off the train onto our platform, but, equally, the terrorist must have stepped off a platform somewhere else in order to board the train in the first place. So should we destroy the train, the platform, neither or both?

Seventy percent of rainforest destruction is carried out for cattle ranching. And we don't even need to eat beef! So the loss of uncounted species from this devastating clearance is really to satisfy some unnecessary luxury consumption. Something like one tenth of this land could provide the same food energy in the form of crops (based on cattle capturing ten percent of the available energy in plants). That's why food pyramids are pyramids, not cubes. The higher up you go, the less energy is passed on. So the higher up the pyramid you live, the more land is needed to sustain you. However, as omnivores, we have a choice.

It is the carrying capacity that holds the key to understanding what has happened human populations. So let's return to our hockey stick curve.

Chapter Twenty-Four
The Hockey Stick Curve Revisited

Many people think that the curve of human population growth is like Verhulst's logistic curve - there is a lag phase, then a rapid growth phase (which they say we are in) and then it will eventually level out when we reach our carrying capacity. In other words, the hockey stick curve is just an example of how everything else grows. It just looks weird because we haven't reached the limit yet. But there is no need to panic, because in a century or two it will level off. So we are not in a geometric growth curve, escalating ever-upward to our destruction. Malthus is irrelevant.

Let me explain why this is a dangerous misinterpretation. The hockey stick curve is *not* a logistic curve. We are not on some natural growth path. The hockey stick curve represents extreme manipulation of the carrying capacity across our globe. Secondly, the human population of the planet cannot be equated to the squirrel population of a forest. By this I mean that the human population is not a single population at all, but many populations, in many different habitats, each with their own carrying capacity, and each in a different place in time as well as space, in terms of their growth.

For example if we look at annual human population growth rates, the global figure is 1.14% (i.e. doubling every sixty years, calculated by $r^t N$ (where r = 1.014 and t = 60), whereas that of Niger is 3.66% (doubling every twenty years) and that of the Northern Mariana Islands is -5.57% (halving every thirteen years). So the hockey stick curve hides lots of different stories within it.

Also, the handle of the hockey stick is far too long to be a logistic curve. The human population appears to have been in a lag phase for most of its existence, only recently entering the hockey blade phase of rapid increase. This is not what should happen. The reason for this is that the human race reached its natural carrying capacity a very long time ago.

It's just that the current population size drowns out earlier changes. When we fit the data onto a set of axes, in order to have it reach the seven billion that it has, the earlier population changes don't even register. But these earlier changes warrant our attention, as they clearly support Malthus' thinking, where disease, famine and war have had very significant impacts on the global population.

War
The Mongol attacks on China, during the thirteenth and fourteenth centuries AD, decimated the population within eighty years, reducing it from an estimated sixty million to just ten million (the loss of some sixteen percent of the world's population at that time). The Spanish invasion of Mexico reduced the population from twenty-five million in 1519 to two-and-a-half million in 1608. The Thirty Year War (1618 to 1648) reduced Germany's population from twenty-one million to thirteen-and-a-half million. Although the Second World War accounted for some sixty million lives, this was only about three percent of the world's population, while the An Shi Rebellion in China, around 750 AD, accounted for some fifteen percent of the global population. That's the equivalent of over a billion people today.

War, then has had a very significant impact on populations, particularly in the past.

Pestilence

Smallpox killed at least three hundred million people in the twentieth century alone, and many more before this. Thankfully it is now eradicated. Bird flu killed over eighty million people in just two years at the end of World War I. The outbreak was called Spanish flu, although it is now thought to have originated in Étaples in France. Étaples was at the centre of the supply wagon wheel of the allied forces, where troops assembled, then dispersed to the various frontline areas. It was a perfect place for a virus to spread from.

Plague in Europe in 1340 is thought to have claimed between a third and two-thirds of the population of Europe, and many more globally. Europe was irreversibly changed by this vast mortality, and it altered the balance of power in many countries. Plague continued to pass across the face of the Earth at regular intervals. In 1629, plague in Italy killed a quarter of the population in the north of the country. Malaria, although not of the death count of the plague, kills two million people regularly, and mostly children. However it is on the rise, possibly encouraged by climate change.

Famine

In terms of famine, there have been some terrible events. By far the worst in recent times was the Great Chinese Famine between 1959 and 1961, when up to forty-three million people are believed to have died. This compares to the one million Ethiopians whose deaths spurred the famous *Live Aid* concert in 1985.

Four famines, also in China, in the nineteenth century, are thought to have claimed another forty five million lives. Earlier than this, in the tenth century AD, the Mayan civilization was wiped out by a drought-induced famine and millions died. Perhaps the biggest famine event, in terms of demography, may have occurred seventy thousand years ago, when, as was mentioned earlier, a volcanic eruption in Indonesia is thought to have led to the collapse of ecosystem structure, and reduced the human population to as little as a few thousand people (Williams *et al.*, 2009).

Going back further in time, mass extinctions have often operated through famine, due to significant drops in temperature or available sunlight, or both, caused by dust in the atmosphere generated from volcanic or asteroid impact origins. The deaths here are mostly caused by the food chains collapsing, with the result that animals starve to death. So famine has probably had a vast role in shaping the zoology of our planet over geological time. Indeed the rise of the primates was indirectly due to the famine following the KT event.

In fact, just about all natural catastrophes, be they floods, fires, droughts, tsunamis or asteroid impacts, will ultimately kill through famine, as primary productivity is impacted upon.

These factors would have kept the population of humans at a steady state, with births equalling deaths. The carrying capacity for man as a nomadic hunter gatherer would have been much lower than today. It has been estimated at one hundred million. Peter Kunstadter, the demographer, refines this idea, in his crisis model, saying that intermittent disasters, like the Toba supervolcano, would have kept the population in check (Kunstadter, 1972).

Disease may not have become a major issue until humans moved from a nomadic lifestyle to settlements. Because they lived in tight-knit, isolated groups, not staying in one place long enough to create filthy conditions, then infectious diseases would not be able to spread, and other conditions, such as cholera, that require dirty water, would not have the opportunity to occur.

War, for early man, is unlikely to have been an issue. So famine, be it from drought or volcanic ash, would have been the main limitation, as well as a series of ice ages which dominated the last two million years, coincident with the existence of man. During an ice age, moisture becomes trapped in glaciers, thus dramatically reducing rainfall. This, combined with a decrease in temperature, would have realized itself as famine, given the fact that man is a warm-blooded creature, whose maintenance costs rapidly increase in cold weather.

The key to understanding human populations at this time is to understand the vegetation, particularly the food plants needed by humans directly, and by the animals they hunted. Any change in the carrying capacity of these plant and animal species would directly impact on the carrying capacity for the humans themselves.

Chapter Twenty-Five
What If We Were All Seventy-Kilogram Lizards?

So the long handle of the hockey stick was a result of natural processes controlling the carrying capacity. The human population was governed by classical Malthusian checks. Humans were living at their carrying capacity. True there were relatively few of us, but then there are relatively few of any species of seventy kilogram, warm-blooded, milk-feeding, huge-brained omnivores.

We're a bit like a big car, whose fuel consumption is very high. We have lots of modern conveniences, but they are all very expensive to run. I often reflect that of all the animals to take over the world and expand their populations, we are the worst, because of the huge expense it costs just to keep us alive. If cold-blooded lizards, each weighing seventy kilograms had swollen to a population of seven billion, they would be a much lower burden upon the Biosphere than we are!

As we moved into settlements, and developed farming, disease increased, keeping the populations low. Domestication of animals brought humans in contact with insect disease vectors, tapeworm and animal faeces. Water became infected with cholera and dysentery. Soon, as population densities increased, vector-free diseases appeared, including tuberculosis, which did not require intermediaries such as flies, but, rather, passed directly from human to human.

As Graunt demonstrated, cities became drains on populations, with London sucking in and spitting out, dead, six thousand people per year from rural England. City economics did not produce healthy people, but dead ones. In Japan, by the mid-seventeenth century AD, a similar situation emerged. Akira Hayami demonstrated, by careful historical demographic analysis, that the large cities of Japan also drew rural people in and killed them. They became stagnated in terms of population growth (Hayami, 2001).

The story of the long handle is one of populations living at their carrying capacity. Nature oversaw this, and, combined with crisis events, the hunter gatherer stayed at a relatively low numbers for a long time, mainly limited by food. So famine was the key controller. Settlement brought disease and war, the two other controlling factors. Although agriculture advanced to ease the pressure from food limitation, the new pressures of war and disease kept a lid on any population explosion. Cities became killing zones, with disease rampant. Trade, free and otherwise, between nations spread disease further, from city to city across the globe.

Chapter Twenty-Six
The Hockey Blade: of Fleas and Teas

So why the hockey blade? In other words why did things change so dramatically since the eighteenth Century? Although agriculture was now producing much more food, disease was the main challenge. It was the improvement of hygiene in cities that was so important, and huge progress was made in this area over the last two hundred years. Sharp declines in tuberculosis and scarlet fever, along with the disappearance of bubonic plague, which had ravished Europe for four hundred years between the fourteenth and eighteenth centuries AD, were hugely important.

In terms of the disappearance of bubonic plague, it is thought that this was due to a very unusual cause, the fussy eating habits of the flea! It has been suggested that the flea species involved in spreading the plague stopped biting humans, developing distaste for them (Chambers, 1972). It is also thought that the flea species involved in spreading the plague, *Xenopsylla cheopis*, basically went extinct as a result of the plague, and was replaced by a nest-building species that didn't roam around, therefore not encountering humans (Hirst, 1953). Finally, the black rat (*Rattus rattus*), that was the key source of plague, again suffered considerable losses due to the plague, allowing the brown rat (*Rattus norvegicus*) to replace it. The brown rat, unlike the black rat, shuns human habitation, and so chances of contact were greatly reduced.

The other unexpected contributor to improved health is thought to have been the shift to drinking tea! The reasons for this are as follows. Tea requires boiled water, which kills many significant disease organisms. Also, there was a move from clay to china cups, which are much more hygienic, because being less porous, they provide less room for bugs to hide, and are more easily washed.

Hence, well before the advent of fertilizers and antibiotics, things were looking up for the city dwellers. Public health measures played a huge role in lifting the check of disease. Now the new settlement plan, of rural agriculture supporting city dwellers, could work much better, without the cities acting as killing zones. So the carrying capacity had been raised, with the checks of famine and disease partly removed. They are still there, but not to anything like the extent that they were. Wars, unfortunately continue.

The development of free trade led to an increase in export. Thus, industrialized cities were not only producing goods for their own nations, but also for an expanding world. This led to a huge growth in production capacity, needing more people to work in the cities and putting greater demand on agriculture. This positive feedback, between free trade and agricultural demand, fulfilled Malthus' concerns with putting economics ahead of agriculture. He recognized agriculture as key.

Fertilizers were the next big discovery, hugely increasing agricultural productivity. As more and more land was brought under the plough, much of it was unsuitable for intense farming. The ecosystems that had existed in these areas, such as rainforests and heath, were low nutrient systems, carefully controlled to recycle everything. Agriculture doesn't work like this. The harvest time is like a giant vacuum cleaner, sucking up the goodness of the soil and taking it away for humans to eat.

You cannot keep taking. Eventually, you need to start giving back. As cities grew, the taking had to increase. Fallow years just couldn't happen anymore. And so the Haber-Bosch process, which produces nitrogen fertilizer, and the mining of phosphates allowed us to pour the goodness back in, quickly. No need to wait on Nature's recycling organisms, the fungi, bacteria, earthworms and the like. We could just spray the fields.

And so we have continued, ever raising the bar, allowing the population to continue its geometric rise. Pushing the carrying capacity further and further up, we have now escaped the Malthusian checks to a great extent. As I said, the hockey stick is not a logistic model; it is a contortion, created by technology, allowing more and more energy to flow through the human race. Occasional wars, famines and disease outbreaks still occur, killing millions, but because the background population is so large, and is in a geometric growth state, these terrible events have little effect on the global population.

Surely then, you say, the philosophers of the Enlightenment had it right after all, and Malthus had it very wrong. We can just keep pushing the bar upwards. We control carrying capacity now, not the other way around. We'll just keep raising the invisible ceiling and never bang our heads on it. The lift is never going to reach the top of the building, because we can build another storey on to the top of it. What then is the problem? Why don't we just enjoy the ride and stop all of this pessimistic gripping?

The problems come in two forms, and each requires careful consideration due to their significance for our future. One is ecological, and one is philosophical. And we need to wake up to both of them. The hockey stick curve is trying to tell us something, and if we don't listen, then we really do deserve all that we get.

Chapter Twenty-Seven
The Man Who Built His House on the Backs of Four Elephants

Once upon a time, long ago, there was a man who lived in the forest in a land far away beyond the horizon. He had the amazing ability of training animals to do exactly what he said they should do. He had a lion that would fetch his newspaper from the newsagents, a wombat that shined his shoes every morning and a very large ostrich who cooked for him. But his crowning achievement was his house. He built it on top of four huge elephants.

Sitting in his living room, he could order them to go wherever he wanted. In the summer, they carried the house up into the coolness of the high hills. In winter, they moved it to the sunny southern coast. He could visit his friends without ever leaving his veranda. And as for the drive-in cinema, or the fast food restaurant, well he could reach them without leaving his favourite rocking chair. It certainly saved on delivery fees.

He was the master of all that he could survey, and everything obeyed him. For nature was there for the sole purpose of making his life enjoyable. And nature was a lot less insightful, imaginative and, to be honest, intelligent than he was. Anyway, all these creatures were much better off serving him. Otherwise, the place would be chaotic – things eating other things, disease, injury, death. For, as that American film director, Woody Allen, once said, *"To me, nature is... I dunno, spiders and bugs and, big fish eating little fish, and plants eating plants, and animals eating...it's like an enormous restaurant"*.

It was also like a garden without a gardener, gone to seed, order lost and nothing but disorganization. What it needed was firm-handed management, and that's exactly what this man recognized was his role. Trimming, training, digging, sorting, moving, and, occasionally, killing, destroying and eradicating, these were the things that only he could do. It was better for nature, and it was definitely better for him. After all he and he alone had the big picture.

The only problem was that to maintain his house at such a lofty position, way up there on top of those massive elephants, he had to feed them. They were very hungry. I suppose you had to expect them to work up a bit of an appetite holding up such a heavy house, day and night. So every evening, he had to cut down huge amounts of foliage and bring it to the elephants. And each day he had to walk a little further to collect the foliage, as he'd chopped down all the trees and shrubs in his immediate area. So he found himself moving his house quite often, and lost his remaining links with where he had originally grown up.

But it didn't matter. He was living in a whole different world than his old friends. It was the brave new world of houses on elephants, of nature serving him rather than *vice versa*. His was the journey of progress, rational man and his machines, with nature tamed, the utopian vision he had once read about, now being realized.

Of course, he lived in a forest that seemed to go on forever, so it wasn't a problem...until, that is, the forest fire.

It hadn't been expected. No-one recalled anything so destructive happening in their lifetimes. But happen it did. The trees and shrubs and bushes all burnt down. Others, who lived in little houses on the ground, away from the trees, survived. And the man initially survived too. He told the elephants to run away from the forest fire. See how useful it was to have the bigger picture?

However over the coming weeks, he realized that there was no foliage left to feed his elephants. It had all burnt down. Soon they were grumbling, their stomachs rumbling. Then, one evening, as the man relaxed in his favourite sofa, made from the finest elephant hide, and sipped his quinine-loaded gin and tonic, there was an enormous crash, and everything in the room, including his elephant hide sofa with him on it, slid towards one corner.

He picked himself up, bruised, but otherwise fine, and climbed outside to see what had happened. One of the elephants had collapsed. It was dead. He heard a creak behind him and swung around, just in time to see his house slowly slide off the backs of the other elephants. It crumbled around him, killing him instantly. He'd failed to feed the elephants and now the whole house had come crashing around his ears.

Chapter Twenty-Eight
The Moral of the Story

The problem with building your house on the backs of four elephants is that you have got to keep feeding them. Elevating our carrying capacity, by increasing the flow of energy through the Biosphere, in order to produce the food and recreational energy needed to sustain our energy-expensive lifestyles, means that we are no longer living at our natural level. Many people seem to think that if we freeze the population at where it is today, or even in twenty years time, then there will be no problems. Wrong. We will still need to maintain the massively exaggerated numbers of people.

Professor Joel Cohen (Cohen, 1995), from Rockefeller University, New York, writing in *Science*, has calculated that between 1860 and 1991, the human population quadrupled. Over that same period, energy usage increased by ninety-three-fold. So the problem isn't actually the number of people, *per se*, but rather the amount of energy needed to maintain us in the way that we have become accustomed to.

The *per capita* energy use is escalating rapidly, exacerbating the problem of a geometric rise in population. And, as resources run low, we must work harder to keep the population elevated. Of course if any kind of large scale disaster should strike, we will be much less resilient to the trauma than if we were living on the ground. Elephants can die of starvation.

If you still think that our population at present is not a concern, then let's drop by the health centre for planetary well-being. Planet Earth has just been visiting to have its medical check-up. Just like us, samples were taken and analysed. As you look through the window into the doctor's office, Earth is sitting in a rather uncomfortable little chair at the side of the doctor's desk. However the doctor is shaking his head, and all is not well. There are clear signs, symptoms if you like, of a serious illness.

The planet looks concerned. When she'd looked in the mirror this morning, she didn't look any different than usual – her large deep blue oceans and green landscapes glinting in the morning Sun, with a few fluffy clouds scattered across her ample globe. True there was a rather unpleasant swirling hurricane, angry and powerful, cutting a swathe across her surface, but nothing particularly worrying. The doctor checks some paperwork and arrives at a diagnosis. She's suffering from what is known as the *human condition*, a horrible infection that afflicts planets like hers occasionally.

The energy flow, upon which we are so reliant, leaves behind some rather unpleasant side-effects. The three greatest causes of extinction at present are global warming, habitat destruction and eutrophication. Each one of these is directly a consequence of our attempts to maintain the human carrying capacity on the planet.

Global warming stems from our use of fossil fuels, in industrial processes, including the Haber-Bosch process, used to produce fertilizers for agriculture, on which some forty percent of the world's population depends for their very existence. The industrial revolution, hailed by adherents to the Enlightenment philosophy of Hume and Condorcet, has set in motion a technological spiral of consumption.

Habitat destruction is carried out to clear areas for crop plants and animal husbandry. Rainforest in the Amazon, equivalent to the area of France, has been cleared for cattle ranching alone.

Swamps are drained and forests felled to convert land for industrialized food production. Habitats are also fragmented by human infrastructure. Meanwhile our desperate need for water leads us to dam rivers and flood areas of important biodiversity.

Eutrophication is a silent killer. Here, the powerful fertilizers used to force the soil into greater productivity, leach out into the water, and horrifically distort natural habitats, leading to huge species loss and the crippling of sustainable ecosystem function.

Chapter Twenty-Nine
The Three New Apocalyptic Horsemen of the Twenty-First Century

So instead of the three horsemen of the Malthusian apocalypse, famine, disease and war, we have introduced three new destructive characters: global warming, habitat destruction and eutrophication. It is ironic that in our efforts to free ourselves from the original Malthusian checks, we have engineered three equally blood-thirsty killers across the globe.

What have these deadly dragoons, unleashed by humans in pursuit of that utopia, done to our Biosphere? David Woodruff (2001) estimates that current extinction rates are fifty to five hundred times higher than background. The International Union for the Conservation of Nature (IUCN, 2001) reported that over fifty percent of animal species are vulnerable, endangered or critically endangered. A quarter of all mammals, a third of all fish and up to a third of all plants are predicted to face extinction in the next few decades.

Please take the time to read this last paragraph again, slowly and out loud. If there is someone else in the room, don't be put off. They need to hear it. Gary Snyder, writing in 1990, summed up the appropriate reaction powerfully when he wrote *"The extinction of species, each one a pilgrim of four billion years of evolution, is an irreversible loss. The ending of the lines of so many creatures with whom we have travelled this far is an occasion of profound sorrow and grief. Death can be accepted and to some degree transformed. But the loss of lineages and all their future young is not something to accept. It must be rigorously and intelligently resisted."*

But it's not really about the individual species, tragic though this is. After all, the enlightened human-centric cynic might say *"What difference does it make to me if a six legged bright orange insect living in a tree in Paraguay goes extinct?"* Biodiversity isn't just about lots of pretty butterflies in your garden, or the opportunity to see a red squirrel in the park. Diversity maintains ecosystem function and provides ecosystem services to us. Reduced diversity leads to the collapse of ecosystems, as resilience is lost, due to increased susceptibility to disease, drought and floods. We are part of these ecosystems, and so our own resilience is threatened. Diversity is serious stuff, and decreasing it will have serious consequences.

What are these *ecosystem services*? In other words what does Nature actually do for us? According to the Millennium Ecosystem Assessment released by the United Nations in 2004, these services fall into four categories: supporting, regulating, provisioning, and cultural.

Ecosystems support life through the production of oxygen, the absorption of carbon dioxide, the formation of soil, dispersal of pollen and seeds and the recycling of nutrients and water. They regulate climate, water purity, pests and diseases, ameliorate flooding and carry out waste management. They provide food, fuel, hydropower, fibres and pharmaceuticals and they are central to cultural aspects of human society, such as education (that is of the Geddesian form, involving stimulation and inspiration), artistic and scientific research and recreation.

The Millennium Ecosystem Assessment found that of twenty-four ecosystem services on which we depend, seventy percent were degraded or unsustainably abused. Remember, again, the abuse will need to continue just to stay where we are, let alone if the population increases.

We aren't heading for a crisis, we are already in it. The symptoms of our misconceived ideas of progress, technology and superiority over nature, are all around us. *"He that hath an ear let him hear"*.

If Dr Dolittle was here, he'd tell us all about the conversations he'd had with the rest of the Biosphere. But, of course, we don't listen to the Biosphere, because it is not worth listening to, an irrelevant jumble of bugs and bushes that can't think, speak, or direct. Surely Dr Dolittle wouldn't get any sense from nature, because nature has neither reasoning nor awareness. Nature appears completely irrelevant to the twenty-first century machine that is the human race.

Technology, the great deliverer of the Enlightenment philosophers, has placed us in a trap, albeit one of our own making, and has unleashed three new equestrian assailants on the very ecosystems that support us. We are living far beyond our natural means, destroying the rest of the Biosphere. We are becoming increasingly dependent on the very technology that we thought was the swash-buckling sabre of progress. Alas, technology has turned out to be a two-edged sword.

We are paying a huge rent on a vast property, and we must keep paying the rent if we want to continue our high spending lifestyles. Seven billion bed-rooms, seven billion meals, seven billion holidays, seven billion cups of coffee. Of course not everyone can have all these things at present, but our aspiration is for the entire human race to have a lifestyle like ours. Banish poverty and join the energy orgy.

Yet from an "enlightened" viewpoint everything is working out as it should. Technology works to keep us moving forward along the path of progress. I speak to many people on this who say things like: *"Well what are the alternatives? Do you want us all to live in a cave? Surely you can't think that living in a Victorian slum is a thought worth contemplating?"* To be honest, there is little point in even answering these questions, because the questions reveal exactly where so many of us are living at present, in an isolated existence far removed from our true context. In this book, I want to attempt to burst this bubble. But what exactly is the bubble I am referring to? This brings us to the second great message of our curve.

Chapter Thirty
Bubbleworld: the Empirical Inheritance

Bubbleworld is a magical place. Those of us who live inside the bubble feel very content, gazing out through the almost transparent, extremely thin film that surrounds us on all sides, we can see the Biosphere. It's not particularly relevant to us, and we have no need, and certainly no desire, to interact with it. We can just float along, oblivious to the strains and groans out there, safely encapsulated in the calm comfortable space within. All of our points of reference are inside this film, and so, from this perspective, everything makes sense to us. Thoughts from outside the bubble are at best without value, and at worst, downright dangerous.

To understand life in *Bubbleworld*, we need to reflect on its inspiration. The Enlightenment really was an amazing period of philosophical thought. Never has a philosophy grown legs and arms and reached into the world quite like it. Of course, Communism has impacted on many people, as have religious philosophies such as Islam, Christianity, Hinduism and Buddism. But I would argue that nothing has had a greater influence on more people than the Enlightenment.

Why is this? Well, it is because it embraced and attempted to unite our understanding of human nature, politics, economics, technology, and education, while promising a utopia here on Earth and including lots of the yellow stuff, gold. Not bad for starters. It emerged from a reaction against state and church control, and sought to break free of these controls, bringing responsibility down to the individuals. These individuals, together, guided by some invisible hand that emerged from social interaction, would progress towards a perfect state. God was unnecessary. However in the earnest pursuit of a society freed from God and King, the focus was on man and man alone.

No need for a king, for a government, for a god, and no need for nature. This is why the philosophy of the Enlightenment, which was to lay the foundation for almost every nation on this Earth, was a philosophy of isolation. To escape both God and State, these thinkers turned to humans as the sole point of reference, socially, economically, technologically and morally. And it was then that we entered fully into *Bubbleworld*.

It is no co-incidence that many hockey sticks started to grow their blades at this time. Painted as progress, no room was left to look back and wonder. All the signposts pointed forward, and the past was an irrelevance. This included our natural context, the very essence from which we had emerged, kicking and screaming, and the fundamental system within which lies our only hope of a sustainable future, the Biosphere.

To further establish its credentials, the Enlightenment embraced the sexy topic of the day, science. All of the philosophers involved hailed technology as the way ahead, through which humans would discover the answers to all the problems facing them. Combining rational thought, moral reasoning and technology, anything and everything was possible. The philosophy of technology and science is a special one. It is called *Empiricism*.

Empiricism holds that knowledge only comes from sensory experience. By measuring things, we can work out how to manipulate processes for our own gain. By carrying out experiments we can understand these processes. Experimental science is the foundation upon which we test ideas (called hypotheses), and come up with theories. These theories can then be used to invent new solutions.

A key point relating to Empiricism is that in order to test an idea, the experiment must be extremely simple. Questions can only have one of two possible answers. Let me give you an example. If you want to know what makes a plant live in a particular place, we would need to design a whole series of experiments each one with all the conditions the same except for one.

If we change more than one thing at a time, then we won't be able to tell which one is having the effect. So we reduce the situation down to a simple one, where we can control one factor only. In fact we often carry out these experiments in a lab, where we can further simplify things.

If we did the research in woodland, where the plant normally lived, then sunlight, day length, humidity, temperature, predators, pollinators, disturbance and many other things could change from day to day, or even minute to minute. The soil is very heterogeneous, unlikely to be the same even a few centimetres apart (Averiss and Skene, 2000). Indeed, a given location in any particular woodland is quite possibly unique on this planet, with no one sod exactly the same as any other. Hence, many experiments on plants are carried out in acid-washed sand, or in nutrient solutions.

Think about what this means. Much experimental science advances by isolating subjects of study from their meaningful context, and by simplifying things, or reducing them. It is isolationist at its core, and so is a perfect bedfellow for the thinkers of the Enlightenment.

Another aspect of Empiricism is that it is a bottom-up system. This is called reductionism. In other words it looks at a building and sees it as being built from little bricks. The building is a product of the bricks. So by understanding the bricks we can understand the building. Take genetic engineering. Science says that genes make proteins, and proteins make everything else. So understanding the genes will open up our ability to understand the rest of it. The Human Genome Project is another classic case in point. It was believed that by sequencing the human genome we could work out how to cure diseases, and start to realize Godwin's dream of immortality.

So if we take a plant and put some new genes into it, reductionist thinking says that this can produce some outcome that is useful, to humans at least. We can add and take away blocks, changing the building, as we wish. Technology allows us to do this. Of course we may not realize what repercussions this could have on other organisms. Will the plant degrade and recycle as well as it used to? By giving it extra things to make, will we not affect how it can balance its energy budget? Many genetically modified plants only have an advantage if their new genes actually work, for example, in killing herbivorous insect pests.

Bruce Tabashnik reported, in Nature Biotechnology, that insect resistance to genetically modified crops, engineered with bacterial genes intended to kill the insects, has already appeared (Tabashnik, 2008). The altered crop will now actually be worse off than the original, un-amended plant, because it will still have to make the extra proteins, even though they don't work anymore. So they have an additional tax on them, leaving them less effective. Energy required in the production of now useless proteins doesn't go into making juicy corn. If, then, we have replaced all the plants in the farmers fields with our new genetically modified crop, as America has done with its soybean plants, and resistance has already been established, we will be left with a weaker plant than the original one.

Reductionist thinking, based on isolationist science, is a key symptom of *Bubbleworld*. We have cut ourselves off from the Biosphere, and we have removed context from our science. It is not surprising, then, that we find ourselves where we do. Our thinking is corrupted by the philosophy of the Enlightenment, whether we've even heard of the Enlightenment or not, entwined with a reductionist approach in science, and separated from the context of the Biosphere.

That's why decisions like pumping iron into the ocean to absorb carbon dioxide, releasing cane toads in Queensland to kill the insects, drilling the Arctic (and no doubt the Antarctic later) for further oil resources, spraying DDT on our crops, re-engineering the very plants that originally fed us, and continuing to pour fertilizers onto the soil to feed the world all make perfect sense.

Without a context, deep inside *Bubbleworld*, the planet reduced to its building blocks, enlightened by philosophy and strengthened by technology, it all appears quite sane. Yet outside the transparent film lies a completely different reality, one of interactions, of balance, of feedback, of intertwined priorities, where we are part of the thing, not separate from it.

Chapter Thirty-One
Conversing with the Curve

Isolationism: if it is all about us, then it makes sense. Whether created in the image of God, or sitting at the very top of the evolutionary tree, our genius, great wisdom and ability sets us far apart from the rest of it. And, isolated, we fail to grasp how out of step we are. Yet, human population growth is not following a natural path. It is not what we see in other populations, because the hockey stick curve is not a logistic curve. It is a disturbing corruption, distended, cruelly stretched from what it should be.

It keeps rising, but so does the smoke from a man whose shoes are on fire. Up may seem utopian. Look what we can do! We can defy Malthus! We can make smoke by setting our shoes on fire! Look how high the smoke goes – way up in the sky – it is wonderful. *"The only way is up, baby"* as Yasmin Evans, (stage name, *Yazz*) sang in 1988, while performing her manic cycling dance!

Adam Smith thought it was great. Increased wealth, he argued, led to decreased mortality and increased wages led to increased procreation. Demand for labour regulates population, so with greater demand comes better wages, and an increasing population. And of course, increased wages meant you could buy more resources. So although he stated *"every species of animal naturally multiplies in proportion to the means of their subsistence, and no species can ever multiply beyond it"*, half of a very Malthusian idea, he failed to consider that this could ever become a crisis.

However, the hockey stick blade cannot stretch forever. We will eventually reach its tip, and this is not a pleasant thing. Let's listen to the curve, let's feel what it tells us. This curve has teeth – it hurts to ride this bend, more than we can really ever imagine in our comfortable, artificial world. Remember the people locked in the room: starving, children dying, the putrid, rancid, overwhelming smell of decay and toxic waste, disease, conflict, accusation, anger, guilt, panic, pain, groaning and death. That pale horse.

Curves carry meaning. We'll see it again and again. Their clean lines on white paper tell nothing of the reality they represent. Think of each of your senses, the sights, the sounds, the smells, the pain, the taste of reaching the end of the blade. I used to think of the logistic curve as an elevator, starting slowly from the ground floor then rising quickly, before slowing down gradually to reach carrying capacity. However, the hockey stick doesn't work like this. It's an elevator ride to hell, one fit for a Stephen King novel, all your worst nightmares rolled into one horrific ride.

It's not an elevator we want to get into. Yet we have no choice because we are born into it. Imagine how much worse is the predicament we find ourselves in, because we are not on a logistic curve. Our own special curve, the hockey stick, promises even greater misery ahead, because we don't face a levelling off, but a significant downward correction. And falling is much more serious than levelling off. We will soon be in a position where not only will we struggle to support continued growth, we will find it difficult to stay where we are.

There's a wonderfully dark irony to all of this. Originally kept in check by Malthus' three natural horsemen of the apocalypse (famine, pestilence and war), we have instead created three new horsemen (global warming, habitat destruction and pollution) which have been unleashed on Nature in our very attempt to avoid her own equestrian incursion, yet the great likelihood is, that if we continue on this path, or fail to deviate from it sufficiently, these three original horsemen will return, as a direct result of our attack on nature. People who live in glass houses shouldn't throw stones, and beating the elephant upon whose back your dwelling rests is a strategy of doubtful value.

Condorcet thought we'd know when to stop, while Godwin thought we'd eventually become immortal and give up sex for good. And anyway, as Hume would say, science and technology will always find a way. More basically, according to the philosophers of the Enlightenment, humankind would work it all out, because progress, prosperity and happiness were where we were all heading.

The shift of governance, from Nature to human, lies at the heart of our problems. We have moved from being part of the Biosphere, governed by its invisible hand, to taking control. We evolved within a natural space and found our place in the intricate system that is the Biosphere. Our population growth was governed by nature, and the long handle of the hockey stick resulted.

Our expanded neo-cortex gave us a greater sense of self, and we named ourselves the wise, wise men (*Homo sapiens sapiens*). The philosophers of the Enlightenment told us that within us lay the answers and that together we could build a better world, because sympathy and benevolence flowed from a unified, contented people. The focus was on humankind, alone, freeing itself from the superstitions of religion and nature, and thereby isolating itself from its original meaning.

No longer a part of a greater whole, we instead began thinking within an isolated solution space, where the solutions only needed to serve ourselves. Nature is good, but not that good.

After all, Nature cannot reason, let alone formulate a plan. It is the outcome of raw competition and random mutation. And it certainly isn't sentient. We envisage ourselves as the gardeners, taming an unruly garden.

This came to a head with genetic engineering. Now we knew so much that we could re-design Nature, correct its deepest imperfections, and align it with our great progressive vision. These plants and animals were flawed, through no fault of their own, but we can correct their foolish ways. We drained the swamps, cut the forest, improved the soil, enriched the ocean, burnt the coal (which we described as Nature's bounty) and drilled the gas and oil. We knew best. Progress is worth the effort, our progress, that is. It all made sense, if you use isolated thinking. If your reference point begins and ends with the human race and your belief is that we are the superior beings on the planet, then our actions are both justified and reasoned.

It makes *no* sense if you use connected thinking. The trail of destruction that we have left behind us damages the very context within which lies our only hope of sustainability. We, on our own, cannot find a sustainable future, and we, alone, cannot be resilient. It is the Biosphere that is the unit of sustainability, and the source of resilience. If we do not think within the Biosphere, then we will never co-exist peaceably within this world. Because it is the Biosphere, ultimately, that is as much a part of each one of us, as we are of it.

The hockey stick curve tells us how far we are from a natural, sustainable, resilient future. It shows that through isolated thinking, we now find ourselves in *'enlightened'* isolation. If we think that we can work this out on our own, we miss the entire point of what life means. Life is an interactive, integrated whole, all of the levels of which, from organism to biome, are interdependent. We are part of it, and a sustainable future can only be found within this context. We need to recognize the bubble and burst it, before we can ever start thinking properly about progress and utopia.

Our huge self-awareness, consequent from our massively swollen neo-cortex, has robbed us of our Biosphere-awareness. We no longer resonate with all else that lives, conversing with the natural rhythms that flow throughout our world, but, instead, we strut around, talking to ourselves. It is not a matter of linking with our fellow humans. The solutions will not be found within an improved human society.

Rather we need to re-discover our place in the larger scheme of things. The hockey stick graph exposes us for what we are – isolated and trapped by our very efforts to escape the Malthusian traps. And let's be clear about this, our efforts to maintain and expand the human population have come at a significant cost to the rest of the planet, as epitomized by the three new horsemen of the apocalypse: global warming, habitat destruction and pollution. These three stand to remind us that Malthus did get it right after all. There will always be a cost if we attempt to defy nature.

Finally, we need to recognise that the blade on our hockey stick is not a symbol of progress, but of disastrous, misguided failure.

REFERENCES

Abbott, M.B., Binford, M.W., Brenner, M. and Kelts, K.R. (1997) A 3500 ^{14}C yr high-resolution record of lake level changes in Lake Titicaca, Bolivia/Peru. *Quaternary Research* 47: 169-180.

Aubrey, J. and Dick, O.L. (1972) *Aubrey's Brief Lives.* Penguin Books Ltd., London.

Averiss, R.J. and Skene, K.R. (2001) Changes in nutrient heterogeneity in a sand dune succession at Tentsmuir Point, Eastern Scotland. *Botanical Journal of Scotland* 53: 45-56.

Bar-Matthews, M., Ayalon, A., Kaufman, A. and Wasserburg, G.J. (1999) The eastern Mediterranean paleoclimate as a reflection of regional events: Soreq cave, Israel. *Earth and Planetary Science Letters 166: 85-95.*

Bolero, G. (1979) *Treatise, Concerning the Causes and Magnificence and Greatness of cities.* Walter J. Johnson Inc., New York.

Buckley, B.M. , Anchukaitis, K.J., Penny, D., Fletcher, R., Cook, E.R., Sano, M., Nam, L.C., Wichienkeeo, A., Minh, T.T., and Hong, T.M. (2010) Climate as a contributing factor in the demise of Angkor, Cambodia. *Proceedings of the National Academy of Sciences* 107: 6748-6752.

Carson, R. (2002) *Silent Spring.* Mariner Books, New York.

Chambers, J.D. (*1972*) *Population, Economy and Society in Pre-Industrial England.* Oxford University Press.

Cohen, J.E. (1995) Population growth and Earth's human carrying capacity. *Science* 269: 341-346.

Condorcet, M. de (1980) *A Sketch for a Historical Picture of the Progress of the Human Mind.* Hyperion Books, New York.

Cullen, H.M., deMenocal, P.B., Hemming, S., Hemming, G., Brown, F.H., Guilderson, T. and Sirocko, F. (2000) Climate change and the collapse of the Akkadian Empire: Evidence from the deep-sea. *Geology* 28: 379-382.

Dalfes, H.N., Kukla, G. and Weiss, H. (Eds.) (1997)*Third Millennium BC Climate Change and Old World Collapse.* Springer, Berlin.

Dawson, D. (1993) Is Sympathy So Surprising? Adam Smith and French Fictions of Sympathy. In: Dwyer, J. and Sher, R.B. (eds.) *Sociability and Society in Eighteenth-Century Scotland.* Mercat Press, Edinburgh.

Forbes, M.S. Jnr. (1992) Fact and Comment (Editorial). *Forbes Magazine,* June 8, 1992, p25.

Godwin, W. (1820) *Of Population.* Longman, Hurst, Rees, Orme and Brown, London.

Godwin, W. (1970) *Things as They Are, or the Adventures of Caleb Williams.* Oxford University Press, Oxford.

Godwin, W. (2009) *Enquiry Concerning Political Justice, and its Influence on Morals and Happiness.* Dodo Press, Gloucester, UK.

Goring-Morris, A.N. and Belfer-Cohen, A. (1997) The articulation of cultural processes and Late Quaternary environmental changes in Cisjordan. *Paléorient* 2.3: 71-93.

Graunt, J. (1662) Natural and Political Observations Made upon the Bills of Mortality. Reprinted 1973, in: Laslett, P. (ed.) *The Earliest Classics: Pioneers of Demography.* Gregg International, Farnborough, UK.

Hacking, I. (2006) *The Emergence of Probability: A Philosophical Study of Early Ideas about Probability, Induction and Statistical Inference.* Cambridge University Press, Cambridge.

Hata, H. and Kato, M. (2006) A novel obligate cultivation mutualism between damselfish and *Polysiphonia* algae. *Biology Letters* 2: 593–596.

Hayami, A. (2001) *The Historical Demography of Pre-modern Japan.* University of Tokyo Press, Tokyo.

Hirst, L.F. (1953) *The Conquest of Plague.* Clarendon Press, Oxford.

Hodell, D.A., Brenner, M., Curtis, J.H. and Guilderson, T. (*2001*) Solar forcing of *drought* frequency in the Maya Lowlands. *Science* 292: 1367-1370.

Hume, D. (1955) [1739] *A Treatise of Human Nature: Being an Attempt to Introduce the Experimental Method of Reasoning into Moral Subjects.* Oxford University Press: Oxford.

Ilic, B., Craighead, H.G., Krylov, S., Senaratne, W., Ober, C. and Neuzil, P. (2004) Attogram detection using nanoelectromechanical oscillators, *Journal of Applied Physics* 95, 3694-3703.

IUCN (2001) *IUCN Red List Categories and Criteria: Version 3.1.* IUCN Species Survival Commission, Gland, Switzerland.

Jones, S. (2007) Chapter 8. The Toba supervolcanic eruption: Tephra-fall deposits in India and paleoanthropological implications. In: Petraglia, M.D. and Allchin, B. (Eds), *The Evolution and History of Human Populations in South Asia: Inter-disciplinary Studies in Archaeology, Biological Anthropology, Linguistics and Genetics. Vertebrate Paleobiology and Paleoanthropology*, Part II, 173-200.

Kemp, J. (1992) Quoted in *High Country News,* Paonia, Colorado, 27 January, 1992, p4.

Kunstadter, P. (1972) Demography, ecology, social structure, and settlement patterns. In Harrison, G.A. and Boyce, A.J. (eds.) *The Structure of Human Populations.* Clarendon Press, Oxford.

Malthus, R. (2007) *An Essay on the Principle of Population.* Dover Publications Inc., Mineola, New York.

Mandeville, B. de (2007) *The Fable of the Bees: Or, Private Vices, Publick Benefits.* Penguin Classics, London.

Martin, M. (1983) *Science and War*. In: Birch, A. (editor), *Science Research in Australia: Who Benefits?* Centre for Continuing Education, Australian National University, Canberra. Pp. 101-108.

Marx, K., Engels, F. and Arthur, C.J. (1987) *The German Ideology: Introduction to a critique of Political Economy.* Lawrence and Wishart Ltd., London.

Meeks, R.L. (1953) *Marx and Engels on Malthus: Selections from the Writings of Marx and Engels Dealing with the Theories of Thomas Robert Malthus.* Lawrence and Wishart, London.

Lenin, V.I. (1913) The Working Class and NeoMalthusianism . *Pravda* 137, June 16, 1913.

Pepys, S. (2010) *The Diary of Samuel Pepys: Volume IV - 1663.* HarperCollins, London.

Robock, A., Ammann, C.M., Oman, L., Shindell, D., Levis, S. and Stenchikov, G. (2009) Did the Toba volcanic eruption of ~74 ka B.P. produce widespread glaciation? *Journal of Geophysical Research*, *114*: 1-9.

Simon J. (1993) Economic thought about population consequences: some reflections. *Population Economics* 6: 137-152.

Smith, A. (1994) *The Wealth of Nations.* The Modern Library, New York.

Smith, A. (2010) *The Theory of Moral Sentiments*. Penguin Classics, London.

Smith, J.M. (1958) *The Theory Of Evolution*. Cambridge University Press, Cambridge.

Snyder, G. (1990) *The Practice of the Wild.* North Point Press, San Francisco.

Tabashnik, B.E., Gassmann, A.J., Crowder, D.W. and Carriére, Y. (2008) Insect resistance to *Bt* crops: evidence versus theory. *Nature Biotechnology* 26: 199 – 202.

Wallace, R. (1969) *Various Prospects of Mankind, Nature and Providence.* A.M. Kelley, New York.

Williams, M.A.J., Ambrose, S.H., Kaars, S. van der, Ruehlemann, C., Chattopadhyaya, U, Pal, J, and Chauhan, P.R. (2009) Environmental impact of the 73 ka Toba super-eruption in South Asia. *Palaeogeography, Palaeoclimatology, Palaeoecology* 284: 295–31

Woodruff, D.S. (2001) Declines of biomes and the future of evolution. *Proceedings of the National Academy of Sciences, USA* 98: 5471-5476.

General reading on particular topics covered in this section:

John Graunt
Glass, D.V., Ogborn, M.E and Sutherland, I. (1964) John Graunt and his natural and political observations. *Proceedings of the Royal Society of London. Series B, Biological Sciences* 159: 2-37.

Kreager, P. (1988) New light on Graunt. *Population Studies* 42: 129-140.

Thomas Malthus
James, P. (1979) *Population Malthus: his Life and Times.* Routledge and Kegan Paul, London.

Petersen, W. (1999) *Malthus: founder of Modern Demography.* Transaction Publishers, New Brunswick.

Wrigley, E.A. and Souden, D. (eds) (1986) *The Works of Thomas Robert Malthus,* 8 vols, Pickering & Chatto, London.

Marquis de Condorcet
Goodell, E. (1994) *The Noble Philosopher: Condorcet and the Enlightenment.* Prometheus Books, Amherst, New York.

Williams, D. (2004) *Condorcet and Modernity.* Cambridge University Press, Cambridge.

William Godwin
Clark, J.P. (1977) *The Philosophical Anarchism of William Godwin.* Princeton University Press, Princeton, New Jersey.

Graham, K.W., (2001) *William Godwin Reviewed: A Reception History, 1783–1834.* AMS Press, New York.

Marshall, P.H. (1984) *William Godwin.* Yale University Press, New Haven.

The Enlightenment
Buchan, J. (2003) *Crowded with Genius: The Scottish Enlightenment: Edinburgh's Moment of the Mind.* HarperCollins, London.

Dupré, L. (2004) *The Enlightenment and the Intellectual Foundations of Modern Culture.* Yale University Press, New Haven.

Israel, J.I. (2006) *Enlightenment Contested: Philosophy, Modernity, and the Emancipation of Man 1670-1752.* Oxford University Press, Oxford.

Rousseau, J.-J. (1993) *The Social Contract and the Discourses.* Everyman's Library, London.

Adam Smith
Fay, C. F. (1956) *Adam Smith and the Scotland of his Day.* Cambridge University Press, Cambridge.

Nicholls, D. (1992) *The invisible hand; providence and the market*, in Heelas, P. and Morris, P. eds. The Values *of the Enterprise Culture: the moral debate*, 217-236, Routledge, New York.

Ross, I. S. (1995) *The Life of Adam Smith.* Clarendon Press, Oxford.

SECTION III
THE SELECTION PRESSURE-VARIATION CURVE: DID DARWIN GET IT WRONG?

Our next curve is a beautiful one that is encountered countless times in all sorts of different contexts. Its form, whose ends seem to never quite end, nor touch the ground over which they hover, is a thing of grace. It is a frequency curve or, more mundanely, a normal distribution, and is shown below (Fig. III.1). Its mathematical properties, and the importance of these properties for everything from probability theory to logistics, and from marketing to product design, are discussed in more detail in Appendix I.

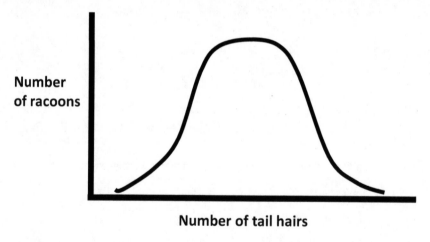

Number of tail hairs

Figure III.1 The normal distribution, or frequency curve, showing the variation in tail hairs in a population of racoons.

Its significance is that it shows how a particular property, such as height, life-bulb longevity, or the number of hairs on a healthy young racoon's tail, varies in a population. Basically, most racoons will have a similar, or near average, amount of tail hairs.

There will be a few with far less hairs than average, and a few with far more hairs. So the distribution will look something like Figure III-1.

The x-axis represents the range of possible values of the characteristic under consideration, while the y-axis represents the number of individuals with a particular value.

The normal distribution will occur many times throughout the rest of this book, so central is it to so many aspects of life and our relationship with the Biosphere. In this section, I want to examine one of the most important applications of this curve in modern science: its use in understanding biological evolution. The normal curve has much to tell us, and questions to the core the theory of evolution by natural selection, thus undermining the foundations of important aspects of modern biology, and associated thinking in social and economic sciences. This curve, ultimately, posses questions and provides solutions for our search for sustainability, while also addressing themes of equality, race and diversity.

Chapter Thirty-Two
A Bad Day at School

The classic school and university textbooks will all contain a figure similar to Figure III.2, as a testament to how natural selection works. It all seems very straightforward. Yet a closer inspection of this cluster of magic curves reveals some significant problems, and points to natural selection acting as a *force majeure* for non-evolution rather than evolution. These graphs should have a health warning attached!

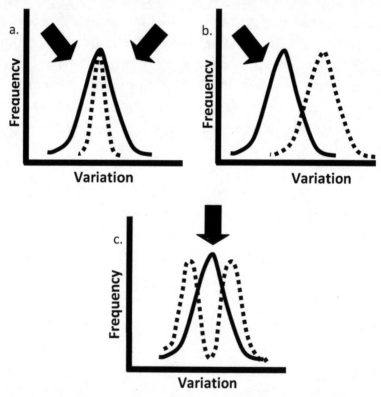

Figure III.2 a. Stabilizing selection; b. Directional selection; c. Disruptive selection.

I remember a particular lesson at the Royal School in Armagh, the ecclesiastical capital of Ireland and my home town, when I was eleven years old. The teacher led us out to the playground beside the crumbling walls of the handball courts, which resembled a scene from a Dickens novel, set in inner city London in the 19th century. This was a very strange event in itself, as we never normally got out of the classroom. I was quite excited, thinking we were going to do something really interesting.

Then, in a strained voice that intimated his own discomfort in this exotic teaching environment, he ordered us to assemble ourselves in order of height, shortest next to the handball court walls, whose crumbling edifice added a sense of drama to the entire proceedings, tallest towards the new science block across the playground, with its astronomical observatory atop.

The observatory couldn't be used due to a design fault that meant the floor vibrated if you stood on it, thus making it impossible to see anything through the telescope, without the stars and nebulae dancing, dizzyingly, in front of you. Its green observation dome remained, forever closed, as a great folly, and a warning to us all of what poor design could produce! A few years ago, I remember thinking that I might build a small observatory in the garden, but then I dismissed the idea as my mind wondered back to the folly of the Royal!

However, on that day, my concerns were far removed from the consequences of poor design. I was equal smallest in the class with another lad, and we wrestled with each other not to be nearest the harbinger walls of the handball courts. It wasn't that we feared impending death following the structural collapse of this ancient arena of red-handed athletic challenge (especially when the ball was wet), but rather that neither of us wanted to be the smallest.

To be smallest...well you were a very clear target for selective pressure! It was of no comfort that Julius Caesar and Alexander the Great were all vertically challenged. More poignant was the fact that Zacchaeus was a very little man (and a tax collector to boot) and that, rumour had it, Napoleon wasn't very tall either. Opportunities to develop a global military empire seemed fairly limited to my young mind in 1977, with the Soviets and Americans seemingly having the show sewn up. Was I, therefore, destined for a career of tree climbing and accountancy, or to be exiled on some far flung island in the middle of the Atlantic Ocean?

There could only be one *"Shorty"* or *"Leprachaun"* in a class, and once labelled, that was you placed in your pigeon hole, barring a supernatural growth spurt. Indeed, such a moniker often outlasted the condition it described. I recalled seeing a clear-faced sixth former who could have modelled for the after effects of a face cream advert, so smooth was his skin, being referred to as *"spotty dog"* regularly. I used to stare at him trying to detect the remnants of a lunar surface that must have formerly existed, but to no avail.

Standing there, beneath the heavens, and the observatory that could never actually observe, I realized that I could wear this sobriquet to my grave, however far in the future that would be. I could envisage the scene: weeping relatives gathered around a resplendent milky green tombstone of Connemara marble, on a hillside running down from an ancient church, a yew tree off to one side and a raven, freshly flown in from Camlann, calling, mournfully, *"kronk, kronk, kronk"*.

Focusing on this morbid necropolis, the writing on the stone became all too clear. *"Here lies the body of Shorty Skene, he lived to one hundred, a tax collector he'd been."* A hundred years, and still that damned nickname persisted!

So we kept pushing each other into last place, two restless midgets embroiled in a struggle for our dignity, until we became aware of the menacing presence of our sickle-like and extremely tall teacher. He separated us, putting me next to the wall. My fate was sealed in that moment, in the twinkling of an eye, and in a perfunctory manner that indicated nothing of the drama that played out in my mind. Of course I knew better than to complain (caning was still an option in the array of disciplinary tools available to the educational facilitators of that time), but felt gutted and betrayed by him. Surely the gravity of the situation could not have passed him by?

There was nothing in his eyes to indicate any sort of awareness of the life-changing, career-determining, soul-destroying immensity of his actions. This new outdoor classroom was turning into a nightmare. I actually thought about making a run for it! We stood for what felt like an age, all eyes seemingly boring down on me from the ever taller line of boys, and the cloudless sky offered no hope of a rain shower to end this agonizing, open-air spectacle. My not quite so vertically challenged companion smiled in relief as much as pleasure. This was turning into a very bad day in *Skeneworld*!

Finally, after what was probably a number of seconds rather than days, we came to the point of the lesson. A chalk line was drawn along the ground and, every five metres along the line, a mark was made, creating a scale. Each mark represented ten centimetres. We were asked to position ourselves along the line within the height range that represented us. The boys in each ten centimetre range then formed a line at right angles to the axis. Fortunately, there were now three other boys within ten centimetres of my own height and this was strangely satisfying to say the least! I felt that I'd dragged others into my small world of darkness and damnation.

The overall result was interesting. The outline of an arch could be seen, with the longest queue of boys at the middle of the height range, and descending numbers either side. The tallest in the class were now somehow as isolated as the smallest, far from the madding crowd at the centre of the curve. Those middle-sized boys were exuding a certain confidence at being the majority group, casting their eyes along both tails in judgement.

We each drew the shape and went back into the classroom, where the teacher introduced us to the normal distribution, or bell-shaped curve. Soon we learnt all sorts of interesting facts about it. Lots of things have a bell-shaped distribution. From light bulb longevity to length of fox tails, from income to carbon footprint, and from IQ (contentiously) to the time it takes to run one hundred metres.

Chapter Thirty-Three
Of Champagne and Fat Camels

Most individuals (be they light bulbs or eleven-year-old children) will be clustered around the centre of the curve, because most of us are similar to each other in lots of ways. A few will have lower values, and a similarly small number will have higher values than this central group. The further we go from the average value, the lower number of individuals we find. So there are very few very small people, and very few very tall people. In other words, most of us are *average Joes*. One important point to note is that we may not each be average at everything. We're usually better than average at some things, and worse than average at others.

Another key characteristic of the bell-shaped curve is the shape of the bell. Some distributions have a narrow base, and form a tall, slender bell, like an upside down champagne flute. Others are squat, with a wide base, resembling a camel's hump (Fig. III.3). The difference in these two curves tells us a lot.

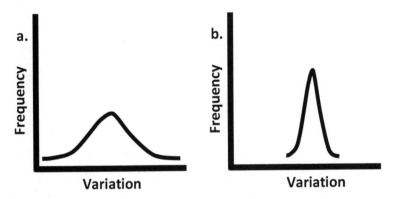

Figure III.3 a) The *Fat Camel Hump* frequency curve; b. The *Inverted Champagne Glass* frequency curve.

The base of the curves represents the range of different values we find in the set of individuals represented by the curve. For example, if everyone was basically the same height, with just a small difference between the shortest and tallest, then the curve would have a short base, like the champagne flute. If there was a big difference in the smallest and the tallest, with lots of different heights in between, then we'd have a wide base, more like a camel's hump.

So the shape of the curve indicates the amount of variation in the group being measured. This is extremely significant, because having lots of variation is very important in terms of evolution and survival of species. In other words, camels' humps are good, while champagne flutes, as much as it pains me to say it, are bad.

Why are camels' humps good (and champagne flutes bad)? Variation within a group means that there are options. If things change, and a new question is posed, then there will be more likely be a solution if there are lots of options. If, on the other hand, there are few options (as is the case in a population with low variation), then it is much less likely that a solution will be found. This is because, in the champagne situation, everyone has the same answer, which is the answer to the main question being asked. All the other answers have been selected against and disappeared over time.

However if the question now changes, then there is trouble. Questions can change, for example, when famine or global warming occurs. Variation allows survival of lineages in a changing world, and survival is the first step towards sustainability. So in terms of biological sustainability, fat curves are good, but skinny curves are bad! What is the relevance of all of this for evolution?

Chapter Thirty Four
What is Evolution?

The evolution of life on Earth has been much debated over the millennia. While Anaximander, the Greek philosopher, is often credited with being the first recorded thinker to address the issue of how life evolved, many earlier writings, relating to the origin of the Universe as a whole, include stories of the origin and evolution of life on Earth, as we have already mentioned in Section I.

So what do we mean by evolution? It is defined, strictly speaking, as *"an opening of what was rolled up"*. Charles Lyell, the famous Scottish geologist, first used the term within the context of biology, but, interestingly, Charles Darwin didn't like the word, and only mentioned it once in his most famous work, *The Origin of Species* (Darwin, 1994), and this in the final paragraph!

However Darwin's fellow supporters used the word, and so it has become inextricably linked to his theory, and the more modern expression of it, neo-Darwinism. Indeed the modern idea of evolution carries with it the assumption that there is only one theory, and the theory of evolution is commonly equated with the theory of neo-Darwinism.

However the original meaning, the opening of what was rolled up, is actually the most appropriate. Evolution is, ultimately, the outcome of matter responding to the laws of the Universe. What happens can never run contrary to these laws, and thus there is a script that ultimately must be followed.

The Universe itself is following such a script, moving from the big bang through to equilibrium, and everything in the Universe is on the same wagon, and thus is travelling a path determined for it by these laws. We will see this more clearly in Section IV, but the point I wish to make at the moment is that there is a script, and its realization in the world of biology, as in all the other "*worlds*", is called evolution. Change happens, and this is what an evolving universe actually represents.

The unrolling scroll of life, over many millions of years, is a wonderful read. Species come and go, and so the biological landscape changes. It is this journey of change that the study of evolution is all about. We can describe the changes and then try to understand what, if anything, has led to these changes. Darwin's theory of evolution by natural selection is one such explanation. However there is a significant change in the thinking of many scientists, related to the work of Charles Darwin. In this section, we will examine a curve that sheds light on this whole debate, and points to a very different understanding of evolution. Its implications are far-reaching: from racial and social diversity to economics, and from ecology to industry.

Chapter Thirty-Five
Charles Darwin Solves a Problem

In 1838, Charles Darwin admitted that he was really struggling. Two years earlier, he had returned from his adventures on board *HMS Beagle*, where he had travelled around the world and had observed the depth and breadth of life's diversity, from Tasmania to the Galápagos Islands and from Madagascar to Valparaiso. As is well known, he had long had an interest in biodiversity, and had a particular attraction to beetles, the most diverse group of animals on the planet (representing one quarter of all known eukaryotic life forms).

Darwin had compared this to the diversity of domesticated animals such as fancy pigeons and pigs, where humans had, through deliberate breeding programmes, produced a whole variety of different forms, colours and even behaviours. Yet he could not work out how nature could do this, without some master breeder overseeing the entire operation. He was looking for a natural solution, but none came to mind. What possible mechanism could drive the selection of forms, and what could produce such diversity?

In his autobiography, he recalls what happened.

"*In October 1838, that is, fifteen months after I had begun my systematic inquiry, I happened to read for amusement Malthus on Population, and being well prepared to appreciate the struggle for existence which everywhere goes on from long-continued observation of the habits of animals and plants, it at once struck me that under these circumstances favourable variations would tend to be preserved, and unfavourable ones to be destroyed. The* results of this would be the formation of a new species. Here, then I had at last got a theory by which to work" (Darwin, 2003).

Quoting from the great man again, in his later book, *The Variations of Animals and Plants under Domestication*, "I saw, on reading Malthus on Population, that natural selection was the inevitable result of the rapid increase of all organic beings" (Darwin, 1998).

And in a letter to his competitor in the niche market of radical new theories on diversity, the Welsh naturalist, Alfred Russel Wallace, on 6th April, 1859, he wrote: *"You are right, that I came to the conclusion that selection was the principle of change from the study of domesticated productions; and then, reading Malthus, I saw at once how to apply this principle"* (Darwin, 2006). Again, in *The Origin of Species*, he stated, when referring to the theory of natural selection: *"This is the doctrine of Malthus, applied to the whole animal and vegetable kingdoms"* (Darwin, 1994).

And so from the pen of Darwin himself, he clearly points to the two great inputs to his thinking: domestic breeding and Malthus.

Since I was a school student, first encountering Darwin's writings, I have had significant concerns about his theory of evolution. At first, I thought it was just a matter of not being bright enough to understand it. As I studied further, completing my Bachelors degree and Doctorate in evolutionary and developmental botany, then writing papers on the subject of plant evolution, and, finally, a book on evolution (*Shadows on the Cave Wall*), I became more and more convinced that there were some very significant problems with Darwin's logic.

And I am not alone. Indeed there have been many papers published in the leading scientific journals in the world, all reflecting very worrying gaps and errors in his thinking. I want to present the scientific evidence here that points to a completely different theory of evolution, and one that has huge significance for us at this time on our planet. It all stems from the curve with which we started this section, and it begins with Thomas Malthus.

The bridge between Malthus and the theory of natural selection rested on a number of key arches, which, under close inspection, do not appear to touch the ground. In other words, the bottom row of bricks is clearly missing. What are these arches?

Chapter Thirty-Six
Applying Malthus to the Natural World

The first arch is all to do with an erroneous extrapolation. Darwin extended Malthus' theory on human populations to apply to all species on Earth. This brought him into direct conflict with the many groups who opposed Malthus, such as the Socialists (Todes, 1989), who found it difficult to embrace Darwinian Theory because of its Malthusian inspiration. So how valid is it to assume that all of nature has found itself in the same situation as Malthusian humans? Do we find species multiplying beyond their resources, and then having to compete for limiting resources? Does nature enter into a crisis, driven by the desire to reproduce, like our humans trapped in the room?

Certainly there is little evidence of any of these scenarios. We see, rather, that natural systems, unperturbed by human activity, tend to be in a balanced, equitable state. The forest, the lake, the alpine meadow, the tundra, the desert: none of these appear in a state of all-out war and over-population. Any of these environments that are out of balance, such as a polluted lake, tend to be the results of human input. For example, if we dump nutrients onto fields surrounding the lake for agriculture, the nutrients will eventually enter the lake (and all the more quickly if we've also cut all the trees down) and populations of algae will spiral out of control. This is not a natural phenomenon, but one caused by us.

However, natural systems tend to be self-regulated. No boom and bust here, but a fine, balanced Swiss watch, with all of its cogs, big and small, working together. On the whole, nature isn't a starving, desperate creature in crisis (or at least it wasn't until we came along), but rather a balanced, complex, interactive entity.

The harbingers of death, the Malthusian horsemen of pestilence, war and starvation, do occasionally visit, but this is no chaotic world of selfish exploitation, and no single species has the arrogance to expect the whole show to revolve around them, nor to find the secret to harmonious living within their own reference points. None, that is, except *Homo sapiens sapiens*.

As we have seen in the previous section, our population and its dynamics have nothing to do with the logistic model anyway. We have raised the carrying capacity of our species, high above where it ought to be naturally. And the cost of this has been another set of horsemen, climate change, habitat destruction and pollution, which so distort the natural world that we must dig deep to find the answers that lie only within the shattered remnants of that world.

And so for Darwin to extend Malthus' theory to all of nature is completely erroneous. There is no understanding to be gained from our bloated population in terms of how live diversified before we ever came to be in this state. For although the world of Malthus portrayed populations that were out of control, where competition was extreme, and where the fittest, the *average Joes*, would survive, this is not what nature looks like.

Darwin envisioned a curve where the arrows of selection were heavy and oppressive, a world where there could be no escape from it. Natural selection was the fundamental constant in a changing world. Maybe in a vastly overpopulated planet we will find this outcome, but if we do, two things are clear, it won't lead to diversification, and it will not be natural! Darwin grasped and ran with an idea that was not relevant to the natural world.

Human population dynamics are artificial products of human efforts to escape a Malthusian crisis. They rely on four large elephants, and have nothing to do with a natural balance.

Chapter Thirty-Seven
Tickling Darwin's Fancy: Pigeons, Pigs and Dogs

The second issue is that Darwin combined this extension with another one, producing what I call his *theory of erroneous extrapolation squared*. Not only did he assume that all species acted like Malthus' human population, but that the process was analogous to our breeding of domesticated animals. Thus he applied a Malthusian method to an animal breeding model.

Darwin clearly stated that the breeding of domesticated animals, be it for agriculture or for pleasure, from dogs to sheep and from pigeons to pigs, was the first great inspiration for his solution to the origin of the planet's diversity. Initially it is an appealing comparison. There are lots of different colours, shapes, sizes and temperaments in dogs, for example.

Domesticated dogs are an interesting case in point. Now thought to have arisen around sixteen thousand years ago (around the same time that the cave men of Lascaux drew their birdman), in an area south of the Yangtze River in China, the appearance of our canine friends coincided with the onset of rice cultivation (Pang *et al.*, 2009). It spread to Europe around ten thousand years ago, and to the Americas some eight thousand six hundred years ago. Female lineages from these early Chinese dog populations can be traced through many generations, indicating that the breeding was not a random event, but was carefully managed.

The dog is the only domestic animal that has spread with man across the ancient world, and actually forms a marker of human movement. It is a sort of smoking gun, acting as a useful sign of contact between different cultures in the absence of archaeological evidence. For example the dingo, found in

Australia, can be shown to have arrived from East Asia some five thousand years ago, and so provides the only evidence of interactions between aboriginal Australian people and the Chinese at this time.

There is a significant problem with breeding programmes. They dramatically lower the variation within the breed. This leads to significant anatomical and physiological problems, basically due to inbreeding. For example, within boxer dogs, for every twenty thousand dogs, we find the variation that would be expected for a population of seventy dogs, while for twenty thousand rough collies, the variation is equivalent to fifty dogs, or 0.0025% of what we would expect (Calboli *et al.*, 2008). As a result of this inbreeding, boxers are prone to heart disease, Dalmatians are prone to deafness and German shepherd dogs suffer from high levels of hip dysplasia.

Humans select the qualities they want, and deliberately breed suitable animals together. As a result we have four hundred million dogs, of around four hundred types, the greatest behavioural and morphological variation of any land mammal. However each type has extremely low genetic variation. They most probably wouldn't survive in the wild. They are artificial creations of mankind, existing only in *Bubbleworld*.

Vets and high quality food keep them going, and many suffer extreme pain. Indeed, in 2008, one of the world's leading dog food producers, Pedigree, as well as the RSPCA, withdrew their sponsorship and support, respectively, from *Crufts*, the largest dog show on the planet, when it was uncovered just how much many of the highly inbred dogs displayed at this annual event were suffering. It was the particularly disturbing example of spaniels with brains which were too big for their skulls, having been deliberately bred to reduce the size of the skulls, which finally put paid to public support.

Domestic breeding, or *artificial selection*, has nothing to do with the real world at all. There is no context, no reference to the greater Biosphere, no compromises within a positive conversation of participation and sustainability, the kind of conversation happening every day in nature. In short, to equate domestic breeding with natural diversification within the Biosphere is a typically human action, one at home with the Enlightenment, but not with the greater whole.

We seek to make nature in our own image, rather than to place ourselves within nature's context. Darwin, in *The Origin*, defended his inspiration from domestic breeding as follows: *"Man selects only for his own good: Nature only for that of the being which she tends."* This demonstrates the reductionist focus of his thinking. Nature selects for the good, in isolation, of the individual.

This statement by Darwin not only reflects a *Bubbleworld* mentality, reducing the whole down to single individuals, but also applies such reductionism to nature. If nature solves its problems by focusing down on the individual, then man can find his solutions by focusing down on himself. The message was clear.

I remember talking with a newly appointed lecturer in genetic engineering in my Faculty, and listening as she told me that what she was doing was exactly what nature did. I begged to differ. The amusing circularity of her logic defied belief. Darwin created a world view of nature in the image of domestic breeding, and now she sat and told me that genetic engineering was, consequently, a natural thing to do!

Yet the circle is broken at the very outset. Nature shares no common ground with domestic breeding. The self-centred, profit-driven, morally-corrupt alteration of our natural plants with genetic elements from bacteria through to fish, aimed at stock markets and dependence, cannot be seen as a *"natural"* approach. Sustainability will not be found in the laboratories of international industry. For the balance of nature requires all aspects of the Biosphere to be involved.

There is absolutely no possibility of finding anything of relevance within pig breeding, nor do fancy pigeons contribute a jot to our understanding of the diversification of life on Earth. To imagine that it has relevance is, frankly, extremely misdirected. Thankfully most of nature is running about without excruciating headaches.

Chapter Thirty-Eight
Competition and the Bloody Claw

Another issue is the thorny subject of competition. Let's make no mistake about it. Darwin's theory was *all* about competition. It required a Malthusian world, packed full of organisms competing for limited resources. The weak were selected against, the fit were selected for. Natural selection was driven by competition. If there was no competition, then there would be no selection. Selective pressure was exactly that. There had to be pressure for the thing to happen.

In case anyone is in doubt concerning the centrality of competition to his cause, the great man himself concluded his greatest work (although he himself claimed his last book, on earthworms, was his greatest!) by summing up his theory as *"From the war of nature, from famine and death, the most exalted object which we are capable of conceiving, namely, the production of the higher animals, directly follows"* (Darwin, 1994).

Alfred Russell Wallace, who had, independently, come up with the same idea, a year prior to the publication of *The Origin of Species,* wrote: *"It is, as we commenced by remarking, "a struggle for existence," in which the weakest and least perfectly organized must always succumb"* (Wallace, 1858). Sir Thomas Huxley, one of the staunchest defenders of natural selection, and known as *Darwin's bulldog,* wrote: *"The animal world is on about the same level as a gladiator's show. The strongest, the swiftest and the cunningest* [sic] *live to fight another day ... no quarter is given"* (Huxley, 1896).

Ultimately, the world that Darwin painted was a competitive one. It seemed to make sense. When the going gets tough, which it ultimately did in a Malthusian diorama, the tough get going, and the weak get buried! Natural selection is not a pleasant process. It involves the removal of the rejected and their genes. It is not like selecting a chocolate from a chocolate box. It involves the eradication of the other chocolates. Poor designs are rooted out, and the strongest, most reproductively successful designs take over. The weak are displaced in a fight to the death. Alfred Tennyson (1809-1892), the great English poet, explored this harsh reality when he wrote, in his *"In Memoriam A.H.H."* (a poem inspired by the death of his close friend, Arthur Hallam):

"Who [humankind] *trusted God was love indeed*
And love Creation's final law
Tho' Nature, red in tooth and claw
With ravine shriek'd against his creed"

This powerful stanza juxtapositions man's concept of the love of God with the great cruelty and violence inherent in nature. It was adopted by supporters of Darwin through the generations, including Richard Dawkins, probably the last of the *bulldogs*, who referred to it in *The Selfish Gene* (1976). Yet it was actually written before *The Origin of Species* was first published.

Chapter Thirty-Nine
Does Competition Really Lead to Diversification?

So competition lies at the heart of Darwinian evolution. Competition acts at two different levels – within a species (called *intraspecific* competition) and between different species (called *interspecific* competition). Let's consider each of these in turn.

Intraspecific competition is all about our curve (Fig, III-1), and was directly inspired by Malthus. As a population increases in size, resources become increasingly limited, leading to competition. The argument goes that the best adapted individuals will survive, while those less perfect will be wiped out. The better genes will replace the weaker genes, in modern day parlance. Pressure will come to bear on organisms that are less fit. This results in the classic curve (Fig. III-2a) that we have already discussed, demonstrating that selective pressure, within a competitive environment, leads to the extremes of our curve being selected against. Gradually, the curve becomes narrower, changing from a camel's hump to an inverted champagne glass. The selective pressure, represented by the two arrows, *narrows the base of the curve.*

This is very important. Natural selection leads to a narrowing of the curve. In other words, it leads to a decrease in the variation. In fact, we can define natural selection as any process that reduces variation within the population. It selects, and thus rejects. So any time there is selection, there is rejection. Rejection in evolutionary terms means removal of genes and traits from the population. And so natural selection always reduces the genetic variation available within a population. Arguments that try to get around this all fail because they are based at the individual level, not the population level.

Now this is a problem, because as Darwin himself stated (In *The Origin of Species*): *"Unless such* [variations] *occur, natural selection can do nothing"*. In other words, in order for selection to act, there must be a range of things to select for and against. If there isn't, then no change can occur. However, if natural selection occurs, it reduces the very variation needed for it to operate. Natural selection is not a self-fulfilling prophecy, but rather a self-destructive one. Its very action leads to its deactivation!

Stabilizing selection leads to a reduction in this variation, so the very process of selection, reduces the stock upon which selection must act. It is a self-fulfilling fiasco! Natural selection cannot possibly produce variation, but rather, it must reduce it. Reducing variation is, of course, useful, as it stabilizes species, and prevents endless evolution from happening. But it is in no way a mechanism for diversification.

But, you may say, aren't there three kinds of selection: stabilizing selection, directional selection and disruptive selection? Yes indeed there are. Let's have a look at the other two forms.

Chapter Forty
Directional Selection: Should I Stay or Should I Go?

Figure III.2b shows the classic textbook example of directional selection. Again, we have our bell curve, and this time the arrow is only on one side. The idea is that this pushes the bell along the x-axis, away from the arrow. If the bell curve represented the temperature at which a species of animal worked best, then if we had climate change and the planet heated up, we would expect animals to be able to live at increasingly higher temperatures, and any individuals who couldn't (at the extreme left of the graph) would be selected against.

Surely, this all sounds reasonable enough? However, in the real world, we don't find this. Animals don't sit and adapt, they move. Before the last ice age, Britain was covered in forests of oak and pine. These all migrated to mainland Europe during the big chill, and then migrated back, thousands of miles, afterwards. They didn't stay and evolve. In the present global warming episode, species are again on the move.

Gian-Reto Walther and his team, writing in *Nature*, reported that significant movement of species was already underway (Walther, *et al.*, 2002). This was corroborated by two studies in the *Proceedings of the National Academy of Sciences* (Kelly and Goulden, 2008; Breshears *et al.*, 2008). If you want more references on this, these are provided at the end of the section (*Climate Change* references).

Concerns exist as to whether or not species will be able to migrate fast enough, but we do not know if the migration rates that occurred during previous warming and cooling periods were maximal or merely appropriate to the rates of change at that time. In other words, we don't know if the trees were merely jogging or were moving flat out, and so concerns that they may not be able to run faster are merely hypothetical.

Migratory birds have been shown to migrate and breed earlier with increasing temperatures, and leave later, in many studies. Giant fossilized tropical ants, five centimetres long, were found recently in Wyoming. The species, *Titanomyrma lubei,* is one of many who crossed the Arctic during extremely high temperature events in the Eocene (56-34 million years ago), much higher than today. At this time, the Arctic was thought to have warmed to 8 degrees centigrade, due to a large release of greenhouse gases. Professor Bruce Archibald, from the University of British Columbia, reported his findings in the *Proceedings of the Royal Society*, highlighting climate change as a key driver for species moving between the *"Old"* and *"New"* Worlds (Archibald *et al*., 2011.

Meanwhile Allison Perry, working at the Marine Biological Station at Millport, Scotland, reported in *Science* (Perry *et al*., 2005) that fish distributions were being dramatically altered, with species moving northward as global warming led to ocean temperatures rising.

While some have argued that local, non-climate-related factors fudge the issue, so that we cannot be sure if the movements of species are down to climate change, Camille Parmesan, from the University of Texas, presented a sophisticated and beautiful analysis across two hundred and seventy-nine species of plants and animals, in *Nature* (Parmesan *et al*., 2003), that clearly indicated movement away from the equator, separating out any local effects.

The point is that when conditions change in a directional way, organisms don't sit and evolve, they move. Animals literally walk or fly away, while the rain of seeds produced by plants gradually finds more success in a direction away from the change. Whole communities shift. Many ice ages occurred over the last two and a half million years, but throughout this time of dramatic change, when, for example, Northern Britain was under two kilometres of ice, life came and went, without any dramatic evolutionary outcome.

Therefore directional change does not lead to directional selection, but, rather, to directional movement. Plants and animals don't just sit there and evolve; they get on their bikes and pedal away. What they are doing is maintaining a *status quo* in their surroundings. And this is where they differ from humans. We don't move from a forest that threatens fire, or harbours a predator. We chop the forest down and kill the predator. We don't move from a river that occasionally bursts its banks, we build a dam to control its flow, or build levees. Our solutions do not stem from our comprehension of our place within our natural context, but, rather, we alter that context to meet our own demands.

We don't recognize our fellow organisms as being able to perceive anything, to pack their bags, to move from change. Rather we view the entire world beyond the bubble as tangled, chaotic and directionless, susceptible to the power of natural selection, sitting ducks in front of the hunter, trembling deer before their predator. However, in reality, it is we who are trapped in *Bubbleworld*, not the rest of nature.

This enclosed thinking is also evident in the work of those harbingers of doom who claim that because the rate of climate change is far faster than at the end of the last Ice Age, poor little defenceless Mother Nature will not be able to cope. It can't possibly travel that fast! This assumption reflects our patronizing view of Nature. These scientists cannot possibly know if nature will cope or not. The experiment cannot be done in a laboratory. Future generations will see if they can cope.

Certainly they have coped with cataclysms before. The venting of greenhouse gases in the Eocene is likely to have been a rapid series of events. The Little Ice Age at the end of the last Ice Age, when the giant Lake Agassiz in North America (it covered eight hundred and forty thousand square kilometres, almost four times the area of the United Kingdom), containing vast amounts of glacial melt, burst its banks and flowed into the Atlantic, disrupting the Atlantic Conveyer, is another case in point. This event moved Britain back into glaciation within 70 years!

And so their statements are indefensible. It's like looking at a man walking past your house and concluding that he cannot run. Only when the dog next door escapes its leash, will we really know! Plants are experts at managing their resources. They don't spend more than they have to, unless they have been genetically modified to do so.

Take St John's Wort, a little plant from Europe that has excellent fungal defence chemicals that ward of pathogenic fungi found in its homelands. When it was moved to America, it was discovered that it had switched off the genes that make the defence, and put the energy into greater growth and reproduction. This isn't the action of a stupid, chaotic organism. The fungi that attacked it in Europe did not exist in America, and so there was no need for the defence.

Many organisms carry out such budgetary recalculations throughout their lives. Given the extreme events that a species will encounter in its millions of years of persistence on our planet, it is more than likely that the show will carry on long after we are gone. Nature today is not a sinking *Titanic* with us and all else on board. Rather, it is more like a submarine, with us sitting on its deck on chairs. The submarine will dive eventually, as it evades the increasingly difficult conditions around, but unless we climb inside, it is we who will get wet. The longer we ignore this reality, the more imminent and likely it is that we will be locked out. I use these last words very deliberately, for by closing ourselves off from the natural world, we become barred from it.

Chapter Forty-One
Disruptive Selection: How Likely is it?

What then of disruptive selection? Figure III.2c shows the commonly represented curve relating to this. The selective arrow exerts pressure on the middle of the distribution, at its highest point, and leads to two little curves emerging to the left and to the right. This looks promising. Those two little curves could represent two new baby species! Diversification could be occurring here!

The key to this curve is what the middle of the curve represents. What it is asking for us to do is to imagine a situation where the fittest, most common types of organism are suddenly turned on by nature, and become the least fit. Organisms that are at the centre of the original curve will most likely excel in more than just one characteristic. They will be matched to their environment in many ways, according to Darwinian Theory, because they are the fittest. You can't be the strongest chain if one of your links is weak. Therefore the fittest must be strong in every aspect, according to Darwinian Theory at least.

Given that organisms tend to move spatially to areas that resemble the ecological space in which they formerly lived, it is unlikely that disruptive selection will have much impact. Don't forget that stabilizing selection is viewed as working most of the time, and so we will already have narrow variation as a result. So there will be little variation to choose from here. Furthermore, there are hardly any examples of truly disruptive selection provided in the literature. So it certainly cannot explain the emergence of the millions of species that we see today.

Finally, because genes are not isolated, but work in groups, the overall combination of genes that account for the majority of individuals in any population are strongly held together, and so the destruction of this group in favour of outliers would seem unlikely. Some have suggested that if we had a population of white, grey and black mice, with only white and black rocks, then the middle part of the colour scheme, the grey, would be selected against. However if there had never been any grey rocks, the population would never have been stabilized in the grey part of the curve. Where did all the grey rocks go?

It was Theodosius Dobzhansky (1937), the Ukranian evolutionary biologist and geneticist, who set out the main idea (now called *the modern evolutionary synthesis*) of how evolution could actually work through genetic mutation and selection. Large populations will dilute new mutations, he said, and so there would be little chance of any significant change. However if a small part of this big population became separated from the larger group, he claimed that this would be more likely to evolve into a new species. He argued that by moving away from the ideal conditions, where the bulk of the population exists, selection pressure would increase, because they were in a more stressed environment. This would result in a shift from stabilizing to directional selection, the direction being towards the new set of conditions.

There are, of course, several problems here, that we have already established, plus a glaring assumption. Firstly, animals are more likely to move away from uncomfortable ecospace than evolve towards it. Secondly, if selection pressure increases, variation will decrease, and thirdly, the assumption that selection pressure will be higher in the new location is not a guarantee. If conditions were particularly unsuitable, then the small group wouldn't survive at all. We'll come back to this when we visit the cathedral of Darwinism, the Galápagos Islands.

Chapter Forty-Two
The Competitive Exclusion Principle and the Paradox of the Plankton

Interspecific competition is competition between two species. The idea of interspecific competition driving evolution came to its zenith in the *Competitive Exclusion Principle*. It was Georgii Gause (1910-1986), a Russian ecologist, who set out this theory, in *The Struggle for Existence* (Gause, 1934), a direct reference to Darwin's use of the same term in *Origin*.

Gause claimed that field work could never lead to any comprehension of ecological relationships, and advocated simplified laboratory experiments, the classic reductionist, and empiricist approach. That should ring alarm bells immediately! And so he placed two species of a little aquatic organism, called *Paramecium*, into a glass jar, and noted that one species ultimately drove the other to extinction. He therefore claimed that if two species are competing for an identical resource, then one will exclude the other. This was in agreement with earlier mathematical models.

It is thought that Gause wrote up his findings in order to try to gain access to a university in the United States of America, which he failed to do. America's loss was the Soviet's gain, however, as he went on to discover the antibiotic, Gramicidin S (S for Soviet), while studying competitive exclusion in two yeast species (Gause, 1932) which worked ideally on skin lesions. This antibiotic saved vast numbers of the Soviet armed forces during World War II.

Yet there was a problem with competitive exclusion, and it was a basic one. You only had to look around, and you are surrounded by biodiversity – millions of species of it. Surely they can't all have different resources? This became known as the *Paradox of the Plankton,* as identified by the great American ecologist, G. Evelyn Hutchinson, in 1961. To resolve this, ecologists determined that the answer lay in how we define resources.

And this subject, if you'll forgive a brief but relevant detour, always takes me to one of the most nerve-wrecking and excruciating experiences of my life, my PhD viva. It was back in December, 1997, when the day finally arrived. It was a Thursday. I was to be examined by one of my heroes of plant ecophysiology, Professor Robert Crawford, from St Andrews University in Scotland. If I am to be honest, my thesis wasn't anything like it should have been. I had been appointed to a tenured lectureship 4 months earlier, and so hadn't had the time or the space to really finish it well. We'd managed to get a number of good papers out of it, but my focus was on trying to get funding in order to build my research group, and write the sixty lectures I had been handed for my first year.

The previous night, I had a dream, though unfortunately not of *Martin Luther King* proportions. No, this was much more mundane. I dreamt that I had lost my suit! I was scrambling up and down the Perth Road in Dundee, visiting all the charity clothes shops, and trying to find a suit, panicked and frazzled to the core. I woke up fairly shaken. Marion, my wife, headed off to her teaching job, and I lazed around for an hour, happy that I could handle any questions on the thesis. I was actually looking forward to the interrogation. Then it was time to put my suit on and head into town from the village where I lived.

I walked into the bedroom, opened the wardrobe door, and started to look for my suit. No sign. I checked the other wardrobe. Again, no sign. I went back over both wardrobes systematically, but ...nothing! This couldn't be happening! A further fifteen minutes slipped by and I was by now feeling very stressed. I had to get going – the viva was only about thirty minutes away!

I remembered an old suit that had been bundled up with other clothes for recycling. I got it out. It was wrinkled and smelt damp. But I had no option. I looked a sight for sore eyes, but I had to face my inquisitor, wrinkles or no wrinkles! I doused the suit in cheap aftershave and headed out. It was as if my dream had been a prophecy of the darkest kind! Gradually, as the day wore on, the harsh smell of cheap *eau de cologne* gave way to the cloying scent of mildew, as I sat, sweating, in my wrinkled costume.

Anyway, the real point of all of this is that the first question that Professor Crawford asked me was *"Do you consider time as a resource?"* I thought about this, and have continued to do so ever since. My answer was, and still is, that a resource exists in both space and time, and so time is inherently part of any resource. This is particularly relevant here. Although two organisms may be competing for what appears to be the same resource, this is often not the case. Since time is a characteristic of the resource and because the organisms are feeding at different times, they are not actually competing for the same resource. Spatial and temporal separation allows this.

My grandfather was a joiner and often travelled to mainland Britain for work from Ireland. He told me of how a group of three workers could share the same, single bed, but each would work a different shift, so that although there was only one bed, each would have a time when they could sleep. It also meant only paying a third of the rent! If we view the bed as a resource, all three workers can use the same resource, as their use is separated by time. Thus they don't competitively exclude each other, by the biggest bloke pushing the other two onto the floor!

However a deeper ecology exists here, one that has significant implications for us. The competitive Exclusion Principle stems from competition being at the core of things. It was derived and tested within extremely simplified lab-based experiments, far from reality, where ecological variables, such as intrinsic growth rates and carrying capacities (see Appendix I), were set as constants. Ecological systems are not usually at maximum competition, and these *"constants"* are not at all constant. Species are not driven to exclusion.

Another issue with the Competitive Exclusion Principle is that if two species were identical, they would act as one species. Thus competition would be within a species, rather than between species, and as we know, species do not eradicate themselves! Thus, the principle is flawed at its ultimate application, since each species is dependent on exactly the same resource. In fact, the more similar two species are in terms of resource use, the more likely they will act as one species. Therefore we switch, in effect, from *inter*specific competition to *intra*specific competition, not a situation of competitive exclusion. Perhaps the greatest problem for Competitive Exclusion lies in something called Functional Redundancy. Let's look at this next.

Chapter Forty-Three
Functional Redundancy

We have seen many examples in science of competition now being disentangled from evolution. And recent research points to a completely new way of looking at things. At the ecosystem level, having a number of organisms doing the same things is very useful. In fact it could make the difference between failure and success. Of course the Competitive Exclusion Principle states that such similarity in function is frowned upon by a Biosphere under the governance of natural selection. However, we have already seen that natural selection is an erroneous extrapolation squared. So it is not surprising that it fails to account for a very significant characteristic of the natural world.

Imagine two ecosystems, one with lots of overlap in jobs, and one with none. If one or two species go extinct in the first case, there will be other organisms, doing basically the same job, capable of replacing them, and the show can go on, rather than waiting for evolution to provide a replacement. However, if there is no other organism around, because it has been competitively excluded, then the entire ecosystem could be at risk.

The literature supporting this concept is vast. I have given a number of references at the end of this Section, under the heading of *Functional Redundancy*. As you will see, support comes from leading scientists across the world, reported in science's leading journals.

Functional redundancy is not something that you are going to discover locked in a laboratory. Unlike Gause, you need to get into the field to see it. It does not come from the individual organisms, but rather from the greater system as a whole.

Unfortunately we have been locked in a reductionist research world for so long, a kind of scientific *Bubbleworld*, and we fail to understand more holistic influences. Yet they are there. The organism is part of the bigger whole, and, equally importantly, that works both ways. Properly designed, context –based observational science is a powerful and useful tool. Experimental science that simplifies nature to some distorted laboratory scenario will tell us nothing of any use whatsoever about how the Biosphere functions.

In the rest of nature, populations influence decisions made by individuals, and ecosystems determine much about populations. To get an example of this, go down to a sand dune succession near you and walk from the beach, inland. You will cross a series of changing habitats, each with different sets of plants. Any sand dune system goes through these same changes. This is one of the biggest differences about how neo-Darwinian biologists, such as Richard Dawkins, view the world, and how ecologists, such as myself view it. We recognize that every level of organization, be it individuals, population or ecosystem, interact differently, yet simultaneously, with the laws of the Universe as well as with each other.

As I explained in *Shadows on the Cave Wall* (Skene, 2009), each level evolves and provides a context for every other level. The whole structure of the Biosphere is evolving, and individuals are just part of this. Ecosystem evolution is called succession. The developmental unveiling of the pattern in succession is impossible for a selfish gene concept to explain. Such higher level development, acting independently of the individual species involved, and, instead, forming a framework within which these species find their place, cannot be understood through the reductionist lens.

The individual species at each stage may differ from succession to succession, be it sand dunes in Fraser Island or in north-east Scotland, but the pattern will be the same, from yellow dunes, to stabilized dunes to forest. That's because the overall change is not being driven by the individual species, but rather by the Biosphere. It is a directional, predictable, developmental process under the control of the larger system. This is why, after each mass extinction, we end up with an identical functional unit, with different forms playing out their roles. We always return to herbs, herbivores and carnivores. That's because the greater system is about function, and not about form. We'll discuss this much more in the next section.

The bottom line is that the reason why we get functional redundancy rather than competitive exclusion, is because it works at the ecosystem level. A reductionist, gene-centric thinker just can't see this, blinded by the building blocks, and failing to recognize the greater whole.

Diversity brings stability. This is as true for engineering as for nature. Reliability engineering is an extremely important aspect of engineering, be it mechanical, micro-electronic or structural. In all cases, redundancy is seen as an essential characteristic of any system, because it provides resilience (Lewis, 1987, Pham, 2003). It was Naeem (1998) who first paralleled the engineering and ecosystem use of the same concept.

And stability is a good thing for ecosystems. In fact, stability is the end point for ecosystems. Sand dune succession ends in a forest, which changes no further. The reason for this stability will be revealed in Section IV!

So applying this to the broader issues facing us, we see that exclusion is not the way of nature, but rather an artefact of reductionist thinking. But then again, so is natural selection as an evolutionary theory. We don't find exclusion out there beyond *Bubbleworld*. Instead, we find a balance in nature, derived from all organisms being a part of the greater whole, where competition and predation are replaced by *quorum sensing* (communication between separate units leading to the co-ordination of behaviour). What I mean by this is that all the organisms out there are communicating with one another, and know their places within the scheme of things. It's called sustainability.

Chapter Forty-Four
Fossil record: Replacement vs Displacement

If Darwin was correct in claiming that competition lay at the heart of evolution, then we should see species displacing other species, as the fit outcompete the less fit, first within the species, and then out-competing other species. However the most recent evidence does not demonstrate this.

Writing in *Nature*, Professor Chris Venditti demonstrated that most biodiversity emerges not from ongoing evolutionary war (the *"struggle for existence"*, as Darwin called it) but from rare and infrequent events (Venditti *et al.*, 2010). Niles Eldridge and Stephen Jay Gould first suggested this when they referred to the evolutionary process, not as a gradual branching of a tree of life, but rather as a process of *punctuated equilibrium* (Eldridge and Gould, 1972).

Professor Michael Benton, a leading palaeontologist from the University of Bristol, wrote, in the *Proceedings of the Royal Society* (Benton, 1996), that displacement has *"probably played a minor role in the history of tetrapods"* identifying only thirteen percent of fossil tetrapods that outcompeted their rivals. Instead, he showed that, usually, new species tended to appear when new niches were available, while others replaced other species when the latter went extinct, writing, that *"family originations were most often associated with expansion into new niches"*.

I have summed this up as follows: *"evolution happens in the empty market place, not in the crowded back alleys"* (Skene, 2009). Stephen Brusatte, of the American Museum of Natural History, writing in the leading academic journal, *Science*, said of dinosaur evolution, *"historical contingency* [luck], *rather than prolonged competition or general "superiority", was the primary factor in the rise of dinosaurs"*(Brusatte *et al.*, 2008). And one of the leading evolutionary biologists of recent times, David Jablonski, also writing in *Science*, stated that during mass extinctions, the reasons for species being removed are random, rather than ecologically related (Jablonski, 1986).

Professor Samuel Alizon and his team wrote, in the *Proceedings of the National Academy of Sciences*, that *"under resource competition there is an exponential slowdown of the apparent rate of evolution"* (Alizon *et al.*, 2008), while Dr Luke Mahler, from Harvard University, wrote, in the journal, *Evolution,* that *"the rate of phenotypic diversity declines with decreasing opportunity"* (Mahler *et al.*, 2010). In other words, competition puts the brakes on evolution.

Yann Hautier, from the University of Zűrich, wrote, in *Science*, that competition for light in plants causes a reduction in biodiversity when nutrients are freely available (Hautier *et al.*, 2009). Meanwhile, Albert Phillimore, from Imperial College London, investigating the evolution of birds, wrote *"speciation slows as ecological opportunities and geographic space place limits on clade growth"* (Phillimore and Prince, 2008).

All of these scientists, writing in our leading research journals, are saying the same thing, and what they are saying is extremely concerning for anyone who thinks that Darwinian evolution is a theory that works. Competition is excluded, by all of them, as being a driver of diversification. Competition leads to a reduction in diversity, not an increase. This attacks the very foundation of Darwinian dogma. And there are still more problems to come.

Chapter Forty-Five
Mass Extinctions

When we look at the change in biodiversity through time, based on the fossil record, we do not see what we might expect to see if mutations drove evolution. Mutation rate is considered to be fairly constant through time, but the change in diversity is anything but constant. Figure III.4 shows what we might predict if mutations and gradualism ruled (a), if there was an exponential increase in evolution through time (b) and the observed change in diversity at the level of the genus (Levin, 2009).

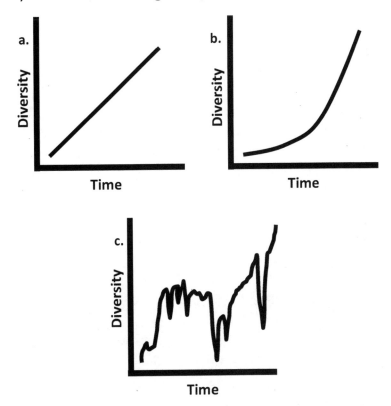

Figure III.4 a. Diversity using a gradual model of evolution; b. Diversity using exponential model; c. Diversity change based on fossil evidence at the level of genera.

Looking at the actual data (Fig. III.4c), we can see two things. Firstly, the overall pattern would appear to increase geometrically, and, secondly, there are lots of ups and downs along the way. So how do we make sense of all of this?

Well, obviously, the actual curve (Fig. III.4c) does not look anything like Fig III.4a. It is not a straight line, gradually increasing through time. So it is not a matter of mutations slowly occurring over millions of years, and these mutations gradually leading to new organisms at a steady rate of increase. There is more to it than that. It is roughly a geometric rise, of the kind we came upon in Section II, when populations of bacteria multiplied to the size of the planet in a matter of months, starting slowly and then rapidly increasing. What could be responsible for this?

Some people feel that the reason diversity seems to have massively increased in recent times is because there have been more niches occupied. More organisms create new opportunities, which lead to even more organisms evolving (e.g. Sahney *et al.*, 2010). New strategies allow new space to be explored. The organisms themselves can also open up new niches for other organisms to find a niche. The idea is that over time, animals, and, particularly, tetrapods, began to both create and move into new types of ecological space, or *ecospace*.

While I would agree that evolution is all about diffusion into ecospace, I don't feel that this adequately explains the patterns we have seen. Rather, it is much more likely that the exponential increase in diversity through time is all about fossil survival. The further you go back in time, the less likely it is that specimens will have made it to the present day.

The greatest proof that the exponential increase in diversity is due to improved preservation, rather than expansion into ecological space, is found in the *Burgess Shale.* Here, under unbelievably ideal fossilization conditions, a small sample of the biology of a shallow sea, in present day British Columbia, was preserved for over half a billion years. That's right, five hundred million years! The Burgess Shale is one of the most exciting fossil finds in history. Here lie the fossilized remains of a vast array of species, suddenly bursting from the rocks, with an incredibly broad range of forms.

I could write a book on this, but instead I will point you to a couple that have already been written: Briggs, Erwin and Collier's *The Fossils of the Burgess Shale (1994)*, and Stephen Jay Gould's *Wonderful Life* (1989). Although there has been some dispute about how many phyla are represented, the bottom line is that a vast number of different niches were clearly exploited. The disparity (i.e. the number of different ways of earning a living) was extremely high. Since then, disparity has declined while diversity (i.e. the number of different organisms practicing these different lifestyles) has risen. But it is disparity that represents strategy. Thus there would appear to have been a decrease, rather than an increase, in the variety of life styles.

The taxonomic breadth at that time was at least as broad as today in terms of invertebrates (vertebrates had not quite evolved, though the earliest known chordate, *Pikaea*, was found in the Burgess Shale). So although the global totals of species recovered from these times is low overall, in areas where preservation was ideal, we see a very different picture. Thus the evidence clearly shows that there were as many different ways of doing things back then, if not more. The geometric rise in species is more likely to be due to improved preservation with time, meaning that we are a lot more likely to find remains of creatures that went extinct closer to our present time than further back. Indeed, given the losses over geological time, we would expect the pattern to be geometric, rising rapidly as we move into the most recent times, since the last mass extinction.

The next important observation is that the curve is by no means smooth. In fact, if we look carefully, we see that there have been a number of very significant spikes, shining through the fog. And they all look basically the same, especially if we allow for the magnification of improved preservation in recent times. In Figure III.5, I detail the five largest events to compare them. These are the mass extinctions of the Ordovician (445 M years ago), Devonian (370 M years ago), Permian (253 M years ago), Triassic (200 M years ago) and Cretaceous (65 M years ago).

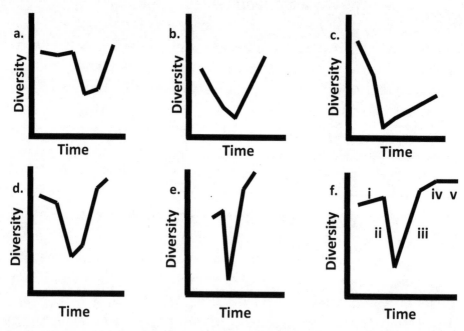

Figure III.5 Extinction and recovery of diversity in: a. Ordovician event; b. Devonian event; c. Permian event; d. Triassic event; e. Cretaceous event; f. Key stages in extinction events: i. Pre-extinction equilibrium; ii. Extinction event; iii. Post-extinction recovery; iv. Slowing of diversification; v. Post-extinction equilibrium.

The changes in diversity around these periods all resemble each other, as indicated on Figure III.5f. Prior to the extinction event, there is a fairly level period, when extinctions equal replacements (Fig. III.5fi). The Earth would appear to be saturated with species here. It's a bit like trying to get into a very popular restaurant. Someone needs to come out before you can get in (this formed the basis of a very funny movie I saw recently called *Date Night*, starring Steve Carell and Tina Fey, where a couple pretend to be someone else in order to jump the queue in a restaurant, with disastrous, though highly amusing consequences!). There is no jumping the queue in nature. Free space needs to be there, and the maître d'hôtel is very insistent.

At times, the walls of the restaurant are blown asunder and the whole building has to be rebuilt. Mass extinctions are not small events. They lead to devastation, often through starvation, as trophic pyramids collapse. The plants are often badly impacted, when the sunlight is blocked by volcanic dust or impact dust, or both. The curve drops dramatically.

Once the dust has settled and the Sun breaks through, the curve steeply increases (Fig. III.5fiii). In each of the five events, this increase represents the fastest rate of evolution in that entire period. This is when evolution really kicks off. There is no competition, because most things are dead. There is no shortage of basic resources, in terms of nutrients (all those dead things), space and sunlight. Nothing will exist that can't find food, and so there is no concern of starvation after the initial kill is over. If you can't find anything to eat, you will be dead already.

This is not a place where natural selection has any place. Instead it is all about opportunity, and diffusion into the empty market place. It's a time for freedom of expression. And that's exactly what I see when I look at the myriad ways in which life is shaped and coloured. What has always struck me, from working around the world in amazing habitats, is the shear breadth of design. It's not about a few fit organisms, excluding everything else. Rather, it is a free-for-all, a diffusion of matter into energetic space. This is not a spectre of control, competition and domination. In fact, it is the opposite.

Gradually, the rate of evolution slows down, and our curve begins to level off (Fig. III.5fiv). Now ecospace has become saturated and the system reaches equilibrium. Evolution slows, and we are into the Darwinian dusk. And, eventually, we return to equilibrium (Fig. III.5fv). This is where Darwin's theory is most likely to have some relevance, as a means of explaining the slowing down of evolution, rather than explaining the process itself.

But then his *erroneous extrapolation squared* couldn't really be expected to have much relevance, its proofs lying in Petri dishes and glass jars, rather than out in the real world. *Bubbleworld* never could reach out and understand what lies beyond its walls. Mass extinctions don't support Darwinian Theory. Rather, they point to a completely different concept of evolution. And we can uncover even more problems if we re-visit that cathedral of Darwinian Theory, the Galapagos Islands.

Chapter Forty-Six
A Heresy in the Cathedral

On a cold winter's day, it's hard to imagine that the interior of our planet is as hot as a star. The inner core has a temperature of five thousand five hundred degrees centigrade. This is similar to the surface of the Sun! Even the mantle ranges from five hundred degrees (near the crust) to four thousand degrees centigrade (near the core). Where did all this heat come from?

Three sources have been identified. Originally forming from cosmic dust that randomly collided and stuck together, as the early planet became bigger, it began to exert a gravitational attraction. This led to it drawing other smaller bodies towards it. These small planetesimals, themselves originally on track to become planets, collided with the Earth, becoming part of it, and releasing heat. Secondly, as the Earth expanded, and its gravitational field strengthened, this gravity compressed the planet, again releasing huge amounts of heat. A final source of heat came from the disintegration of radioactive elements, such as thorium and uranium. This source, unlike the other two, is still ongoing.

The heat of our planet drives the movements of our tectonic plates. In fact tectonic plate movement is the main way for Earth to lose heat. These huge pieces of the crust travel across the globe creating mayhem. They move at about the same rate as your fingernails grow, so next time you clip your nails, you can think that your house has shifted that far since the last clipping!

These plates bang into each other, creating giant pile-ups, like some cosmic road crash between two monster trucks, and huge mountain ranges reach to the sky as a result. The Himalayas rose, literally, from the collision of the Indo-Australian plate and the Eurasian plate, some fifty million years ago. The European Alps resulted in a similar crash, eighty million years ago, between the Eurasian plate and the African plate. Whole oceans can appear and disappear as plates grow or disappear back into the mantle.

At times, huge plumes of rock, originating at the edge of the core, move upwards through the mantle and press on the crust. It's like pushing your finger against a layer of cloth. The raised crust forms a platform just below the surface of the ocean, and from this platform, volcanoes form, creating islands.

Deep beneath the Pacific Ocean, three of the planet's great tectonic plates, called Cocos, Pacific and Nazca, meet at a location called the Galapagos Triple Junction. In this area, the crust of the Earth is extremely thin, and it just so happened that a plume in the mantle has pushed against the crust here, forming a platform, the Galapagos Platform. Volcanic activity at the surface of the platform led to islands popping up. The Galapagos Archipelago was formed, some three thousand kilometres from Rapa Nui, and one thousand kilometres west of Ecuador.

And it was there, on 15th September, 1835, that HMS Beagle arrived, with a young, twenty-five-year-old Charles Darwin on board. The story has grown over the years, and the Galapagos Islands have become the Cathedral of Darwinian Theory. One group of organisms in particular, the so-called Darwin's finches, would take centre stage, as the symbols of his theory. There are a number of interesting points related to these. First they are not finches at all, but, rather, tanagers (Sibley and Monroe, 1990). Secondly, Darwin dismissed them as unrelated, labelling them as blackbirds, gross-bills, finches and a wren, and packaged samples up to be sent back to Britain.

Darwin hadn't even bothered to label which islands the different specimens had come from. He was much more interested in the mockingbirds and tortoises. It was in London that John Gould, the curator at the Zoological Society of London, examined the specimens, and discovered that they were all closely related species. Fortunately, other members of the Beagle expedition had also collected some of these birds and had properly labelled their origins, and so finally the true story of the tanagers was able to be told.

A third important point to note is that we now know that a number of these so-called finches can breed with each other. The medium and small ground finches can mate and produce viable offspring. Medium ground finches also breed with cactus finches (Grant and Grant, 1989; Grant, 1993). The problem here is that a species is defined as a reproductively isolated group of individuals. So these three finches cannot be counted as separate species. Given that most studies have been limited to the ground finches, it is quite possible that other so called "species" also interbreed. So this group, held up as an example of speciation, is more appropriately an example of non-speciation!

What we do know is that sometime between one and five million years ago, according to genetic analysis by Vladimir Vincek and colleagues, some thirty individuals of a single species of finch arrived on the islands in a single event (Vincek *et al.*, 1997). It is thought that they may have been blown by a freak storm to the islands. Although the founding species was from South America, we find none of the *"species"* of tanager, discovered on the Galapagos Islands, on the mainland. So they clearly evolved. That is not in question. The questions are: how did it happen, and why did it not happen on the mainland?

I want to suggest that the opposite of what was claimed to have happened actually occurred. Firstly, let us remind ourselves of the traditional Darwinian version (with genetic additions). These birds found themselves on an island. They spread to other islands, and selective pressure was very high, because they were no longer in the type of habitat where they had come from. Competition was high and so different beak shapes evolved in what is called *character displacement*. The fittest survived, and so the birds adapted differently, natural selection being the driver.

Isolated on these little islands, they became separate genetic populations, and went their own way, resulting in speciation (not actually true), and a whole range of different beaks. Selective pressure led to the squeezing out of these characteristics from a formerly homogenous single species. Back on the mainland, the pressure was stabilizing, and so the original species remained as it was, whereas on the islands, we would have directional selection, or even disruptive selection, acting.

Now let's look at the actual facts. The birds were not on the edge of their main population. They were blown to a completely new place. Hence the rules of Dobzhansky, relating to a peripheral group in sub-optimal conditions, do not apply. As far as we know, based on DNA analysis, no other finches were on the islands, and so there were no competitors. The islands are not small, covering a total area of around eight thousand kilometres squared.

The thirty birds survived as they were (unless you are a Lamarckian evolutionist, believing that they could change within the first generation!), and so the conditions must have been suitable for them already. Indeed, arriving after a traumatic one thousand kilometre wind-assisted flight, they would have needed excellent conditions to make it through. This was not the time to have to struggle for existence. It was the time for some comfortable convalescence. They also must have had all the provisions not only to sustain them, but to build energy resources for reproduction. Birds need to build up significant energy and nutrient resources leading up to egg production.

Then, of course, the new offspring would need a high protein diet, such as invertebrate larvae, to sustain them. All of this must have been available on the islands during the first and subsequent breeding seasons. These insects also require energy and nutrients for their own proliferation, and so we can picture a working ecosystem.

In other words, we cannot envisage a landscape that is placing pressure upon the birds. Furthermore, if the original cohort indeed consisted only of thirty birds, a significant number of successful reproductive events would be required to build up numbers, in order to avoid the risks of inbreeding. It is well known that within birds, inbreeding can lead to significant problems (see, for example, studies by Greenwood *et al.*, 1978; van Noordwijk and Scharloo, 1981; Kempenaers *et al.*, 1996; McRae, 1996).

New beaks don't grow on trees, and certainly don't evolve overnight, and this means that suitable food, such as what they were used to eating with their original beaks, must have been available for a long period of time. So I do not accept the proposition that there was pressure on the system. If there was pressure, it would be a long time before new anatomy would evolve to respond to this pressure. Since the birds survived, and with sufficient variation to evolve into many different niches, then inbreeding could not have been an issue, as this reduces variation (as well as leading to all sorts of issues including sterility). That being the case, selective pressures must have been extremely low, not high.

What we observe on the Galápagos archipelago is not at all unique to this one set of islands. Indeed, islands are famous for the number of endemic species (that is, species only found on a particular island). On New Caledonia, eighty percent of the plants are only found there. For Hawaii, this figure is nearer ninety percent (Whittaker and Fernández-Palacios, 2007). Ninety-five percent of land snails on Madagascar are unique to that extraordinary store of biodiversity. The Canary Islands have over two thousand unique insect species (Izquierdo *et al.*, 2004). All of this tells us that islands are diversity factories. They provide what we call *ecological release*. Here, variation within a species expands because there are few or no competing species and there is therefore empty niche space. Mainland populations have long been under competitive and predatorial pressure, with no free niche space.

Now going back to our curve, if selective pressure is *low*, the arrows disappear, allowing the curve to relax. It takes a big breath inwards! As a result it swells, changing from an inverted champagne glass to a big fat camel's hump. In other words, the variation in the population increases. In my view of evolution, natural selection represents all those things which stabilize populations. Though ill-conceived, this imaginary concept of natural selection represents a force of non-evolution. It keeps things constant. The fittest, in our curve, are also the most common. Natural selection maintains the *average Joe*.

The theory that I propose here is that evolution occurs when pressures are *released*. The birds on the mainland were in a large population, probably not far off its carrying capacity, with lots of competition and predation within a stable, ancient ecosystem. Mature ecosystems are highly balanced, and therefore highly stabilized.

If we destabilize the ecosystem then we release the population to become more varied. All sorts of unusual variations on the theme can thrive, and they won't be snuffed out as outliers. Instead, the curve swells, representing a varied population. On the Galapagos Islands, the population of little birds, freed from predators and competition, expands in numbers and variation. This allows evolution to happen, with new variants able to appear. Later as numbers grow, competition acts to stabilize these new variants, or to remove them.

To me anyway the evidence is clear. Scientists writing in the leading journals of the world point to competition and species displacement as being unimportant. Islands represent freedom from the stability present on the mainland, and mass extinctions remove this stability at a global level. It is at these times that we see evolution working, as variation has the opportunity to expand, and as it does so, it fills the world with all sorts of amazing creatures of every shape and size imaginable. Natural selection has nothing to do with the Galapagos Islands. Rather, the driver is the opposite of this – a decrease in competition, a freedom of expression and an expansion of variation, resulting in a whole new set of beaks.

Before finishing this section I want to draw your attention to a three significant experiments, one old one that has been wheeled out as proof of Natural Selection but isn't, and two new ones that undermine two tenets of Darwinian evolution.

Chapter Forty-Seven
Industrial Melanization: Moths, Trees and the Illusionary Proof of Selection

One of the classic examples of Darwinian evolution that appears in many school and university text books is the story of *Biston betularia*, the peppered moth. The tale goes that before the industrial revolution in England, the peppered moth had white wings with black speckles (as if someone had sprinkled pepper on it). However, between 1850 and 1920, almost all of these moths were replaced by forms with completely black wings.

More recently, according to this legend, this trend has reversed, with numbers of truly peppered wing forms increasing again. This is said to be a beautiful example of evolution in action, through natural selection. As the Industrial Revolution progressed, then soot and acid rain turned tree bark black. Bernard Kettlewell, from the University of Oxford, set out the hypothesis that since the trees were the natural roosts for these moths, then as the bark turned darker, so selective pressure, in the shape of predatory birds, led to the moth population darkening also, in order to be disguised against the surface of the tree. The lighter forms were selected against and the dark forms were selected for.

It was claimed that the speckled wing form had originally roosted on lichen-covered trees, but now, due to air pollution, the lichens were mostly gone, and the dark bark was all that was left. Any speckled moth would quickly be spotted by a hungry passing bird and be eaten. This very effectively removed its genes from the gene pool!

The Clean Air Acts were introduced in the 1950s, and the atmosphere improved, leading to a recovery for the tree lichens.

This was said to explain the recent recovery of the lighter forms of the moth. Kettlewell carried out a range of experiments showing that dark and light coloured moths both chose backgrounds that matched their colour, and that each form, when placed on the wrong background, would be predated upon more than when on the correct background. It all seemed to work beautifully.

However recent work has completely undermined this thesis (Sargent *et al.*, 1998; Majerus, 1998). Firstly, in more than forty years of research, a total of two *Biston betularia* moths have ever been found naturally roosting on tree bark. In other words, tree bark is not their natural habitat. This immediately invalidates the entire story.

Kettlewell's experiments that were done in the field were artificially constructed, and he bred the moths in the laboratory before placing them on the trees. Furthermore, the moths were placed on the trees during the day, while moths will normally choose where to rest at night. Moths are averse to doing anything in daylight, being nocturnal species.

Finally, the recovery of the lighter coloured forms occurred well before tree lichens re-colonized, so even if the moths did rest on trees, which they don't, the lighter forms recovered before their habitat re-appeared! Finally, Kettlewell's results relating to moths choosing an appropriate background that matches their wings has never been able to be replicated, casting serious doubt on its validity. Reviewing this work in the journal, *Nature*, Professor Jerry Coyne of the University of Chicago said *"We must discard Biston as a well-understood example of natural selection in action"* (Coyne, 1998).

Chapter Forty-Eight
A Final Darwinian Teaser: Of Sex, Size and Song

We've all heard the familiar Darwinian tale of the fittest males having the brightest tail feathers, the largest inflatable throat sacs and the loudest calls. Genetic fitness has been tightly linked to physical fitness. This has underpinned much of the eugenics movement, where, for example, the strong Ayrian should defeat a weaker specimen, and should provide the genetic basis for a fitter human race. Indeed the importance of sexual selection, where females favour fitter males, lies at the heart of neo-Darwinism.

The selection of a mate from a choice of mates allows fitter combinations of genes to come together and provides the basis for fitness itself. In fact the idea that competition always leads to improvement is a true *Bubbleworld* phenomenon. And in neo-Darwinism, fitness is defined as the proportion of individuals of a particular genotype that are selected for and go on to reproduce in the next generation. In other words, fitter individuals are more likely to pass on their genes to the next generation.

However, two significant papers, published in 2010, undermine all of this, and instead point to a different theory of evolution being the more appropriate approach. Working on two different organisms, crickets (Rodríguez-Muñoz *et al.*, 2010, in *Science*) and guppies (Evans, 2010, in *Proceedings of the Royal Society B*), these findings all disagree significantly with the accepted story.

With crickets, it was found that when observed in the field (not in the Gaussian laboratory!), using a newly developed camera system never before available, our understanding of reproduction and fitness was very different than that gleaned from laboratory experiments, which had, up until then, been used to support traditional theory. What the British-led team of scientists found has shaken the world of evolutionary biology. Using two hundred and fifty thousand hours of footage of one hundred and fifty-two crickets, filmed in a meadow in Northern Spain, the scientists came to a number of shocking discoveries.

Firstly, many males and many females never mate. It had been thought that males out-competed each other for female attention, but that most females would mate, being the "choosers". So females are not a limiting resource, as had been commonly stated. Also, many females mated often, with different males, and the more matings completed, the more offspring they had, meaning that the offspring were likely to have different fathers, the opposite to the assumption normally made.

More worrying still was the observation that apparently sub-ordinate males have the same numbers of offspring as dominant males. This completely uncouples any link between genetic fitness and phenotype. It didn't matter if you were big or small, you had an equal chance of passing on your genes. No sexual selection here! The small males used song to attract females, while the larger males didn't sing. Again, it had been thought that song was a sign of fitness associated with large males.

The study highlighted two things: that the mantras of sexual selection and of survival of the fittest are not supported, and that laboratory results, previously the basis for the vast majority of the so-called evidence relating to Darwinian Theory, has no relevance to field studies. But then, we have already argued this. I would like to underline that all of the evidence provided for the alternative, energetic theory of evolution, which I will sketch out in the next section, is based on field work, not laboratory work.

The second paper is equally interesting (Evans, 2010). Professor Jonathan Evans, based at the University of Western Australia, discovered that in guppies, one of the most intensely-studied fish, smaller, less ornamented individuals produce faster swimming sperm than larger, flashy fish. It was thought that having greater numbers of colour spots was a sign of fitness, as was size. However Evan's work shows that because resources are limited, then if you put more effort into physical appearance, there is a trade-off, and your sperm will be less fit. Ultimately, it is the sperm that represent the males in reproduction, and so fast sperm are distinctly advantageous.

The outcome is that there will be much greater variation preserved than expected under a survival of the fittest argument. This is because it is not about fitness, but about energetic budgeting. You can have a range of balances between looking good and having fit sperm, but you can't afford to be strong in both traits. The range of solutions to this energetic equation is numerous. And so it is not *survival of the fittest*, but survival of fit. The problems can be solved in a range of ways, and there is no fittest genotype. Rather, each individual represents an energetic compromise of different emphases.

Let's turn, now, to the broader lessons that this curve teaches us.

Chapter Forty-Nine
What is the Significance of All of this to our World Today?

Sure, evolution is all fine and dandy, but what relevance does any of this have to us, and our continuance on the planet? There are a number of key issues here. Darwinian Theory has been embraced by many fields far beyond biology. The idea of the survival of the fittest, of competition delivering the best and of our ability to artificially select outcomes in nature, all feed off this theory. While I certainly would not argue that Darwin produced the eugenic drive of Nazi Germany, there is no doubt that Eugenics certainly embraced the science of evolution as a support in both argument and essence.

Francis Galton (1822-1911), the half-cousin of Charles Darwin, introduced the term *"Eugenics"* in his book, *Inquiries into Human Faculty and its Development* (Galton, 1883). He defined it as: "*the science which deals with all influences that improve the inborn qualities of a race; also with those that develop them to the utmost advantage*". Compare this to the full title of Darwin's masterpiece: *The Origin of Species by Means of Natural Selection or the Preservation of Favoured Races in the Struggle for Life.*

Galton was a remarkable polymath, who counted among his achievements the mapping of Namibia, the first popular weather maps and a new fingerprint analysis that was of significant use to forensic biology. He also founded the field of psychometrics (the science of measuring mental ability). Yet it was for his work on Eugenics that he would become best known.

The application of Darwinian Theory to humans, called *Social Darwinism*, particularly in improving the stock by selection, became extremely popular with a wide number of scientists. In America, Charles Davenport (1866-1944) became director of the Station for Experimental Evolution (now the Cold Spring Harbor Laboratory), founding the Eugenics Record Office (ERO). The ERO focused on constructing family trees, in order to gather evidence of the transmission of social traits, including anti-social behaviour and criminality, as well as intelligence quotients (IQ).

Harry Hamilton Laughlin (1880-1943), the director of ERO, quoted in Henry Friedlander's book, *The Origins of Nazi Genocide: From "Euthanasia" to the Final Solution* (Friedlander, 1995), stated that *"immigrants from Southern and Eastern Europe, especially the Jews, were racially so different from, and genetically so inferior to, the current American population that any racial mixture would be deleterious"*. The ERO research led to the development of sterilization laws in America. Charles Davenport's book, *Heredity in Relation to Eugenics* was published in 1911 (Davenport, 1911). He had close links with German eugenicists at the time, editing two German journals on eugenics in the 1930s.

In 1907, Indiana became the first state with legislation requiring the sterilization of criminals. By 1914, twelve states had eugenic sterilization. Targets were orphans, tramps, deaf, deformed, dependent, feeble-minded, insane, epileptic and the blind. Madison Grant (1865-1937), Chairman of the Zoological Society of New York and another prominent eugenicist, published *The Passing of the Great Race* in 1916, wherein he advocated *"elimination of those who are weak or unfit"*.

Darwin's theory fitted with the overall direction of thinking of the time: progress, competition and fitness. The great possibility of a utopian dream, realized by human thought and technology reached its zenith in the statement that *"Eugenics is the self-direction of human evolution: like a tree eugenics draws its material from many sources and organizes them into an harmonious entity"* as the logo for the Second International Eugenics Congress, held in New York, in 1921, famously put it. This was no meeting of crackpots either. Alexander Graham Bell was the honorary President, Madison Grant was treasurer and Henry Osborn, fellow of the American Academy of Arts and Sciences, and renowned palaeontologist, was the President. It doesn't get much more perverse than this, and clearly ties eugenics to evolution in the minds of many of the leading scientific minds of that time.

President Calvin Coolidge (1872-1933) wrote, in the February edition of the popular *Good Housekeeping Magazine* of 1921, that *"There are racial considerations too grave to be brushed aside for any sentimental reasons. Biological laws tell us that certain divergent people will not mix or blend. The Nordics propagate themselves successfully. With other races, the outcome shows deterioration on both sides."*

In the same year (1921), the influential campaigner for contraceptive rights, Margaret Sanger, wrote that *"the unbalance of the birth rate of the unfit and the fit is admittedly the greatest present menace to civilization"*. 1923 saw the formation of the American Eugenics Society, with thirty-three chapters across the country. By 1924, the US Immigration Restriction Act was passed, and by 1935, sterilization laws existed in America, Germany, Norway, Sweden, Denmark and Switzerland.

In Germany, the experiments in America had a major impact. Adolf Hitler, in *Mein Kampf* (1925), made reference to the Californian studies. German eugenics can be traced back to British and American influence, with ideas exchanged between the leading thinkers of the time. Ernst Hackel, the famous German evolutionary biologist, also known as Darwin's bulldog in

Europe, who coined the term *Darwinism*, as well as *phylum*, *phylogeny* and *ecology*, published his book, *Wonders of Life,* in 1904 (Hackel and McCabe, 2009). In it, he wrote that sickly adults should be eliminated to prevent spreading of their genes, suggesting the use of painless and rapid poison.

In 1905, Ernst Rudin and Alfred Ploetz founded the Society of Race Hygiene. Ernst Rudin (1875-1952) was a Swiss psychiatrist who is acknowledged as contributing to the philosophical framework of the Holocaust. In 1933, he was chosen to head Germany's racial purity programme. He had studied the Californian sterilization programme, and published in American eugenics journals. Rudolf Hess, quoted by Stefan Kuhl in his book, *The Nazi Connection* (Kuhl, 1994), said *"National Socialism is nothing but applied biology"*.

This quote from Hess exposes why the erroneous extrapolation squared that represents Darwinian Theory is more than just an intellectual failure. It matters that it is wrong. What Hess describes as *"applied biology"* is actually Darwinian Theory. As we have shown, this theory fails, abjectly, to describe real biology. It is based on reductionist, Gaussian science. Yet its central tenets of competition, selection, survival of the fittest and sexual selection are nowhere to be seen in the natural evolving Biosphere.

By equating the real world with this erroneous theory, support was gathered for many morally corrupt and horrific actions. Here we see the misrepresentation of the Biosphere, as a harsh, reductionist, selfish, competitive place, where only the fittest survive, being used to promote artificial selection among humans. This is serious stuff, not just some trivial academic debate. And that is why the curve of this section is so important, because it points clearly to the significant errors in Darwinian thinking, and the consequences for how we behave. National Socialism may have a lot in common with Darwinism, but it has nothing whatsoever to do with biology, and neither does Darwinian Theory.

The idea of racial purification, inspired by Social Darwinism, took on a great significance in Germany when combined with the Root Race Theory. This theory focused on the Aryans, thought to be the common ancestors of India, Iran and Europe, as evidenced by the origin of language in these places. The common linguistic root, Proto-Indo-European, was thought to point to the original Aryans. These were thought to have existed in the steppes of Russia, Scandinavia or Germany, and the idea of the northern, or Nordic European being the descendent of the pure Aryan, and threatened by inferior groups such as the Jew, became a strong force in German thinking.

Huge archaeological expeditions were raised to find evidence of the Aryan nature of the German people and archaeologists such as Gustaf Kossinna (1859-1931) strongly aligned the origin of the Aryan race with the early German people, identifying the German nation as the leader of ancient civilization. Hyerdahl's work on South America and Rapa Nui continued this obsession, as we noted in Section I.

The superior race was identified, and the steps needed to ensure its continuance were clear. For the Aryans to dominate, these inferior races would need to be exterminated. This came to a terrible head in the gas chambers of Treblinka and Belzec, and fed a much more ancient drive, the elimination of competitive races in order to preserve the purity of the favoured race, through artificial rather than natural selection. Darwinism had spawned Social Darwinism, and the whole heady mix of survival of the fittest and improving the race was driven forward within the acceptable context of scientific theory.

It is an irony that Darwin's use of domesticated animal breeding (artificial selection) as a way of understanding natural diversity led to the birth of natural selection, which in turn made the application of artificial selection to humans more palatable. After all, nature did it this way, so why should we not apply it to our own race, particularly since we had removed ourselves from nature's selective eye. Indeed, it would be better anyhow for us to decide the genetic destiny of our race, as we are much better than nature at all things. We had replaced the gods and the states and the natural checks, and would take charge of our own evolutionary development too.

Of course, genetic modification of crops and animals has an uncanny similarity to Eugenics in terms of its driving principle – giving Nature a helping hand. Once again, we take control of a natural process in order to alter the very genetic code of our natural plants, playing the gods we have replaced by technology and reason, the wise creators. However, there is no wisdom in altering things without any reference to the context within which these things exist.

Chapter Fifty
A Celebration of Diversity

A competitive world kills diversity because diversification relies on opportunity. If the human race is to find answers, it must be able to diffuse into all of the possible solution-spaces that are out there. Our present system is increasingly pressured on all sides. Deadlines, competition, attack, defence, selfishness, guardedness – these are the walls of suppression that close us in. But the greatest walls are those constructed by the Enlightenment, the walls of human-centric thinking, *Bubbleworld*.

If we want to explore the variety of possible solutions to our problems, we need to celebrate diversity. Diversity thrives when freed from selection, reducing competition and judgement, removing the barriers and walls that prevent us from diffusing outwards. And diversity brings stability. The Competitive Exclusion Principle brings only monopoly and dominance, whereas a finely tuned human society should be like any thriving population within a healthy ecosystem, rich in diversity.

Diversity also brings resilience. When disasters occur, the more alternatives you have, the better. If a country is completely dependent upon one supermarket chain or upon one power source, and something happens to it, then they will be in serious trouble. But with functional redundancy, although there may be some failures, the ecosystem carries on.

Of course what we know as *natural selection* increases as diversity increases, eventually reaching an equilibrium. However this is not the selective force of nature, red in tooth and claw, but rather a diversified, balanced society, at equilibrium with itself. Natural selection is, rather, a product of diversity, and an outcome of creative freedom. This is nature's way. The balance is not within one species. For one person cannot sit on a seesaw and remain in the air. Balance comes when someone else sits on the other side, of a similar weight.

And that is how ecosystems and the Biosphere as a whole work, with all of life expressing itself within the context of the greater whole. Here, selection is not a painful thing, but an acknowledgement of our place in the greater scheme of things. It is a conversation between partners, a comforting rubbing of shoulders, acting as a quorum sensing, where we can "feel" our impacts upon each other. Indeed, as we have seen in this section, natural selection is a consequence of an erroneous extrapolation squared, and so instead of this phrase, I would suggest replacing it entirely with a different one: *Biosphere feedback.*

Biosphere feedback is a much more scientifically legitimate term than natural selection, and carries none of the baggage of the latter expression. It covers the useful aspects that natural selection tried to explain, without the baseless analogy with pigs and dogs. It references the actual context of any individual, the Biosphere, and reminds us of the importance of conversations between the components. By characterizing these conversations, we can understand the processes that define who we are, and understand how to live sustainably.

Sadly, one of the ugliest outcomes of Darwinism has been the celebration of the *"fittest"*. Evolution by natural selection sorts out the fit from the unfit. Judgements are made, and the perfect physique steps out from the imperfect crowd and is crowned. Competitive exclusion of the not-so-fit leads to progress towards a utopian world. This is such a destructive way of thinking.

Nature is full of strange, sub-optimal, creatures, none more so than *Homo sapiens sapiens* himself. We developed terms like "handicapped" and "disabled" to describe those who do not fit the perfect forms of Darwinian thinking. Instead, I would prefer to celebrate all that lives, where each of us is the perfect outcome of energy married to matter, expressing ourselves in all of the varied shapes, sizes and behaviours that we see. There is no "*fittest*". As we have seen, the *fittest* are actually the most common, or the *average Joes*. It is the *different* ones that represent and celebrate variation, and bring new morphologies and thinking to the table.

Not only does an ecosystem need lots of different species, but a species needs lots of different individuals. Therefore we should celebrate diversity within as well as between species. Since fitness is merely commonness, then let's not look on it as something to aspire to. Rather, enjoy where we are, and what we are a part of. The very existence of the peak in our curve owes itself to the process that prevents diversification, and so we should see a focus on fitness as a symptom of too much competition, and too little diffusion.

A nation that celebrates diversity, then, is one that is actively diffusing into solution space, embracing the consequences such as resilience, functionality and productivity. A nation that aspires to fitness, or stereotype, is one that is losing diversity, leading to collapse, depression and war.

Let's take our eyes off the peak in an inverted champagne glass curve and, instead, look for the gently sloping edges of a big fat camel hump. For diversity is a move away from the Darwinian obsession with fitness, and an embrace of the balance of the Biosphere. And finally, sustainability and resilience can only be found within the context of a diverse Biosphere, and never in the self-interested, technology-fuelled *Bubbleworld* that many people use as their thinking platform.

In the next section, we will explore what really makes us tick, and the repercussions of this for just about anything you can think of. Not only does this new approach supplant Darwinian Theory, but has significant implications for sustainability, as it points the way to a new form of thinking. See you in the next section.

REFERENCES

Alizon, S., Kucera, M. and Jansen, V.A.A. (2008) Competition between cryptic species explains variations in rates of lineage evolution. *Proceedings of the National Academy of* Sciences, *USA* 105: 12382-12386.

Archibald, S.B., Johnson, K.R., Mathewes, R.W., and Greenwood, D.R. (2011) Intercontinental dispersal of giant thermophilic ants across the Arctic during early Eocene hyperthermals. *Proceedings of the Royal Society of London B. In press.*

Benton, M.J. (ed.) (1993) *The fossil record 2.* Chapman and Hall, London.

Benton, M.J. (1996) On the nonprevalence of competitive replacement in the evolution of tetrapods. In: Jablonski, D., Erwin, D.H. and Lipps, J. (eds), *Evolutionary Palaeobiology*. Chicago University Press, Chicago.

Breshears, D.D., Huxman, T.E., Adams, H.D., Zou, C.B. and Davison, J.E. (2008) Vegetation synchronously leans upslope as climate warms. *Proceedings of the National Academy of Sciences, USA* 105: 11591-11592.

Briggs, D.E.G., Erwin, D.H. and Collier, F.J. (1994) *The Fossils of the Burgess Shale.* Smithsonian Institution Press, London.

Brusatte, S.L., Benton, M.J., Ruta, M. and Lloyd, G.T. (2008) Superiority, competition, and opportunism in the evolutionary radiation of dinosaurs. *Science* 321: 1485-1488.

Calboli, F.C.F., Sampson, J., Fretwell, N. and Balding, D.J. (2008) Population structure and inbreeding from pedigree analysis of purebred dogs. *Genetics* 179: 593-601.

Coyne, J.A. (1998) Not black and white. *Nature* 396: 35-36.

Darwin C.R. (2003) [1876] *The Autobiography of Charles Darwin.* Icon Books, Ltd., London.

Darwin, C.R. (1998) [1868] *The Variations of Animals and Plants under Domestication. Volume I.* The Johns Hopkins University Press, Baltimore, USA

Darwin C.R. (2006) Letter 71 to A.R. Wallace. In: *More Letters of Charles Darwin Volume I.* The Echo Library, Fairford, Glos., UK

Davenport, C.B. (1911) *Heredity in Relation to Eugenics.* H. Holt, New York.

Dawkins, C.R. (1976) *The Selfish Gene.* Oxford University Press, Oxford.

Dobzhansky, T. (1937) *Genetics and the Origin of Species.* Columbia University Press, New York.

Eldridge, N. and Gould, S.J. (1972) Punctuated equilibria: an alternative to phyletic gradualism. In: Schopft, J.M. (ed) *Models in Palaeobiology.* Freeman Cooper, San Francisco.

Evans, J. (2010) Quantitative genetic evidence that males trade attractiveness for ejaculate quality in guppies. *Proceedings of the Royal Society of London B 277*: 3195-3201.

Friedlander, H. (1995) *The Origins of Nazi Genocide: From Euthanasia to the Final Solution.* The North Carolina University Press, Chapel Hill, USA.

Galton, F. (1883) *Inquiries into Human Faculty and its Development.* First Edition. Macmillan, London.

Gause, G.F. (1932) Experimental studies on the struggle for existence: 1. Mixed population of two species of yeast. *Journal of Experimental Biology* 9: 389-402.

Gause, G.F. (1934) *The Struggle for Existence.* Williams and Wilkins, Baltimore.

Gould, S.J. (1989) *Wonderful Life: The Burgess Shale and the Nature of History.* Penguin Books, London.

Grant, M. (1916) *The Passing of the Great Race or the Racial Basis of European History.* Charles Schribner's Sons, New York.

Grant, B.R. and Grant, P.R. (1989) *Evolutionary dynamics of a natural population: the large cactus finch of the Galápagos.* University of Chicago Press, Chicago.

Grant, P.R. (1993) Hybridization of Darwin's finches on Isla Daphne Major, Galápagos. *Philosophical Transactions of the Royal Society of London, B* 340: 127-139.

Greenwood, P. J., Harvey, P. H. and Perrins, C. M. (1978) Inbreeding and dispersal in the great tit. *Nature* 271: 52–54.

Hackel, E.H.P.A. and McCabe, J. (2009) *The Wonders of Life: A Popular Study of Biological Philosophy.* BiblioBazaar, Charleston, South Carolina.

Hautier, Y, Niklaus, P.A. and Hector, A. (2009) Competition for light causes plant biodiversity loss after eutrophication. *Science* 324: 636-638.

Hitler, A. (1971) *Mein Kampf.* Translated by Ralph Manheim. Houghton Mifflin, Boston.

Hutchinson, G. E. (1961) The paradox of the plankton. *American Naturalist* 95: 137-145.

Huxley, T.H. (1896) The struggle for existence in human society. In: *Evolution and Ethics and other Essays.* Appleton, New York.

Izquierdo, I., Martín, J.L., Zurita, N. and Arechavaleta, M. (eds) (2004) Lista de species silvestres de Canarias (hongos, plantas y animals terrestres) (Consejería de Medio Ambiente y Ordenación Territorial, Gobierno de Canarias, Santa Cruz de Tenerife.

Jablonski, D. (1986) Background and mass extinctions: the alternation of macroevolutionary regimes. *Science* 231: 129–133.

Kelly, A.E. and Goulden, M.L. (2008) Rapid shifts in plant distribution with recent climate change. *Proceedings of the National Academy of Sciences, USA* 105: 11823-11826.

Kempenaers, B., Adriaensen, F., van Noordwijk, A.J. and Dhondt, A.A. (1996) Genetic similarity, inbreeding and hatching failure in blue tits: are unhatched eggs infertile? *Proceedings of the Royal Society of London, Series B* 263: 179–185.

Kuhl, S. (1994) *The Nazi Connection.* Oxford University Press, Oxford.

Levin, H.L. (2009) The Earth Through Time. Wiley, London. Ninth Edition.

Lewis, E.E. (1987) *Introduction to Reliability Engineering.* Wiley, London.

Mahler, D. L., Revell, L.J., Glor, R.E. and Losos, J.B. (2010) Ecological opportunity and the rate of morphological evolution in the diversification of Greater Antillean anoles. *Evolution* 64:2731-2745.

Majerus, M.E.N. (1998) *Melanism: Evolution in Action.* Oxford University Press, Oxford.

McRae, S. (1996) Family values: costs and benefits of communal nesting in the moorhen. *Animal Behaviour* 52: 225–245.

Naeem, S. (1998) Species redundancy and ecosystem reliability. *Conservation Biology* 12: 39-45.

Pang, J-F., Kluetsch, C., Zou, X.J., Zhang, A.B., Luo, L.Y., Angleby, H., Ardalan. A., Ekström, C., Sköllermo, A., Lundeberg, J., Matsumura, S., Leitner, T., Zhang, Y-P., Savolainen, P. (2009) mtDNA data indicate a single origin for dogs south of the Yangtze River, less than 16 300 years ago, from numerous wolves. *Molecular Biology and Evolution* 26: 2849-2864.

Parmesan, C. and Yohe, G. (2003) A globally coherent fingerprint of climate change impacts across natural systems. *Nature* 421: 37-42.

Perry, A.L., Low, P.J., Ellis, J.R. and Reynolds, J.D. (2005) Climate change and distribution shifts in marine fishes. *Science* 308: 1912-1915.

Pham, H. (Ed.) (2003) *Handbook of Reliability Engineering.* Springer-Verlag, London.

Phillimore, A.B. and Price, T.D. (2008) Density-dependent cladogenesis in birds. *PLoS Biology* 6 (3): e71.

RodríguezMuñoz, R., Bretman, A., Slate, J., Walling, C.A. and Tregenza,

T. (2010) Natural and sexual selection in a wild insect population. *Science* 328: 1269-1272.

Sahney, S., Benton, M.J., and Ferry, P.A (2010) Links between global taxonomic diversity, ecological diversity and the expansion of vertebrates on land. *Biology Letters* 6: 544-547.

Sanger, M. (1921) The eugenic value of birth control propaganda. *Birth Control Review*, Oct. 1921: 5.

Sargent, T.D., Millar, C.D. and Lambert, D.M. (1998) The classical explanation of industrial melanism: assessing the evidence. *Evolutionary Biology* 30: 299-322.

Sibley, C.G. and Monroe Jr., B.L., (1990) *Distribution and Taxonomy of Birds of the World.* Yale University Press, New Haven.

Skene, K.R. (2009) *Shadows on the Cave Wall: a New Theory of Evolution.* Ard Macha Press, Letham, UK.

Todes, D.P. (1989) *Darwin without Malthus: The Struggle for Existence in Russian Evolutionary Thought (Monographs on the History and Philosophy of Biology).* Oxford University Press, Oxford.

Venditti, C., Meade, A. and Pagel, M. (2010) Phylogenies reveal new interpretation of speciation and the Red Queen. *Nature* 463: 349–352.

Vincek, V., O'Huigin, C., Satta, Y., Takahata, N, Boag, P.T., Grant, P.R., Grant, B.R. and Klein., J. (1997) How large was the founding population of Darwin's finches? *Proceedings of the Royal Society of London B* 264: 111–118.

Wallace A.R. (1858) On the tendency of varieties to depart indefinitely from the original type. *Journal of the Proceedings of the Linnæan Society (Zoology)* 3: 53-62.

Walther, G.-R., Post, E., Convey, P., Menzel, A., Parmesan, C., Beebee, T.J.C., Fromentin, J.-M., Hoegh-Guldberg, O. and Bairlein, F. (2002) Ecological responses to recent climate change. *Nature* 416: 389-395.

Whittaker, R.J. and Fernández-Palacios, J.M. (2007) *Island Biogeography: Ecology, Evolution and Conservation.* Second Edition. Oxford University Press, Oxford.

van Noordwijk, A. J. and Scharloo, W. (1981) Inbreeding in an island population of the great tit. *Evolution* 35: 674–688.

General references on specific topics

Replacement or Displacement?

Benton, M.J. (1983) Dinosaur success in the Triassic: a non-competitive ecological model. *Quarterly Review of Biology* 58: 29-55.

Roossinck, M.J. (2005) Symbiosis versus competition in plant virus evolution. *Nature Reviews Microbiology 3*: 917-924.

Cadena, C.C. (2007) Testing the role of interspecific competition in the evolutionary origin of elevational zonation: an example with Buarremon brush-finches (Aves, Emberizidae) in the neotropical mountains. *Evolution* 61: 1120-36.

Climate change and directional selection:

Marra, P.P., Francis, C.M., Mulvihill, R.S. and Moore, F.R. (2005) The influence of climate on the timing and rate of spring bird migration. *Oecologia* 142: 307-315.

Studds, C. E. (2011) Rainfall-induced changes in food availability modify the spring departure programme of a migratory bird. *Proceedings of the Royal Society of London B. In press.*

Sokolov, L.V. (2006) Effect of global warming on the timing of migration and breeding of passerine birds in the 20th century. *Entomological Review* 86, Supplement 1, S59-S81.

Functional redundancy

Cowling, R.M., Esler, K.J., Midgley, G.F. and Honig, M.A. (1994) Plant functional diversity and functional redundancy in fynbos communities. *South African Journal of Science* 90: 333-337.

Lawton, J.H. and Brown, V. K. (1993) Redundancy in ecosystems. In: Schulze. E. D. and Mooney, H.A. (eds), *Biodiversity and ecosystem function.* Springer-Verlag, Berlin.

Link, J.S. (2007) Underappreciated species in Ecology: "Ugly fish" in the Northwest Atlantic Ocean. *Ecological Applications* 17: 2037-2060.

Joner, F., Specht, G., Müller, S.C. and Pillar V.D. (2011) Functional redundancy in a clipping experiment on grassland plant communities. *Oikos. In press.*

Schindler, D.W. (1990) Experimental perturbations of whole lakes as tests of hypotheses concerning ecosystem structure and function. *Oikos* 57: 25-41.

Howarth, R.W. (1991) Comparative responses of aquatic ecosystems to toxic chemical stress. In: Cole, J.J., Lovett, G. and Findlay, S.(eds), *Comparative analyses of ecosystems: patterns, mechanisms and theories.* Springer-Verlag, New York. pp.169-195.

Prins, H.H.T. and Douglas-Hamilton, I. (1990) Stability in a multi-species assemblage of large herbivores in East Africa. *Ecologia* 83: 392-400.

Walker, B.H. (1992) Biodiversity and ecological redundancy. *Conservation Biology* 6: 18-23.

Wohl, D.L., Arora, S., and Gladstone, J.R. (2004) Functional redundancy supports biodiversity and ecosystem function in a closed and constant environment. *Ecology* 85: 1534–1540.

Ecological impacts on evolution

Rainey, P.B. and Travisano, M. (1998) Adaptive radiation in a heterogeneous environment. *Nature* 394:69–72.

Geritz, S.A.H., Kisdi, E., Mesze´na, G. and Metz, J.A.J. (1998) Evolutionarily singular strategies and the adaptive growth and branching of the evolutionary tree. *Evolutionary Ecology* 4:1–79.

Turner, P.E. and Chao, L. (1999) Prisoner's dilemma in an RNA virus. *Nature* 398:441–443.

Dieckmann, U. and Doebeli, M. (1999) On the origin of species by sympatric speciation. *Nature* 400: 354-357.

Jansen, V.A.A. and Mulder, G.S.E.E. (1999) Evolving biodiversity. *Ecology Letters* 2:379–386.

Kisdi, E. (1999) Evolutionary branching under asymmetric competition. *Journal of Theoretical Biology* 197:149–162.

Elena, S.F. and Lenski, R.E. (2003) Evolution experiments with microorganisms: the dynamics and genetic bases of adaptation. *Nature Reviews Genetics* 4: 457–469.

SECTION IV
ENTROPY-TIME CURVE: HOW THE COSMOS CREATED GARDENERS

At first sight, the curve below (Figure IV.1) seems a strange choice. It shows the amount of chaos, or entropy, generated by a developing ecosystem (Hodaway *et al.*, 2010). As you can see, it is a classic logistic curve. What, possibly, could be the relevance of this curve to sustainability? The answer is profound. It points to the most significant driving force in our universe, something that impacts on almost anything you can think about. In this section we are going to meet the second law of thermodynamics, and examine how it affects us. We'll revisit the French Revolution, encounter some giant insects and discover a goddess called Sophie! But first, it is time to get to grips with diffusion.

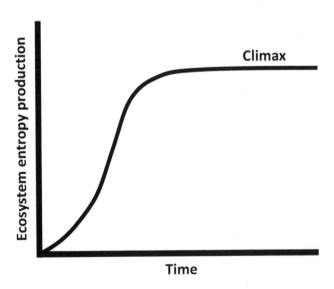

Figure IV.1 Entropy production during the development of an ecosystem.

Chapter Fifty-One
The Seductive Scent of Chaos

She floats through the room in a shimmering silk dress, and all eyes turn towards her. Chandeliers sparkle and the violin music rises and retreats like the waves on a pristine beach. A man dashes from the gothic mansion and runs to the nearest flower shop (appropriately located just down the road), where he has to queue behind a desperate mass of other handsome young beaus in tuxedos, all buying bunches of exotic orchids. He rushes back and falls at the woman's feet, offering his floral tribute. As the camera pans back, more men climb through windows, clutching beautiful bouquets.

Interviewed later, the man, who wished to remain anonymous, described how he had been enjoying a fairly average selection of canapes and chatting to some potential clients when he suddenly became aware of an intoxicating aroma, drifting through the room. His actions beyond this point were out of his control, he claimed, as he found himself running from the building, overpowered by something so profound that he could not attempt to start putting it into words. Finally, the name of a well-known parfumerie appears on the screen. The message is clear: this scent drives men wild with desire, and they'll fall under its spell as soon as they smell it.

We weren't the first to use perfume as an attractant. A species of seaweed living on many coasts around Europe, called bladderwrack (*Fucus vesiculosus*), reproduces with the help of a little *eau de toilette* (Muller and Gassmann, 1978). Iodine was first discovered in this seaweed, and it has been used as a medicine for centuries. Just like most humans, bladderwracks are either male or female. During the reproductive season, the adult plants release female and male cells into the ocean. Female cells emit a chemical called *fucoserraten*, which acts as a sperm attractant, diffusing outward. It may not be the most marketable name around, but fucoserraten is the ultimate in perfumes!

Once a male cell has fused with her, the fertilized cell (now officially a zygote) releases a repellent (an anti-perfume) that deters any unwanted attention! So the bladderwrack really is the queen of perfumes, using her array of scents to make the males do exactly what she wants, when she wants! It is unrecorded if the male cells buy flowers before fertilization, but it is thought unlikely.

The other, more relevant lesson here is that perfume spreads. It will keep spreading until evenly distributed, whether in water or in air. And it is not the only thing that does this. Put a drop of ink into a jar of water, and the same effect can be observed. In fact this process of spreading is a very common event indeed. It is called *diffusion*. Things have a tendency to spread out. And, of equal importance, they don't have a tendency to come back in.

Chapter Fifty-Two
Eating Pizza at the Top of a Tower: Why Diffusion Matters in Evolution

Diffusion is not just about pretty perfumes. Oxygen diffuses across the lung surface into the blood. Carbon dioxide diffuses in the opposite direction. Of course, we have a circulation system to move this blood around, because if we had to wait for the oxygen to diffuse through our bodies, it would take too long. We would use the oxygen much more quickly than it could be replaced. Before circulation systems evolved, the size of an organism was limited by the concentration of oxygen in the atmosphere.

To understand why this is so, try to imagine a huge tower, where food must be brought in through the front door, and carried all the way up to the top. The residents on the top floor order a pizza. As the pizza delivery boy climbs the stairs, he builds up an appetite and eats a slice. Another hundred stairs later, and he eats a slice more. By the time he reaches the top, there is no pizza left.

The only way to improve things is to bring more pizza through the front door, so that although many slices are used up on the way to the top of the tower, there is still some left to feed the hungry man and his wife who live way up there. Otherwise, they will starve and die. Within this analogy, the evolution of a circulatory system represents an elevator, carrying that precious pizza around the building with much less loss *en route*.

And the pizza analogy tells us how the early evolution of multi-cellular life on Earth was held back by diffusion. No, early life didn't eat pizza! But it did need oxygen. Until a circulation system emerged to carry the oxygen around, attached to haemoglobin, multi-cellular organisms were limited in the size they could reach. For at least a billion years, life was restricted to having one fairly small cell. Having a number of cells created a problem. The further a cell at the centre of an organism was from the surface of the organism, the less oxygen reached it, because the cells outside of it would use it all up. So being in the centre meant suffocation and death, and you don't want your inner cells dying!

Earth started with no oxygen in its atmosphere, and it was only when bacteria discovered how to photosynthesise that oxygen was released, as a waste product. Photosynthesis works by using light energy to split water (H_2O) into oxygen and hydrogen. The oxygen is released and the hydrogen is used to drive sugar production.

It took a long time for levels of oxygen to build up high enough for it to allow multi-cellular organisms to exist. As atmospheric oxygen increased, it was like having more pizza delivered to the door. Now, even though cells on the outside of the organism used oxygen, there was still enough to make it through to the inner cells. This freed up multi-cellular evolution.

The first proper multi-cellular life forms were found in rocks in the unlikely setting of downtown St John's, a city in Newfoundland, on the terraced edge of one of its main roads, Duckworth Street. The discovery was made by Elkanah Billings (1820-1876) in 1872 (Billings, 1872), and dated to around five hundred and seventy million years ago. Strictly speaking, the fossils were discovered by a Newfoundland geologist called Alexander Murray, who dismissed them as inorganic artefacts. It was Elkanah who recognized these creatures, called *Aspidella*, as the oldest animals on Earth. They look like little jellyfish but may actually be holdfasts of a bigger organism.

Elkanah Billings is worth a brief detour. His father, Bradish Billings (what a wonderful name!), was one of the founding fathers of Ottawa, now the capital city of Canada, and his mother, Lamira, developed the educational and medical infrastructure of this new town. Elkanah had tried his hand at farming, aged fourteen, but made such a mess of it, that his father paid to have him educated at boarding school!

The next we hear of him, he has qualified as a lawyer, but shortly afterwards, is caught smuggling forty-two books from New York to his home in Canada! His brother tried to blackmail him, but he had none of this and handed himself over to the authorities. Dabbling in journalism for a while, he finally decided that palaeontology was to be his career, and for the last twenty years of his life, he identified over five hundred new species of animal, including *Aspidella*.

Aspidella lived near the end of what was a very significant ice age on our planet, possibly lasting over one hundred and fifty million years. The Earth was almost completely covered in ice at one stage, and the situation was only rescued by the venting of huge amounts of carbon dioxide, possibly raising levels to four hundred times what they are today. *"Global Warming Saves the Planet!"* would have been the morning headline!

We know that cold water contains more dissolved oxygen than does warm water. It is thought that this huge cooling event led to levels of oxygen rising high enough in the cold water to allow multi-cellular life to spring forth (Shen *et al.*, 2008). Similar organisms from the same period have been found around the world, in Namibia, Australia and Russia. However, subsequent warming led to the disappearance of this early experiment, and it would take tens of millions of years before photosynthesis eventually raised oxygen levels enough for another animal explosion to occur. We have already encountered this next explosion of diversity. Its signature was the Burgess Shale.

Chapter Fifty-Three
Giant Insects on Planet Earth

Insects do not have a blood circulation system. Instead they have a network of tubes that begin as small openings at the surface of the organism, spreading throughout the internal structure. They carry oxygen and carbon dioxide throughout the body. It is thought that the maximum length for these pipes to support cellular life, at current atmospheric levels of oxygen, is about half a centimetre. That would allow a total diameter of one centimetre, if diffusion occurred from either side.

However, about three hundred million years ago, in the geological period known as the Carboniferous, giant insects inhabited the planet. Dragonflies with wingspans up to seventy centimetres across (that's about the length of your arm!) and mayflies with wingspans up to twenty centimetres (Carpenter, 1992) have been discovered in the fossil record from this time. The body could be up to three centimetres in diameter (May, 1982). That's three times wider than would be possible today!

The oxygen needed to power the flight muscles and support this size of insect could not be supplied by diffusion at current levels of oxygen (twenty-one percent). There just wouldn't be enough pizza entering the building! Professor Jeffrey Graham and his team, based at the University of California's Scripps Institute, suggested, in a paper in *Nature* (Graham *et al.*, 1995), that this was due to a peak in oxygen levels during the Carboniferous. It is known that atmospheric levels rose as high as thirty-five percent at this time. These gigantic insects all disappeared during the Permian mass extinction, when oxygen levels fell to as low as fifteen percent, making it impossible to support their size.

Aquatic invertebrates also increased in size at this time, and elevated oxygen levels are thought to have helped the invasion of vertebrates onto land (Budyko *et al.*, 1985). The argument here is that the increased burden of supporting your own weight and the increased difficulty in achieving movement without buoyancy would have required greater use of muscles, which in turn would have needed more oxygen.

Chapter Fifty-Four
Indian Hedgehogs and the Thermodynamics of Development

So we see that diffusion has had huge impacts upon evolution. Diffusion also lies at the heart of developmental biology. The development of organisms is one of the most interesting of subjects, to me anyway. I have spent much of my scientific life studying it. How we move from a single cell to a multi-cellular, all-singing, all-dancing tetrapod like ourselves is an amazing story, and it is all about diffusion. We have around two hundred and twenty different cell types in our bodies, which must be in exactly the right places if we are to survive. How does the body manage to achieve this?

When we were just a bundle of cells in our mother's womb, little proteins diffused across these cells and triggered other proteins, which formed gradients, from high concentrations at the place where they were made, to increasingly lower concentrations further away, just like perfume. These chemicals are called *morphogens*, as they determine the morphology (shape) of the organism. So each cell experiences different levels of these signal molecules, depending on how far away from the source they are. The clever part is that these cells respond differently in their development, depending on the concentration of the signals. Thus, the cell fate (i.e. what the cell is going to become) is set in place by diffusion.

Any one place in the cluster will have a unique combination of different signals. This leads to different cells changing into particular types of structure, depending on where they were located in the gradient. If a cell was near where the protein was being made, it would experience much higher concentrations of the protein than if it was further away, just like those men who were closest to the woman in silk smelling the perfume more strongly than those further away. This is called the *French Flag Hypothesis*.

The idea was put forward by the developmental biologist, Lewis Wolpert (Wolpert, 1968). If we imagine a morphogen diffusing from the flagpole, across a French flag, becoming more dilute as it moves across, from blue to white to red, the cells in each band of colour react differently, so we would get three different kinds of cells as a result. The first of these morphogens wasn't discovered for another twenty years (Driever and Nüsslein-Volhard, 1988). Called *Bicoid*, it is central to the determination of which end of the tiny bundle of cells will become the head.

Lots more of these morphogens were subsequently discovered, and were given strange names like *sonic hedgehog* (crucial in patterning of limbs, brain and spinal cord) and *Indian hedgehog* (essential for cartilage development). It was a fad of the time to use these unusual names, but this stopped when it was recognized that this could trivialize the often catastrophic consequences of mutations in these genes, especially for children.

Chapter Fifty-Five
What Drives Diffusion?

Perfume, once released from the bottle is impossible to retrieve. It is a one way journey. Put it another way, if you want to get all those little molecules of perfume back into the bottle, it's going to take a lot of hard work, and energy. Even the thought of it seems depressing. Diffusion is like a slope. Things roll down the slope, not up it. And this brings us to a crucial question. Why does diffusion work like this? In other words, why does the perfume disperse across the room?

Sitting looking at a drop of blackcurrant juice spreading in a glass of water, it's difficult to grasp that you are looking at a proof of perhaps the greatest of all the laws of physics, the second law of thermodynamics. This law states that *disorder in the universe always increases*. So when the drop of juice is placed in the glass of water, initially it is organized into a compact little drop, but then gradually loses its "*order*" and spreads. Eventually, the drop and the water reach a state where the molecules of the juice are perfectly spread throughout the water. This stage is called *equilibrium*. At this point, there is no more change. It's the same with perfume, with gas, indeed with anything. Ashes to ashes, dust to dust! This law was discovered by a French military engineer, Nicolas Carnot (1796-1832), inspired by his father, Lazare Carnot.

Chapter Fifty-Six
Lazare Carnot: the Father of the Father of Thermodynamics

It is, most likely, an amazing coincidence of history that we again return to the French Revolution as a context for the next part of our story. Having seen how Malthus had been greatly influenced by the philosophy and events occurring in France at the end of the eighteenth century, and having noted the consequential impact of his writing upon Darwin, we now turn to probably the most important scientific discovery in the history of mankind. Its implications unlock the secret to human sustainability and to everything else in our Universe. *The Second Law of Thermodynamics* lies at the heart of time, gravity, diffusion, religion, diversity, equality, economics, evolution, ecology and life itself.

Nicolas Carnot was born into dramatic times in France. Indeed he owed his very existence to the French Revolution. His father, Lazare Carnot, had been thrown into jail under the Rule of King Louis XVI, for having an affair with an aristocrat's daughter, and could well have died there had he not been freed early in the revolution.

Indebted to the Revolution, Nicolas' father became a key player, the architect of the Revolutionary Army and a brilliant military strategist. He developed a *total war* approach, where all resources available were used to aid the army, including melting church bells to make canons, and developing the leather industry in order to procure more boots. He also introduced conscription to expand the army even further.

Following the execution of Louis XVI, which Lazare Carnot supported, the ruling revolutionaries set in place a slaughter of their opponents, killing forty thousand of them (many of which were fellow revolutionaries, but with differing opinions), without trial. This dark period, called, appropriately, *The Reign of Terror* (*La Terreur*), came at the same time as legislation giving all men the right to vote. It is an irony that while the new constitution pushed for liberty and equality, many were never given the right of a trial and were deprived of the right to life.

There were some very odd things that accompanied the Revolution. The central importance of rational thought, celebrated by the Enlightenment, was marked by the formation of the *Cult of Reason*, where churches throughout France were converted into *Temples of Reason*, with the worship of the *Goddess of Reason* as the highlight of ceremonies. Bizarrely, to avoid accusations of idolatry, this goddess was a living woman, perhaps the only goddess ever to actually exist, in flesh and blood, in the history of religion! The goddess turned out to be Sophie Momoro, the wife of a Parisian printer and bookseller.

Maximilian Robespierre (1758-1794), one of the chief architects of the Revolution and the Reign of Terror, recognized that this had all gone too far, and the peasants, whose support was essential, were generally heavily religious. They found the goddess and her rites extremely insulting. So he set up the *Cult of the Supreme Being* (*Le culte de l'Être supreme*), which he designed single-handedly, and planned for it to be the new religion of the State.

This was the kind of thing that happened in the heady (or, often, headless), blood-splattered days of the Revolution. Whole areas of society were re-written in a matter of months, and then changed just as quickly. But designing a new state religion really was excessive! Of course, the new cult orchestrated the deaths of supporters of the old cult, as revolutionaries continued to execute other revolutionaries. Even the goddess of reason's bookselling husband was separated from his head, and his goddess, forever.

In order to demonstrate the rapidity of change at this time, follow this timeline with me. *The Festival of the Cult of Reason*, complete with its human goddess called Sophie, occurred on 10th November 1793. By 7th May, 1794, the Cult of Reason had been denounced and the new religion, *The Cult of the Supreme Being*, was launched. A month later, on 8th June, *The Festival of the Supreme Being* was held. A huge earth mound was built in the centre of Paris, and Robespierre descended from its summit as Moses.

This was all too much for many people. Soon, opposition built against Robespierre. By 28th July, he was beheaded. So within the space of three months, he had devised a new religion, played the role of Moses at a national celebration, and then been executed by his fellow revolutionaries!

Chapter Fifty-Seven
Lazare Carnot and Napoleon Bonaparte

Nicolas' father, Lazare Carnot, was a key player in the downfall of Robespierre, becoming one of the five *"directors"* of France after this. Unfortunately, this leadership began to argue within itself (a repeated theme throughout the French Revolution), and Napoleon Bonaparte was able to fill this vacuum. In 1799, Bonaparte led a coup, effectively ending the revolution. Lazare Carnot fled to Geneva.

However Bonaparte recognized how important Lazare Carnot was as a strategist. Carnot had been Napoleon's mentor, promoting him from Captain to General, and so Napoleon convinced him to return to Paris and appointed him to the position of Minister of War. During this time, Carnot senior developed a great interest in the machinery of warfare, and wrote an important book, seen as a precursor to much of his son's work, entitled *Fundamental Principles of Equilibrium and Movement* (See Gillespie, 1971).

In this book, he surmised that there could be no such thing as perpetual motion. Of course, his interests were driven by war, and Lazare was looking ahead to a time when supremacy in engine-driven war machines could bring victory. Ultimately, Napoleon crowned himself as Emperor of France (and King of Italy to boot!). This was unacceptable to the republican Carnot Senior, and he resigned.

Napoleon Bonaparte continued to fight battles against various coalitions of European countries for twelve years. Finally he over-stretched himself in an attempt to invade Russia (not the last dictator to make this mistake), and Lazare Carnot returned to help. But after fourteen years of France as an empire, it once again became a kingdom, with Louis XVIII being instated by a coalition of European nations. Napoleon was exiled to Elba, and Lazare Carnot melted into the background.

However, in less than a year Bonaparte had escaped from the small Mediterranean island and landed in France. A regiment of troops was sent to arrest him. In an incredible turnaround, he dismounted his horse alone, invited them to shoot him, and instead they proclaimed him as emperor, and escorted him victoriously to Paris, whereupon King Louis XVIII fled.

Napoleon enjoyed another one hundred days as emperor, appointing Lazare as Minister of the Interior, before defeat at the Battle of Waterloo ended up with the Emperor exiled, this time to the remote mid-Atlantic island of Saint Helena. Louis XVIII was restored as King of France. Six years later Napoleon Bonaparte was dead, most probably of stomach cancer.

The defeat and exile of Napoleon had a significant impact on the history of science in an unexpected way. Carnot's father, having held such a position of authority under Napoleon, was exiled, first to Warsaw and then to the city of Magdeburg. His had been a glittering career. Lazare Carnot remained the only general in Napoleon's army never to have tasted defeat. And he chose well for his exile. Magdeburg had been an important centre of the Holy Roman Empire in the Middle Ages, whose first emperor, Otto I, lived and was buried there. The city had enjoyed a significant position politically ever since.

It is one of those great co-incidences of history that Lazare Carnot had ended up in Magdeburg at this time. For one hundred and fifty years earlier, Magdeburg had been the home city of Otto von Guericke (1602-1686), who was the mayor of the city. He had invented the electrostatic generator, the vacuum pump, the piston and cylinder, and the famous *Magdeburg Hemispheres*. His work had been inspired by an effort to test an ancient idea, that a vacuum could not exist (or *Nature abhors a vacuum*).

On the 8th May, 1654, Guericke, in front of the Reichstag and Emperor Ferdinand III, put two copper hemispheres together (now known as the Magdeburg Hemispheres), sealed with grease, and created a vacuum using a pump. Two teams of fifteen horses were attached to each hemisphere, but could not pull them apart. The power and existence of a vacuum had been graphically demonstrated for the first time.

And so when Nicolas Carnot visited his exiled father, it was no surprise that this great city had an early version of one of the key drivers of the industrial Revolution, and, consequentially of modernity, in use: the steam engine. The steam engine arrived in Magdeburg in 1818, and Carnot's father, already a published expert in the field, dedicated his time to scientific study of this extraordinary invention.

And so the arrival of his son, in 1821, brought together a town with a deep history in steam, whose mayor, some one hundred and forty years earlier, had set in place the critical foundations for the invention of the steam engine, a wise and aging father who had written a foundational thesis on the physics of steam, and a young, highly intelligent man, amidst a Europe recovering from the political chaos of the Bonaparte years.

Yet this meeting in space and time was also consequent upon the Bonaparte legacy, as Carnot never would have visited the ancient city of steam if his father had not been exiled. On such amazing coincidences are huge discoveries built. This was not a direct philosophical link to the Enlightenment, but a spatiotemporal collision of man and machine, the results of which, unexpectedly, promise us a new way of existing sustainably on our planet, and much, much else besides.

Chapter Fifty-Eight
Nicolas Carnot and his Passion for Steam

Having excelled in school and university, specializing in military engineering, the young Carnot had begun a military career, but had become disillusioned with the constant moving and the unchallenging jobs that he was given. He was able to take leave and dedicate himself to study. Spurred on by his visit to Magdeburg, where his father had already immersed himself in thinking about engines, Carnot dedicated his time to the hot topic of the day, steam. The steam engine promised to deliver the technology predicted by the philosophers of the Enlightenment, allowing humankind to move towards the utopian destination by marrying technology to reason.

While a number of early steam prototypes, dating back two thousand years, are recorded, none were capable of doing work. It was only in 1698, that Thomas Savery constructed the first truly working model. It had a tendency to explode, and so in 1712, the much more reliable Newcomen engine appeared. These engines were extremely bulky, and it was not until around 1800 that an engine was designed that could power a vehicle. A number of men have been proclaimed as the inventor of this more compact engine, but the truth is that so many people were working simultaneously on the project, that is impossible to definitively name a winner. Challengers included Richard Trevithick, Nicolas-Joseph Cugnot, William Murdoch, and Oliver Evans.

Most credit is given to Trevithick as the man who designed the engine that drove the Industrial Revolution. Ironically, he died without a penny and was buried in an unmarked grave, although his invention would make many industrialists wealthy beyond their wildest dreams. Of course, the Industrial Revolution also laid the foundation for global warming and population increase, and so in terms of the Biosphere, Trevithick would not be viewed as a hero.

The arrival of a steam engine in Magdeburg, based on the Trevithick design, was an exciting event, completing a circle. Some of the key components had been invented in this city by Guericke one hundred and fifty years earlier, and these ideas had spread across Europe, inspiring, ultimately, the steam engine that had now returned to them. There was poetry to this! No wonder people were talking. Another interesting aspect was the fact that a meeting between a father and a son had stimulated the son into his great work, just as was the case with Thomas Malthus.

And there were two questions that arose from these discussions. Firstly, what is the maximum work that heat can do, and, secondly, was there anything more effective than steam? Nicolas published his findings in *"Réflexions sur la Puissance Motrice du Feu"* (*Reflections on the Motive Power of Fire*) in 1824 (Carnot, 2010).

He came to three conclusions:
- that heat could neither be created nor destroyed, and that the total heat in the Universe was constant;
- that when a temperature gradient exists, work can be done;
- that there can be no such thing as perpetual motion.

The foundations of these ideas could be found in his father's earlier works. In these statements the young Carnot had discovered the first and second laws of thermodynamics, that energy can neither be created nor destroyed and that the Universe is becoming more disorganized (i.e. that there is no such thing as perpetual motion, because some energy is always lost to the Universe).

The full implications of his work, published in 1824, and reviewed favourably at the time, went unrecognized for another thirty years (similar to Mendel), until William Thompson studied them, and developed the laws of thermodynamics more formally. Sadly for Carnot, just like Mendel, he would not live to see his work recognized. In June 1832, he contracted scarlet fever. In a weakened state, on 24th August, he then contracted cholera, dying within twenty-four hours. He was only thirty-six years old. The Paris Cholera Epidemic of 1832 would kill nineteen thousand people in the city alone, and was part of a huge pandemic, originating in India. At that time, the practice was to destroy all personal belongings of victims. Thus, most of Carnot's notebooks were burnt, and so we will never know what other discoveries lay in these research records.

Chapter Fifty-Nine
The Two Great Laws of the Universe

Energy is the key to understanding how our universe behaves. There are two central rules that apply to energy, called the first and second laws of thermodynamics. It all started with steam. *Thermo-* means heat (like in *thermo*meter) and *-dynamics* means power or movement. It was work by Carnot, and, subsequently, others, that led to key discoveries about how the Universe works.

The two laws are simple, yet profound. First, energy cannot be created nor destroyed. It is infinite, a bit like a god (though not like Sophie!). It always has been there and always will be there. In other words, the total amount of energy in the universe is constant. The second law is the one that adds colour to the whole picture. It says that the Universe is becoming less structured. The energy is spreading out, and becoming less useful.

Ultimately, the Universe will be a completely flat landscape, no hills (gradients) around. There will be no difference in the concentration of anything. This is called equilibrium. At the moment there are mountains and plateaux, structures and the like, but gradually all will be evenly spread. Think of that drop of ink. The total amount of ink doesn't change. That's the first law at work. It gradually spreads, until equally dispersed. That's the second law at work. So we have a constant and a change.

It's so simple, yet confuses many. Ultimately, the second law provides an arrow. It points in a direction. The Universe is moving to a destination, called equilibrium. During the journey, it becomes more chaotic. And we can measure the journey by measuring the increase in chaos. This measure is called *entropy*.

The word *entropy* is from the ancient Greek, εντροπια (entropia), meaning *"turning inwards"*. It is represented by the letter **S** (which, annoyingly, doesn't even occur in the word!!). It is a measure of the amount of energy that is not available to do work. Gradually all energy in the Universe will be converted to less useful energy, and no further work will be possible. This is a quality of the equilibrium state of the universe, where we are all going.

We can measure entropy. It has the units of energy per unit temperature (Joules/Kelvin). The entropy of a system is a measure of how disorganized it is, and entropy continues to increase until we reach the amazing location of total chaos. This place is, as we have said, equilibrium. You can't get any more chaotic and so you stop trying!

My four-year-old son, works to the second law. The longer he is in a room, the more chaotic it becomes. I have often wanted to let him carry on without me tidying up, just to see what the final equilibrium state of his bedroom might actually look like! Basically what he is doing is giving the toys random movement, and they jostle about, losing their structure and organization, until they are evenly spread throughout the universe that is his room. It's all entropy at work.

Entropy gives direction to things, including time. Entropy creates the change that is time. I remember asking the Professor of Biology at the University of Dundee, who was also a bit of a biophysicist, about what the Universe would be like if there was no entropy. He said it would be timeless, because nothing would change. And that, of course is where we are heading. At equilibrium, the end point of the Universe, time will stand still.

Mini-Summary

So where have we got to? We have discovered that a drop of ink in a glass tells us a lot. There is a direction to the Universe, one of increasing chaos, and driven by entropy. The Carnot team, father and son, laid the foundations for this discovery. This same drive leads to perfume and the Universe spreading. Its observed effect, diffusion, plays a central role in almost every physiological and developmental process that you can think of.

It is a big arrow, and hangs over everything. It is important for us to understand, because it holds the explanation for just about everything, including our own survival. Why don't we just take a moment to let this sink in? Get a glass, put a drop of food colouring, or diluting juice in, and watch it. Go on, it will only take a moment.

There it is, entropy at work, right before your eyes, not an analogy, but a real part of the whole universal event. The little drop of dye is spreading, irreversibly and will eventually reach equilibrium, where every particle is the same distance away from every other particle, and where there is no longer any discernable structure, just pale, evenly coloured water. The system has moved from being far from equilibrium, to equilibrium, driven by the second law of thermodynamics. Now enjoy the great director of the Universe at work. Amazing, right?

Chapter Sixty
The Second Law is Huge!

The second law of thermodynamics certainly has some huge repercussions for almost any area of thinking. Don't just take my word for it. Here is what some of the leading thinkers of recent times have said. Sir Arthur Eddington, one of the most influential astrophysicists of the twentieth century, stated: *"The second law of thermodynamics holds, I think, the supreme position among the laws of Nature. But if your theory is found to be against the second law of thermodynamics I can give you no hope; there is nothing for it but to collapse in deepest humiliation"* (Eddington, 1928).

Ivan Bazarov, the Russian physicist had no doubts of its importance: *"The second law of thermodynamics is, without a doubt, one of the most perfect laws in physics. Any reproducible violation of it, however small, would bring the discoverer great riches as well as a trip to Stockholm. The world's energy problems would be solved at one stroke"* (Bazarov, 1964).

Writing in *Nature*, Professor Seth Lloyd, the leading quantum physicist based at M.I.T., Cambridge, Massachusetts, summed it up as follows: *"Nothing in life is certain except death, taxes and the second law of thermodynamics"* (Lloyd, 2004). Nobel Prize winner and French biochemist, Jacques Monod, stated: *"Evolution in the biosphere is therefore a necessarily irreversible process defining a direction in time; a direction which is the same as that enjoined by the law of increasing entropy, that is to say, the second law of thermodynamics. This is far more than a mere comparison: the second law is founded upon considerations identical to those which establish the irreversibility of evolution. Indeed, it is legitimate to view the irreversibility of evolution as an expression of the second law in the biosphere"* (Monod, 1972).

Howard Resnickoff, in *Illusions of Reality* wrote: *"Life is nature's solution to the problem of preserving information despite the second law of thermodynamics"* (Resnickoff, 1988). Slightly more crudely, Woody Allen stated, in his 1982 movie, *Husbands and Wives*: *"It's the Second Law of Thermodynamics: Sooner or later everything turns to shit."*

But what has this second law got to do with all the things we are looking at in this book?

Chapter Sixty-One
Making Ends Meet in a Separating Universe: Rubber Ducks in a Leaky Barrel

We have learned that our Universe is gradually becoming more and more chaotic, and will eventually reach a point where it is completely disorganized. And this point is called equilibrium. It is the equivalent of the perfume becoming evenly spread throughout the room. Minute by minute, the entire show is slipping slowly towards this end point. That is what the Second Law tells us.

If the universe is slipping down a slope, increasing in chaos and heading for complete disorganization, then how can we possibly build anything within this model? Surely everything must fall apart. Many people have used this argument to support an idea that evolution cannot happen within an increasingly chaotic universe. If the perfume is constantly escaping from the bottle, how can you put it back in? Surely the Second Law of Thermodynamics stands against evolution, whose course seems to run in the opposite direction, with increasing order rather than increasing disorder. This idea is incorrect, and to understand why, we need to visit a rubber duck in a leaky barrel.

Imagine a barrel, full of water, with a rubber duck floating in it, sitting in a yard. There are holes in the barrel, and so the water gradually leaks out. The holes can't be plugged. The duck sinks down in the barrel as the water level falls. If things keep going like this, soon there will be no more water left in the barrel, and the duck will lie at the bottom.

In this analogy, the barrel represents any organism, and the floating duck represents life. Water represents energy. The holes in the barrel represent the second law of thermodynamics, and the leaking water represents entropy. The yard is the Universe. Life requires energy, but, according to the Second Law of Thermodynamics, energy slowly is lost to the Universe, like the water from the barrel, and becomes less useful as it sinks into the cosmos.

So the duck sinks. Not good news for ducks. How can the duck be kept afloat? Don't forget, the holes can't be plugged. There is only one way to do this. Pour more water in. If you do this, then you can keep the duck afloat. You need enough energy, of course, to replace that lost, if you want to keep the level constant.

So we eat to stay alive. And the energy in the food that we eat ultimately comes from the Sun. That is why plants and algae are so important. They capture some of the energy from sunlight and convert it to edible energy, sugar. They are the water taps. If we turn them off, we die. If we stop eating, our duck will sink! Don't try it at home. Just take my word for it (an important lesson here – just because you can do something, it doesn't mean you necessarily should!).

So by eating we live, and manage to fend off the second law, at least for a while. However, this is not really true. The second law continues to operate, as evidenced by our need to continually eat. By eating we counteract the effect. You cannot escape the second law! And by existing, we contribute to the increasing chaos in the Universe. Once our barrels run dry, no more water flows out of them, and so we no longer contribute to the unravelling of the greater whole. So each of us is assisting the end of our Universe by living!

Chapter Sixty-Two
Evolution: Swimming Against the Stream?

We clearly need a new theory to explain evolution. We have seen that Darwinian Theory just doesn't account for what we observe in nature. The key tenets of evolution by natural selection have been shown not to be correct. In Section III we examined all the evidence. Let's review this briefly:

- Malthusian foundation: not applicable to the rest of the Biosphere;
- Domestic breeding foundation: not applicable to the rest of the Biosphere;
- Competition as a driver: not recognized as significant;
- Competitive Exclusion Principle: functional redundancy suggests otherwise;
- Species displacement: species *replacement* is what we observe;
- Interspecific competition drives character displacement: not observed;
- Stabilizing selection: leads to reduction in variation, slowing evolution;
- Directional selection: organisms move rather than evolve;
- Disruptive selection: rare and difficult to envisage within a stabilizing context;
- Reproductive advantage of fittest: not seen in real field experiments (guppies and crickets);
- Sexual selection: not seen in real field experiments (crickets).

So how do we explain evolution? Well I would suggest that the answer lies in the observation that laboratory experiments do not produce the outcomes that we see in the field. This was clearly demonstrated with the experiment on the crickets, which overturned the results of laboratory science in such a clear way (Rodríguez-Muñoz *et al.*, 2010). Why is this? It boils down to one thing. Evolution is not just down to the genes. Rather it operates at many levels, and the outcome is a balance, arising from the context of the organism within an evolving Biosphere. We cannot reduce the Biosphere to a laboratory experiment. It must be studies within its true setting. So what is this context? There is no single unit of selection. Rather evolution emerges from the interaction between all the different levels of organization. And there is no agent of selection. Rather, there is an agent of organization: energy. It is the second law that gives direction to evolution, as it does to every other natural process.

To understand where energy comes into all of this, let's look at the levels of organization in the Biosphere.

Cellular reactions: whether a reaction can happen or not is determined by how much entropy is produced, and how much energy is released or consumed.

Genetic sequence: the code is thermodynamically determined (we'll cover this in detail in Section VII). Mutations represent increasing chaos in the code.

Protein structure: modification and folding is thermodynamically determined. Change in the energetic context around a protein alters the shape of the protein. This lies at the core of post-translational modification, where changes in the energetic context alter protein shape and function. This is an important area of biomedical research at present.

Cells: Their main function is energetic balance, controlling chemical reactions and protein construction/destruction. Cell fate is thermodynamically determined by morphogen diffusion, driven by the second law of thermodynamics.

Organisms: Life is a thermodynamic process, thus all organisms are ultimately geared to staying away from equilibrium (death), within the context of population, ecosystem and biome. Growth, physiology and development are all thermodynamic entities. Finding energy (food) is central to existence.

Population: Carrying capacity is a consequence of available energy. The more energy available, the larger the population can be. We see this in humans, who, by manipulation of agriculture, have been able to massively increase the population size.

Species: represent the diffusion of life into energetic space. Thus speciation occurs rapidly when energetic space is available, and decreases when energetic space is reduced. This is clearly seen in mass extinctions and post-extinction recovery.

Ecosystems: their structure is fundamentally driven by the passage of energy through the system, called trophodynamics. Ecosystem development is also an energetic process, as we shall see shortly.

Biomes: are dependent on incident radiation from the Sun. Rainfall and temperature vary depending on energy density.   As we move from the equator towards either pole, we find the same biomes in both directions, as energy density decreases, from tropical forest, to savannah, to desert to Mediterranean scrub, to temperate rainforest, to taiga to tundra.

In other words, every level is an energetic outcome. Thus, fundamentally, the Biosphere is structured by energy. In other words, the architect of structure is energy. The architect of change is also energetic. Entropy drives change. We would expect things to increase in complexity, because the more complex something is, the more energy is needed to maintain it. And the more energy that is needed, the more wasted energy (entropy) will be produced and distributed to the Universe. A two-cell organism needs more energy than a single-celled organism. A cold-blooded lizard needs much less energy to live than does a warm-blooded mammal.

In fact the evolution of our own species demonstrates this principle beautifully, each step involving an increase in energetic complexity.

Transition I: from chemical reactions to an organized single-celled organism.

Transition II: Multicellularity.

Transition III: Division of labour into specialist cells within this multicellular organism.

Transition IV: Move onto land, with increased costs of support and locomotion.

Transition V: Warm-bloodedness – huge increase in heating bills.

Transition VI: Milk production: extremely expensive parenting bill.

Transition VII: Huge increase in brain size – the largest user of energy in the body.

Transition VIII: *Recreational energy* – heavy and light industry, transport, electricity - things we don't need but things we like (as opposed to *survival energy* – the basic requirements for survival).

Each of these transitions has increased the production of entropy. Basically, of all the animals to take over the world and live a lifestyle well beyond its natural context, warm-blooded, lactating, large creatures, such as humans, are the worst case scenario. As we have already noted, if cold-blooded lizards had taken over the world we would all be in much better shape!

Organisms evolve within their energetic contexts to maximize the amount of entropy produced. If there is any *"progress"* in evolution, it is a progressively greater generation of entropy, because, ultimately, all arrows point that way. Increasing entropy gives direction. Equilibrium is the universal destination, where your bus, my train and his speedboat are all heading.

Chapter Sixty-Three
Entropy and the Almost Naked Scientist

So everything falls under the shadow of entropy. We can measure entropy, and much work is now being done to look at how much entropy is released in biological processes. One of the most recent efforts has focused on Amazonian forests, and has examined how an ecosystem changes. The curve for this section (Fig. IV.1) is based on this work, published in the *Proceedings of the Royal Society of London* by Robert Holdaway, then a PhD student at the University of Cambridge (Holdaway *et al.*, 2010).

His paper was not actually aimed at looking at succession at all, but, rather, at the effects of deforestation. However, for me, as an evolutionary ecologist, there was a much more important meaning hidden in the data, and when I saw the graph, I was very excited. It was almost an Archimedes moment, but I didn't jump out of my bath and run naked down my village street, thankfully for my longsuffering neighbours! I did imagine doing it though! It was one of those fist-pumping *"oh-yeah"* kinds of moments, when the idea that you had suddenly puts clothes on and starts singing and dancing before your eyes. The Scots have a term for that kind of moment: *"Stoatin"*!

So why was I so excited by Figure IV.1? Well it answered a question that I'd been puzzling with for a very long time, which is all about sand dunes. And it also supported a key part of my theory of evolution, that I pushed upon the world in 2009 (Skene, 2009).

Let's just remind ourselves what succession is. It is the directional, predictable development of an ecosystem. It starts with bare soil, or sand, or rock. Gradually, life fills the void, changing through time and finally reaching a stable ecosystem, such as a forest. There are very few good examples left in the Western World, as we have destroyed most of these natural sites. A classic example is the sand dune succession, often found at mouths of rivers. Most of these have been turned into links golf courses. Indeed the game of golf originated on one such succession, at the mouth of the appropriately named River Eden in Scotland. Here, sediment deposited by the river builds over time and forms sandbanks. These accumulations of sand eventually become significant enough to break the surface and form dry land.

Early plants need to be salt-tolerant to cope with the seawater, and gradually, wind blows more sand onto the banks and they rise. Soon a layer of freshwater (from falling rain and snow) can float on top of the salt water, and more plants can arrive. Gradually the surface changes, with plants dying and forming compost. Shrubs come in and diversity increases, as more and more species find a place to live. This developmental process ends in a forest. Forests are very special places. They don't need gardeners to pull out weeds and trim the edges. They don't need clipping. They don't need mowing. They don't even need strimming. In fact, they don't need any maintenance at all. It's my dream garden. Hang up the tools, set down the pruning shears, sit back and listen to the birdsong!

The forest is the endpoint. My question has always been: why does ecological succession grind to a halt at the forest stage? Why doesn't it change anymore? Also, what leads all successions to do the same thing? Why do they all reach an end point and then stop? It's not the species that run the show, because all sand dune successions go the same way across the world, even though the species are quite different from region to region.

No, there must be some higher rule here, something driving succession forward in the same way across the planet, no matter what the individual species are. But then that something suddenly stops. I always suspected it was something to do with energy, but was never sure what exactly it would be. Yet it had to be something significant, as the process was so obvious.

Something directional. Something predictable. Something universal. Ring any bells?

The answer to all of this lies in Figure IV.1, and the answer is entropy. What we see is that as an ecosystem develops, it increases in the amount of entropy it generates. And it does so in an S-shaped way – a pleasing piece of luck, given that the symbol for entropy is S! On the beach, the initial community is a very basic one, and has low energy flux through it.

With time, diversity increases and more and more different ways of producing entropy develop. Food webs increase in complexity, as do the organisms that make them. Populations increase in size as energy flow through them allows this. In this mid-stage, the system is developing rapidly. Then, later in the development, the rate of increase in entropy production slows, and later still, levels off. This is where the forest is fully developed and becomes the stable final state.

No further increase in entropy is possible. A ceiling has been reached. There is a maximum amount of entropy that a system can deliver to its thermodynamic master! And succession is all about the journey to this point. Increasing diversity and ecosystem complexity creates more and more entropy. But eventually, maximum entropic production is arrived at. And so the end point of succession is dictated by this maximum amount of entropy. In fact the whole journey is about the Second Law of

Thermodynamics. The arrow of entropy is directing the ecosystem. Similar results have been found for lake (Aoki, 1995; Aoki, 2006; Ludovisi, 2004), marine sediment (Meysman and Bruers, 2007) and Mediterranean (Celesti and Pignatti, 1988) ecosystems.

This observation, of entropy production increasing up to a ceiling, and then levelling off, has become known as the *Maximum Entropy Principle* (MEP). This principle states that systems with energy flowing through them (such as life) are arranged so that the rate of entropy production is maximized. And a maximum means an upper limit.

Maximum entropy production can be observed in a range of different situations. Organisms stop growing when they reach maximum entropy production (Aoki, 1995). Evolution in lineages draws to a halt when a particular design type reaches its maximum in entropy production. In other words, lineages have a limit to their evolutionary potential.

For those of you who are interested in the mathematics behind MEP, I have expanded this thinking in Appendix II, where I relate entropic output to a logistic model, developing a few equations and examining how maximum entropy output provides an excellent framework for understanding succession, population growth, carrying capacity and even the determinate growth in organisms.

As *Perez-España* and *Arreguin-Sanchez* (*1999*) said, the overall strategy of life is focused towards obtaining a structure as large and diverse as the environment allows. The Maximum Entropy Principle is now a major subject of research in areas such as genetics (Bernaola-Galvan *et al.*, 2000), climate modelling (Lorenz, 2010), mantle convection (Vanyo and Paltridge, 1981), planetary heat transport (Paltridge, 1979) and planetary science (Kleidon, 2004). Indeed a complete issue of the *Philosophical Transactions of the Royal Society B: Biological* Sciences (Volume 365, issue 1545, 2010) has recently been dedicated to the subject, entitled *Maximum Entropy Production in Ecological and Environmental Systems: Applications and Implications.*

So why is there a ceiling? I suggest that there are two reasons. Firstly, a system can only have a limited amount of energy flowing through it before it suffers harm. And secondly, no part of the system can act in isolation. Let's explore these two important statements.

Eventually any system, be it a cell, an organism, a population or an ecosystem will reach a maximum ability to produce entropy. Think of our barrel again. We can drill more and more holes in it to allowing the water to flood out, and, as a result, we need to pour more and more water in. However, eventually, the structural integrity of the barrel will be jeopardised by all those holes. The whole barrel will collapse!

So, pouring more and more energy in, to support greater and greater entropic production, will have a limit. An example of this is the number of heartbeats in a lifetime. This number is constant for many animals. This means that if a mouse's heartbeat rises, it lives a shorter time. Dr Herbert Levine states: *"Life span is predetermined by basic energetics of living cells and the apparent inverse relation between life span and heart rate reflects an epiphenomenon in which heart rate is a marker of metabolic rate"* (Levine, 1997). In other words, too much energy flowing through the mouse means more holes in the barrel, which means the barrel collapses sooner. Living a high energy lifestyle has consequences.

If we think about this, it makes sense. Wear and tear happens to living as well as non-living machines. Proteins need replacing to maintain function. Take the crucial process of photosynthesis. Too much light energy leads to the destruction of an essential protein in the chain of proteins involved in the production of sugar. The more solar energy hitting a plant, the more damage is done, and this leads to a decrease in sugar production. This damage is called *photoinhibition* – basically, light (*photo-*) inhibiting the process of photosynthesis (Aro *et al.*, 1993).

"No man is an island". This famous quote, from John Dunne, is a central tenet of holistic thinkers. It has particular relevance here, and it is a theme that we will come back to in the rest of the book. In *Shadows on the Cave Wall* (Skene, 2009), I described how the Biosphere is organized into different levels, and each of these interacts with energy differently. It is this interaction that determines the characteristics of that level, and the subsequent interactions of all of these levels that moderate each other. I call this the *Energetic Theory*, for obvious reasons!

Figure IV.2 sums up the key differences between this approach and the other two major scientific theories, Gaia and neo-Darwinism. What we see is that the *Energetic Theory* represents a *"transductionist"* rather than reductionist (neo-Darwinism) or holistic (Gaia) approach. Transduction means the conversion of one form of energy to another. I use the word to indicate that the Biosphere is the product of energy transformation, working through every level of organization simultaneously.

The word *"simultaneously"* is important here. It is not a hierarchical flow, like a current passing through a series of structures, one after the other. Rather, every level is interacting directly with energy in a unique way. And at the base of evolution lies this energetic conversion, at every level.

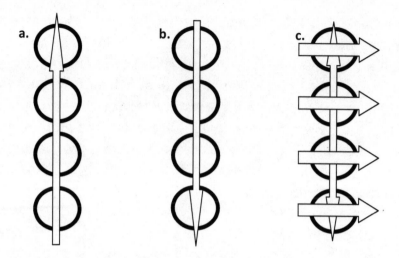

Figure IV.2 Scientific theories on how the Biosphere evolved and functions: a. Neo-Darwinism; b. Gaian Theory; c. Energetic Theory.

So rather than a bottom-up approach (where the selfish gene lies at the heart of everything else), or the top-down approach (where the planetary super-organism ultimately controls all processes under it), we have energy flowing through each level, and each level is of equal importance, and equally integrated with every other level.

So to summarise:

- Each level is organized by the same agent of organization, thermodynamics.
- Each level exhibits behaviour, defined here as the response to one's energetic context.
- Each level undergoes directional change over time, driven by entropy in each case. This has been referred to as evolution.
- The conversations of these levels of organization lead to compromise and balance. This process has been mistakenly referred to as natural selection.

So each level is tuned to producing the maximum amount of entropy possible (Maximum Entropy Principle). However this level is intrinsically limited, by the make-up of the level, and externally limited by the other levels. I visualize this as a multi-armed see-saw (Fig. IV.3).

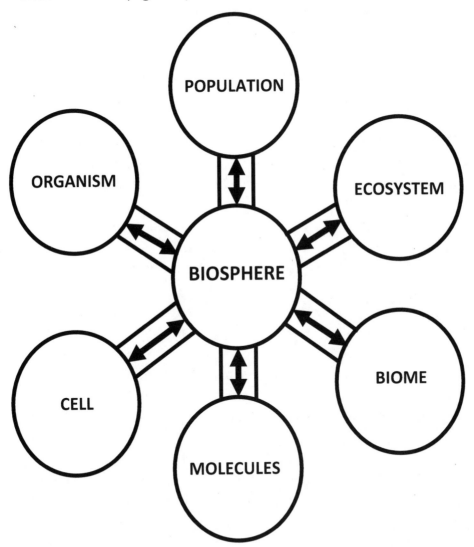

Figure IV.3 The See-saw of maximum entropy output, where each level of organization adjusts its output to maintain balance within the Biosphere.

Each level is represented by a person sitting on one arm of the see-saw. The weight of the person represents the intrinsic limit to generating chaos for the Master of the Universe (sounds more exciting than "*the second law*"!). The external factors are represented by a balanced see-saw. In order to achieve balance, each person can move either towards or away from the centre, which, as we know from basic physics, increases its strength the further away from the centre it goes. Thus the entropy generated by each level is dependent on the requirements of the overall system.

All the components of the Biosphere are on board the one see-saw. In the Energetic Theory of Evolution, each level, from chemical reaction to biome, has an independent conversation with the laws, and this conversation is then shared with the other levels, achieving a balance. This is the natural way: interaction, feedback, balance. This is not a natural world at war. It is a Biosphere responding to its thermodynamic master.

Entropic production is paramount, and drives processes such as development, evolution, sustainability and stability. This is because stability, ultimately, is achieved at maximum entropic output. In other words, it exists at the plateau of Figure IV.1. However, this balance can be perturbed, because it is a balance. If anything shifts on our multi-armed see-saw, the whole thing will go into a wobble.

It is important to note that sustainability and resilience are not the same. Resilience represents the ability to stay on the see-saw, whereas sustainability represents the continued balance of the system. Resilience requires flexibility and the ability to respond to change. If you try balancing on a floating log, you need to be able to continuously shift your centre of gravity. Remaining static will lead to you getting very wet! So a resilient system has the ability to change and move as required. This necessitates variation and diversity.

I want to suggest that there is a *cone of resilience*, increasing with each level of organization. Species are less resilient than ecosystems. This is shown by the existence of functional redundancy in ecosystems. By this I mean that ecosystems are designed to lose species by having *"spare"* species around to do their work. Populations are less resilient than species. Individuals are less resilient than populations. The loss of an individual will have little impact on a population.

Many previous workers have attempted to use thermodynamics to understand evolution (e.g. Lotka, 1922; Fath *et al.*, 2001; DeLong, 2008) but always keeping the Darwinian theory of evolution by natural selection at the centre. As we have seen in the last section, natural selection is not a valid concept, nor can it explain evolution. Scientists writing in the leading journals of modern biology, including *Nature, Science, Proceedings of the Royal Society* and *Proceedings of the National Academy of Sciences* all support the central problems identified in Section III, as we have noted.

Yet we see similar patterns running through the Biosphere. Growth rate of a body, growth rate of a population, and entropy output of an ecosystem all follow a logistic model. These patterns are set in place by the driver of entropy (Appendix II). And each level of organization is attempting to operate at its maximum entropy output. It is the response of each level, from chemical reaction through to biome, to the rules of thermodynamics, and the subsequent balancing of the see-saw, that produce what we know as evolution.

Chapter Sixty-Four
So How Did the Cosmos Create Gardeners?

Getting back to the title of this section, we need look no further than our gardens to see all of this in action. Gardening is a challenging business. Things keep growing, and weeds keep appearing. It is a lifetime commitment. It is also responsible for the introduction of many exotic species into countries, which can escape over the garden wall and have significant damaging inputs on our native species, but that's a whole other discussion.

How did the Cosmos create gardeners? Well ecological succession, as we have seen, is driven by the second law, with communities of organisms gradually changing and diversifying, called, ultimately, to maximize entropic output. Thus nature has a driver, who sits in the front seat of the universal limousine, steering us all towards equilibrium. But it's such a jolly ride!

When you set up your garden, you, most probably unknowingly, decide to act like King Canute, and stop the tide. It is actually much more impossible than what King Canute is rumoured to have tried. He was merely attempting to stop the gravitational interaction between the water on our planet and the moon. As gardeners, you are attempting to stop Entropy! Armed with your spade and secateurs, your strimmer and weed killer, and dressed in your gardening gear, complete with gloves and kneeling mat, you walk out each morning to wage war against the powers of darkness that would destroy your beautiful borders and beds.

Nature works to reclaim this patch of land that you have taken from it, and return it to its right and proper path, the path of ecological succession. And the plants you refer to as weeds, are actually ruderals. Ruderals are the foot soldiers of succession, whose job is to prepare the way for the shrubs and, eventually, trees, leading to the balanced forest that needs no gardener, because it is maximally producing chaos. Ruderals begin the job of covering all the bare soil with vegetation, so that the soil isn't washed away. They also get to work altering the soil, transforming it as part of the journey to balance. Our attitude to these amazing little plants reflects our seclusion in *Bubbleworld*, displaying our complete ignorance of the natural processes.

And so you do battle, in a war you will never win, until one day you die, and, if left untouched by human hand, nature will take back its child and lead it to balanced harmony, brimming with native species, all in conversation with the laws of thermodynamics, and with the other levels of organization.

Chapter Sixty-Five
A Word on Conservation

Unfortunately we have applied the same logic to conservation as we have to gardening. Captive breeding programmes, re-introductions, tree-planting, tree-hugging, culling, weeding, excluding, we try it all. Basically, it's all about us *doing* things, and philosophically, it is underpinned by the principle that humans know best. Once again we interfere with nature; that chaotic, confused and directionless mess. How wrong we are. For nature is organized, balanced, directed and intricately interactive. It is we who are the tangled, confused, separated, unbalanced, unbalancing, ignorant, isolated disasters.

But, you say, surely we must act to correct the terrible things that we have done to nature. My message is simple, nature knows best. The only way to restore nature to its former prime, is to remove as much of our interference as possible, and to resume our roles as participants in the Biosphere. Participants listen, they respond in a context-appropriate manner. They contribute to maintaining entropic generation at a level that is required by the greater system. They behave by directly conversing with the laws of the Universe, and, equally, finding their place on the see-saw. It is all about listening, then participating, then listening again.

By removing our interference, I make reference towards much of the conservation movement. Let's look at a couple of examples. The first one is a general point on tree planting. Surely it is good to plant trees? They replace forests that have been chopped down. They provide habitats for birds and insects. They restore the damage we have done to our planet. Let's examine these statements. A forest is the end point of succession. It is maximally producing entropy. It takes some one hundred and fifty years for an ecosystem to move, naturally, from bare soil to a forest. In between the start and finish of this journey, there is a gradual developmental process, directional and energetically driven.

If you decide to stick some trees in a field you will not have planted a forest. You'll have stuck some trees in a field. It's like gluing a beard onto a baby and expecting it to act like an adult. It isn't an adult. It's a baby with a beard glued to its face. Ecosystems are complex, subtle things, involving a balance derived from their energetic character. Forests sit at maximum entropic capacity. They are stable ecosystems because of this. But they are there only because they have grown and developed through time. Many species will have come and gone in the process.

Conservation is not about the species in isolation, in space or time. Rather it is about the energetic journey of the landscape. Species find a place in this great scheme for a while, but then their contribution is done, and new species come in. Populations and individuals are even less permanent fixtures, yet are equal in terms of conversing with the laws.

So how should we conserve nature? We shouldn't. Nature is capable of self-repair. It came back from five mass extinctions, countless intermediate extinctions and numerous ice ages. Tectonic plate movements have not hindered it. Huge volcanic events have been coped with. Giant bolides, the size of Mount Everest, have not derailed it. Don't get me wrong, there is a lot we do need to be doing. We need to completely realign our thinking, and escape from *Bubbleworld*. Then we need to listen to the laws of physics and to the conversations around us. And finally, we need to change what we do in response to this, and continue listening.

We need to wake up to the fact we are on the see-saw and work out how far we should be along our beam of wood, in order to restore the balance. But as for the rest of it, we need to leave it alone. Stop treating our wildlife like a garden. We need to trust the Biosphere, and acknowledge that it knows best.

Nature will take an area, if left alone, and lead it along the path to maximum entropic production. It will take more than a century to do it, but you'll never have to lift a finger. That is the ultimate proof of proper conservation — there should be no ongoing maintenance. If the changes you make are in accord with the natural direction, there will be no problem. If you have to start correcting things, then you are not working with nature. So leaving nature to operate as it knows best is also the most economically efficient approach. And in these times of austerity, the natural solution is a winner every time. Otherwise you'll have to continue trimming and pruning and strimming and mowing and restocking. And that costs money.

This is what has happened at a nature reserve near me. Managed (or, should I say, mismanaged) by the most powerful conservation organization in the country, Scottish Natural Heritage, the site, Tentsmuir Point, is designated as a Site of Special Scientific Interest (SSSI), and a National Nature Reserve. Here is a quotation taken from their website (SNH, 2011): *"A major programme of tree and scrub removal has been carried out here in recent years. This has achieved the aim of restoring 95 per cent of the reserve to dune habitats — mainly dune grassland and heathland."*

I have carried out research on this reserve for almost twenty years, publishing several papers on this wonderful place. I know it well, and it has inspired me in much of my thinking. However, this sentence, above, from the SNH website, is extremely worrying for a number of reasons. They are trying to halt succession. It has become a National Gardening Reserve, instead of a National Nature Reserve. Of course there are pine trees owned by the forestry commission nearby. However the direction here should be the removal of this plantation, not the destruction of all the shrubs and native birches.

Instead they use chainsaws, herbicides and a large herd of highland cattle, who destroy the lichen heath and disturb the delicate soils, ruining the site in terms of a research base for soil heterogeneity (Averiss and Skene, 2001). Cutting down shrubs, and important species such as birch, is unforgivable. They claim to be preserving the dune system, but instead, what they are doing resembles plastic surgery. I may have my face reconstructed to look like a young James Dean (not that there was, tragically, any other sort), but I will still be aging underneath.

Sand dune successions change. That is the whole point! The gradual change is part of the system, and is a subtle but widespread thing, reaching into every soil pore and every nematode species on the reserve. Chopping down trees, many of which are part of the natural succession, is tantamount to tragedy. It represents another Canute moment. The irony is that, for years, the rare coralroot orchid or *Corallorhiza trifida* (so called because its roots resemble coral), has been found in much higher numbers on the outer edge of the reserve than within it!

Of course, this orchid grows best in birch woods, most of which have been chopped down in the reserve. Meanwhile the marauding cattle disturb the soil, allowing rose bay willow herb (*Chamerion angustifolium*), a pernicious invasive hybrid that requires bare soil to infest an area, to spread like wildfire (it's no wonder the Canadians call it *fireweed*). Another research project, carried out by an honours student working with me, found invertebrate diversity significantly greater just outside the reserve, where scrub and birch wood had not been prevented from growing.

It is unforgivable, to me and many other ecologists with whom I have discussed the issue of Tentsmuir, to carry out this aggressive management of such an important habitat. Not only are their approaches ruining the site in terms of research, as you don't know if the plants you were studying are going to be there when you return, or if a huge pile of cattle faeces has altered your historical measurements of nutrient heterogeneity, but, more fundamentally, SNH are irrevocably altering the system, and in such a way as to spoil it for future generations. Their work is leading to a dramatic drop in diversity. This is no longer a nature reserve. It's a disaster. Put it this way, if you want to examine the natural ecology of Tentsmuir, go just outside the reserve – it's far more relevant. That's where you will encounter the greatest diversity and the rarest plants, safe from human management!

What would I recommend for Tentsmuir? I would, firstly, request the compulsory purchase and removal of the Forestry Commission plantation, as this is a critically important sand dune area. A very small decrease in industrial forestry will be no great loss, given the uniqueness of Tentsmuir Point. Then we need the removal of all human interference from the site. We have no place there, except to listen to and to learn from its conversations.

And as for tree planting? Don't do it. Purchase the land and leave it alone. Nature will take care of the rest in its own time. It's been doing so for the last four billion years. And for the vast majority of this time, it has managed quite happily on its own.

Chapter Sixty-Six
Thermodynamics and the Tempo of Evolution

Where does all of this entropy generation lead when applied to understanding the tempo of evolution? Well, as we have seen from the last section, evolution works by diffusing into available space. This space is energetic space. The individual species, along with all of the other levels of the Biosphere, are moving towards the maximum entropy output possible for that level. And the evolution of all levels will be similarly geared towards this. Thus the species, like every level, is a compromise between maximizing its own entropy production and that of the Biosphere as a whole.

When evolutionary space opens up, the forms of life diffuse into this space. This is why we have so many different forms on our planet. Evolution is the opportunistic expansion into space, just like a gas. It works at its most rapid in the empty marketplace. In a similar way, perfume diffuses into space, or a drop of ink into water. If you open a door for evolution, something must push it through the door. Why does it go through? The answer is entropy.

The key point is that the direction of evolution is fundamentally driven by the arrow that drives everything else: the second law of thermodynamics. Of course, the evolution of individual species must be within the context of everything else. This is a significant difference compared to neo-Darwinism. And so each level finds its energetic meaning on the entropic see-saw. After a mass extinction, many species are extinct, and whole ecosystems re-emerge through ecological succession. They gradually build up their production of entropy, but may be slowed by having to wait for suitable species to evolve.

Thus the evolution of a species requires it to fit into a succession, and so the species must contribute appropriately to the build up of entropy and to the change required at that particular stage in the succession. Some species find their roles as ruderals while others may be members of the forest. Every species on our planet fits into the path from early to late succession, and this fundamentally determines its role, from behaviour to physiology.

Hence, species are not free to evolve as they may wish to. They are part of the great conversation, with the laws of thermodynamics individually, and with all the other levels of organization collectively. This has nothing to do with natural selection. Competition is not relevant here either, as the driver is far beyond all of that. Instead it is a corporate response to thermodynamics, supported by a supply of free energy and driven by entropic increase. Again, it is not a matter of selection at any particular level, but rather the simultaneous exploration of energetic space by all levels of the Biosphere.

Within the population level, we also see entropy at work. Let's compare two graphs to demonstrate this. The first is what we call a *Boltzmann distribution*, shown below (Fig. IV.4a) and, alongside it, we see the variation-stabilizing selection curve from Section III (Fig IV.4b).

The Boltzmann distribution (named after Ludwig Boltzmann (1844-1906), the Austrian physicist) simply shows how perfume spreads from a source into space. The solid line on Figure IV-4a shows the situation just after release. Most of it is concentrated in the centre of the graph (or the room). The second curve, the dotted line, shows the situation later. Now the curve is much broader, because the perfume has diffused into the space. Now compare this to Figure IV.4b. Here we see the effect of removing our selection arrows on variation. It is the same outcome.

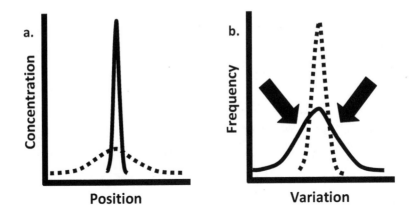

Figure IV.4 a. Boltzmann distribution showing the distribution of a drop of dye at t=0 (solid line) and at t=100 seconds (dashed line) based on van Holde, 1985; b. Change in variation within a population before (solid line) and after (dashed line) application of selection pressure (arrows).

This is no co-incidence. What we see is that when a population is placed in an empty market place, devoid of many of the compromises found in a mature, stable ecosystem, this population will expand in terms of its variation. Thus variation is driven by entropy. This is obvious, when you think about it, because variation is produced by random changes in the genetic code. This randomness is a form of entropy, leading to greater disorganization within the original code, and producing variation.

Just like the perfume particles are jostled by the random motion of the gas particles in the air, and the ink particles are jostled by the random movement of water molecules, spreading as *per* Boltzmann, so variation reflects the spreading of phenotype, jostled by the random mutation of DNA. Entropy within the population drives variation. It is balanced by compromise, as entropic production slows at the ecosystem level.

To summarise, we see that each level of organization undergoes evolution through time, driven by the second law. It works as follows:

1. Energetic space becomes available by local extinction of species or by larger-scale disruption.
2. Variation increases in surviving populations, freed from the compromises of the see-saw, and driven by entropic increase in information (DNA)
3. Sexual incompatibility separates groups of sexually reproducing organisms (speciation)
4. Populations expand based on available energy
5. Ecosystems build and reach maximum entropic output, leading to compromise as entropic production within populations is reduced
6. Reduced variation means reduced evolution
7. It is the interactions of the levels of organization that, together, determines how any single level behaves.

So there we have it! A new theory of evolution, based on thermodynamics, and without any reference to natural selection. It explains what we observe much better than Darwinian Theory, is supported by scientific research, and is therefore a better theory altogether. It also has huge repercussions for sustainability, setting a new agenda for the human race.

In 2011, the Indian Premiere League introduced a new trophy for its 20 over competition. It was engraved with the motto "talent meets opportunity". In many ways this is what evolution is all about. Not competition, but opportunity. It is an exciting exploration, driven by the second law of thermodynamics, and realized in the vast array of creatures, whose context matters most. We can now also understand why laboratory experiments just don't have that much relevance to understanding evolution, as clearly indicated by the study of the crickets.

It isn't at all surprising that what we find in the real world undermines completely the laboratory-based findings of *Bubbleworld*. This is because life is about balance. The context of ecosystem and biome cannot be re-created in laboratories. Yet these contexts matter. That's why, without them, we get completely different results. Only in the natural world can we understand any given element of that world, where the conversations occur, and where all of the impacts of entropy, at every level of organization, come together on the energetic see-saw.

Let's now examine the current crisis facing us and uncover what lies at the heart of it. We are about to discover that thermodynamics will allow us a wonderful insight into these problems, and into the solutions available.

REFERENCES

Aoki, I. (1995) Entropy production in living systems: from organisms to ecosystems. *Thermochimica Acta* 250: 359-370.

Aoki, I. (2006) Min-Max principle of entropy production with time in aquatic communities. *Ecological Complexity* 3: 56-63.

Aro, E.-M., Virgin, I. And Andersson, B. (1993) Photoinhibition of Photosystem II. Inactivation, protein damage and turnover. *Biochimica et Biophysica Acta- Bioenergetics* 1143: 113-134

Averiss, R.J. and Skene, K.R. (2001) Changes in nutrient heterogeneity in a sand dune succession at Tentsmuir Point, Eastern Scotland. *Botanical Journal of Scotland* 53: 45-56.

Bazarov, I.P. (1964) *Thermodynamics.* Pergamon Press, New York.

Bernaoli-Galvin, P., Grosse, I., Carpena, P., Oliver, J., Roman-Roldan, R. and Stanley, H.E. (2000) Finding borders between coding and non-coding DNA regions by an entropic segmentation method. *Physical Review Letters* 85: 1342-1345.

Billings, E. (1872) On some fossils from the primordial rocks of Newfoundland. *Canadian Naturalist* 6: 465-479.

Budyko, M.I., Ronov, A.B. and Yanshin, A.L. (1985) *History of the Earth's Atmosphere.* Springer, Berlin.

Carpenter, F.M. (1992) *Treatise on Invertebrate Palaeontology, Vols. 3 and 4.* University of Kansas Press, Lawrence, Kansas.

Carnot, N.L.S. (2010) {1824] *Réflexions Sur La Puissance Motrice Du Feu Et Sur Les Machines Propres À Développer Cette Puissance.* Nabu Press, Charleston, South Carolina.

Celesti, L. & *Pignatti*, S. (*1988*) Analysis of the chorological diversity in some South-European vegetational series. *Annali di Botanica* 46: 25-34.

DeLong, J.P. (2008) The maximum power principle predicts the outcomes of two-species competition experiments. *Oikos* 117: 1329–1336.

Driever, W. and Nüsslein-Volhard, C. (1988) The bicoid protein determines position in the *Drosophila* embryo in a concentration-dependent manner. *Cell* 54: 95-104.

Eddington, A.S. (1928) *The Nature of the Physical World.* Michigan University Press, Michigan.

Fath, B.D., Patten, B.C. & Choi, J.S. (2001) Complementarity of ecological goal functions. *Journal of Theoretical Biology* 208: 493–506.

Gillispie, C.C. (1971) *Lazare Carnot Savant: A Monograph Treating Carnot's Scientific Work.* Princeton University Press.

Graham, J.B., Dudley, R., Aguilar, N.M. and Gans, C. (1995) Implications of the late Palaeozoic oxygen pulse for physiology and evolution. *Nature* 355: 117-120.

Holdaway, R.J., Sparrow, A.D., Coomes, D.A. (2010) Trends in entropy production during ecosystem development in the Amazon Basin. *Philosophical Transactions of the Royal Society B* 365: 1437-1447.

Kleidon, A. (2004) Beyond Gaia: thermodynamics of life and earth system functioning. *Climate Change* 66: 271-319.

Levine, H.J. (1997) Rest heart rate and life expectancy. *Journal of the American College of Cardiology* 30: 1104-1106.

Lorenz, R.D. (2010) The two-box model of climate: limitations and applications to planetary habitability and maximum entropy production studies. *Philosophical Transactions of the Royal Society B* 365: 1349-1354.

Lloyd, S. (2004) Going into Reverse. *Nature* 430: 971

Lotka, A. (1922) Contribution to the energetics of evolution. *Proceedings of the National Academy of Sciences USA* 8: 151–155.

Ludovisi, A. (2004) Biotic and abiotic entropy production in lake ecosystems *Ecological Modelling* 179:145-147.

May, M.L. (1982) Heat exchange and endothermy in Protodonata. *Evolution* 36: 1051-1058.

Meysman, F.J.R. and Bruers, S. (2007) A thermodynamic perspective on food webs: quantifying entropic production within detrital-based ecosystems. *Journal of Theoretical Biology* 249: 124-139.

Monod, J. (1972) *Chance and Necessity: An Essay on the Natural Philosophy of Modern Biology*. Vintage, New York.

Müller, D.G. and Gassmann, G. (1978) Identification of the sex attractant in the marine brown alga *Fucus vesiculosus*. *Natur Wissenschaften* 65: 389-390.

Paltridge, G.W. (1979) Climate and thermodynamic systems of maximum dissipation. *Nature* 279: 630-631.

Perez-España, H.   and *Arreguin-Sanchez*, F. (*1999*)   A   measure   of ecosystem maturity. *Ecological* Modelling 119: 79–85.

Resnickoff, H.L. (1988) *The Illusion of Reality*. Springer, Berlin.

Rodríguez Muñoz, R., Bretman, A., Slate, J., Walling, C.A. and Tregenza, T. (2010) Natural and sexual selection in a wild insect population. *Science* 328: 1269-1272.

Shen, Y., Zhang, T. and Hoffman, P.F. (2008) On the coevolution of Ediacaran oceans and animals. *Proceedings of the National Academy of Sciences, USA* 105: 7376–7381.

Skene, K.R. (2009) *Shadows on the Cave Wall: A New Theory of Evolution.* Ard Macha Press, Letham, Angus, UK.

SNH (2011)http://www.snh.org.uk/publications/online/designatedareas/nnrs/TentsmuirPoint/TentsmuirPoint.asp last accessed 20/05/11.

Vanyo, J.P. and Paltridge, G.W. (1981) A model for energy dissipation at the mantle-core boundary. *Geophysics journal* 66: 677-690.

Wolpert, L. (1969) Positional information and the spatial pattern of cellular differentiation. *Journal of Theoretical Biology* 25: 1–47.

SECTION V
THE DIVERSITY-ENERGY CURVE: MASS EXTINCTIONS AND WHY NUMBER SIX IS SO DIFFERENT

(Parts of this section are expanded from an article to be published in *Contemporary Review* (Skene, 2011)).

In this section we will examine another frequency curve, or normal distribution. This one looks at the relationship between diversity and the energy flowing through an ecosystem (Figure V.1). Energy basically represents food. The more food you have, then surely the more diversity you will have. After all, food is good and starvation is bad. More and more food can only be good for everyone! Well, nature just isn't like that. Too much food is as bad as too little food. It's an absolutely crucial point. This chapter is going to look at the relationship between life and energy, and at why we are destroying the Earth by over-feeding it. This subject is crucial to our future survival, and for the survival of our fellow passengers on this little planet of ours.

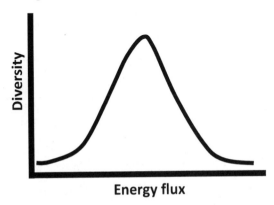

Figure V.1 The relationship between energy flowing through an ecosystem and diversity.

Chapter Sixty-Seven
Form, Function, Forests and Fossils: Sustainability Revisited

"It is the pervading law of all things organic, and inorganic,
of all things physical and metaphysical,
of all things human and all things super-human,
of all true manifestations of the head, of the heart, of the soul,
that the life is recognizable in its expression, that form ever follows
function. This is the law."

Louis Sullivan (1896).

On a hill high above Oban, a small port on the west coast of Scotland, there stands a structure that resembles a Roman amphitheatre. However, never in its history has a lion, a gladiator or, indeed, a Christian battled for their lives within its walls. In fact it has no function, and never has had. It is called McCaig's Folly, after John McCaig, the provincial banker who commissioned it, and it was built a mere one hundred years ago, fourteen hundred years after the fall of Rome. It could be said that it stands to remind us that form, without function, is folly.

Form follows function, or at least that is what Louis Sullivan (1856-1924), the American architect, and so called father of the skyscraper, stated. This maxim has created a lively debate, reaching across many fields of human thought, from architecture to design and from town-planning to web development.

In architecture, it was a Jesuit monk and architectural theoretician from Italy, Carlo Lodoli (1690-1761), who first discussed the relationship between form and function, stressing that nothing should be in the design that was not functional. This appears to be an extremely early version of what would become

Utilitarianism, or Modernism. He was also credited with starting the organic architecture movement (Pearson, 2001).   All of Lodoli's work was lost, but contemporary writers recorded his thinking (Kaufmann, 1955; Memmo, 1973; Wittkower, 1982)

Horatio Greenough (1805-1852), the American sculptor, developed these ideas (Greenough, 1947), having studied the work of Lodoli, and of Georges Cuvier (1769-1832) who believed that anatomical form followed function. Ralph Waldo Emerson, a key figure in the transcendentalist movement in America, said that *"Nature which created the mason now creates the house"* (Honzik, 1947). This idea would feed into the concept of natural architecture. Countering this approach, critics target the problem of a function existing without a form. Thus the *form follows function* dictum is seen as teleological.

Chapter Sixty-Eight
Formism and Biology: Latter-Day Bedfellows

While function tends to have the upper hand in most areas, this is by no means the case in biology. Here, form dominates function in key topics such as taxonomy, phylogeny, evolution, diversity and conservation. This has had significant impacts upon how we understand our planet and in how we respond to the challenges that currently face the human race.

So how did form come to dominate biology? It is an interesting journey, and begins in ancient caves, where humans first drew images of the animals around them, some thirty thousand years ago. From the earliest cave paintings of Chauvet in the Ardèche region of France, and the Altamira Cave in Cantabria, Spain, it is clear that humans had the capacity to accurately record morphology. Subsequently, the field of taxonomy developed, based on structure, both in terms of shape and colour. So if *A* looked like *B*, then *A* was *B*.

This morphological basis for taxonomy meant that species were equivalent to forms. Indeed, when a species has not been taxonomically identified, it is often referred to as a *morphotype*. Thus, diversity became a measure of forms or morphotypes. The number of different forms that a habitat possessed became a measure of its importance and significance.

Form-rich habitats were celebrated, and form-poor habitats condemned. Indeed, the history of biological conservation is a journey steeped in form. How many conservation charities have a cute, fluffy or furry creature as their emblem? Humans are much more likely to help save the panda or the parrot than they are the dung beetle or the slimy nematode.

It is a further irony that the organisms that have the greatest impact on our planet, the Bacteria and Archaea, are not even visible to the human eye, and, when magnified, consist, mostly, of only two forms, spheres and rods. These little creatures manage everything from atmospheric content (they are the main suppliers of nitrogen, which is seventy-eight percent of the atmosphere, and which prevents oxygen partial pressure from reaching dangerous levels) to rainfall (acting as nucleating centres for precipitation, as revealed by Professor Brent Christner and colleagues in a recent article in *Science* (Christner *et al.*, 2008)), and from recycling to digestion in herbivores, where fifty percent of the energy obtained by the herbivore is released from the food by the bacteria living in their guts.

Furthermore, it was within the bacteria that most of the metabolic pathways were invented, which would later be passed onto the rest of life. They are, basically, formless, but very functional. However they are invisible to the naked eye, the equivalent of Adam Smith's *invisible hand*!

Chapter Sixty-Nine
A brief History of Formism in Biology

It was at the turn of the nineteenth century that the form/function debate really became a significant issue in biology. Étienne Geoffroy St. Hilaire (1772-1844) phrased it this way (from Russell, 1916): *"Is function the mechanical result of form, or is form merely the manifestation of function or activity? What is the essence of life -- organization or activity?"* Two natural historians based in France took opposing positions. Cuvier, as we mentioned, stressed that form follows function while Étienne Geoffroy St Hilaire firmly believed that function followed form.

Thoughts on form and function have occupied evolutionary biologists for many centuries. Jean Baptiste Lamarck (1744-1829) believed that function led to form. The need for a particular function would result in the form changing. For example, the need to reach foliage led to the giraffe's neck elongating.

Charles Darwin turned this position on its head. Working from a taxonomy dominated by form, and relating these forms to each other by phylogeny, Darwin put forward a form-based theory of evolution, where tiny differences in forms (variation) were exposed to selection. Function follows afterwards, but it is the generation and then selection of form that comes first.

Interestingly, the formist approach of Darwinian Theory runs in opposition to the modernist, functional approach in design. The modernist approach suggests that designers should approach the solution by designing the best form to achieve the identified function (a Lamarckian idea), whereas the Darwinian architect would generate lots of different available designs, and see which one would best fit the challenge.

The adoption of form as the basis for understanding in biology is the natural outcome of Empiricism and the scientific method. Empiricism was based on observation. Seeing was believing, and form became the ultimate reference point. Never was a philosophy more thoroughly applied than Empiricism within science. Form fitted as an empirical currency.

Forms could be built up of blocks. This allowed experiments to be done, isolating these blocks for intimate study, and then putting the blocks together in a classically reductionist approach. Function was too woolly, especially at higher levels of organization. Anyway, function came from form. Better the shadows on the cave wall, than the unknown world beyond. At least you could see shadows. Ultimately, form reduced to the gene, whose double helix became the iconic form of all biology, and it was selfish! Form had a personality, and displaced any requirement for a functional basis.

Form provided another very significant advantage over function. It ridded the stage of a god-like destiny. If function was seen as the driver, then this driver could be attributed to a deity. By having a randomly-generated set of forms, with the emphasis on *random*, there was no need for directed design. If there was a watchmaker at all, he was blind.

This fitted into Enlightenment thinking perfectly. There was no destiny, just a process of form generation and selection. Humankind could create their own destiny, by reasoning and technology. One irony in this was the use of the term *adaptation*, which actually means *to fit towards.* Yet those who use this term freely would staunchly argue that there is no destination to evolution.

Chapter Seventy
The Consequences of Formism

One of the significant consequences of reductionist thinking is that if it is a matter of building blocks, then engineering these blocks, the genes, would appear to be a strategy of useful value. If we can control the bricks, we can control the cathedral. Little building blocks can be put together to make all sorts of things, and to help solve the world's problems, such as food shortages and disease.

In this new utopia, we could envisage a Gattaca-like population of perfected humans, eating perfected food and living on an altogether perfected planet. Form is controllable, it can be built and rebuilt, and we as humans have the technology to do this. We can re-engineer the imperfect forms produced by nature to build a better future. Godwin, Condorcet, Hume and Smith would be so proud of us.

We have applied our reductionist approach to ecosystem problems too. From the formist point of view, ecosystems are merely built of the organisms that occupy them. So if we have a problem, such as an unruly beast like the cane beetle (*Dermolepida albohirtum*), a pest of sugar cane plantations in Queensland, Australia, we can introduce something that will eat it, such as the cane toad (*Bufo marinus*). This form will eat the "*bad*" form and all will be well. Two hundred million cane toads later, minus a number of native species now extinct or nearly so due to *Bufo marinus* (Crossland and Alford, 1998; Lampo and Giulio, 1998), and this building block approach now looks questionable.

Yet, ultimately, the Biosphere is ruled by energy, both in terms of its dissipation as entropy, and in terms of maintaining its flow. Whatever level you look at (see Appendix III), it is energy that shapes it. Thus function, rather than form, must surely be the best way to understand the Biosphere, and to understand sustainability of the Biosphere. For, as we have said, sustainability can only be achieved at the Biosphere level.

To talk about human sustainability or human resilience is meaningless, and exposes reductionist thinking. Solutions will only be found if we put ourselves back into our original, energetic context. We cannot continue to separate ourselves from the greater order that is the Biosphere, for our survival lies in the hands of that order.

And, ultimately, in order to remain alive we need energy flowing through us. This is because, as we have seen in Section IV, we are constantly leaking energy to the Universe (the second law) and we cannot make energy from nothing (the first law). So we have to get it from somewhere.

Chapter Seventy-One
The Search for Energy: Black Smokers and the Blue Beyond

Originally, the energy came from our own planet, at underwater hot springs called *hydrothermal vents* or *black smokers*. These vents, heated by the hot interior of the Earth, provided the essential elements needed to supply replacement energy. Early life fed off these chemicals. There are still some organisms left from this time on Earth today, using sulphur and iron to run their energy budgets.

However the availability of these chemicals and the number of black smokers were limited. Thus, the most important transition in the evolution of life on Earth was when a group of early bacteria turned to the Sun for its energy. It used sunlight to split water, and then used the hydrogen to power the production of sugar. From then on, most species on Earth either got their energy directly from the Sun, or indirectly, as the energy passed through the food web. So life became dependent on a chain of events: sunlight had to reach the green photosynthetic organisms, they had to be able to convert it to sugar, and that sugar then had to be eaten.

In the oceans, this only proved to be possible near the surface and near the land. This was for two reasons. Firstly, sunlight can only penetrate a certain distance into the sea before it is scattered. Even today, the deepest that organisms capable of photosynthesis can live is only around two hundred metres in depth (Littler *et al.*, 1985).

The second great limitation upon marine algae is the supply of nutrients. Nutrients are essential for handling the energy received from the Sun. If you don't have enough of the right ones, you cannot live.

Nutrients have generally only been at high enough levels near the coasts of land masses. Further out to sea we find what is called the *blue desert*. The use of the word *desert* does not refer to a lack of water of course, but to a lack of nutrients. These areas have such low levels of things like iron, phosphorus and potassium that they are almost devoid of algae. And if there are no algae, then there isn't much else, because energy cannot flow through the system. The waters are clear because there is not much life in them: clear, blue and almost empty.

Of course some things do live there, but nothing compared to the coastal regions. To make things worse, the water is divided by what is called a *thermocline* (literally, *heat bed*). Thermoclines act to separate upper water from deeper water, due to a dramatic drop in temperature over a short depth. Basically, the top part of the ocean is warmed by sunlight, and the heat is moved around by wave action, but below a certain depth, mixing doesn't occur.

Thus the warm water doesn't mix with the cold deeper water. In the transition zone between the warm upper layer and the cold lower layer, the temperature drops dramatically. Further down still, and the water stays at a chilly -2 to +4 degrees C. We end up with three layers, the bottom one not mixing with the top one.

The problem is that most of the nutrients are in the deeper water, and so do not get mixed with the upper layer, where there would be enough light for algae to grow. No sugar means no food chain, and hence the term, blue desert. So we have plenty of nutrients but no light in the deep ocean, and plenty of light but no nutrients in the upper ocean.

Coastal regions are shallow and turbulent enough to avoid the formation of a thermocline, and with lots of juicy nutrients flowing off the land, there is not the same limitation. In fact, the problem instead can be too much nutrition, as we shall see later in this section.

Chapter Seventy-Two
Land-Locked Carbon and the One Hundred and Twenty Million Year-Old Puzzle

On land, life has freed itself from the liquid nutrient solution that is sea-water. Terrestrial plants have direct access to sunlight, with no liquid layer to interfere with the flow of energy. Of course, water now becomes an issue, and nutrients must be gained from soil. So the supply chain is not as restricted in terms of light, but rather it is the second link, the conversion of light to sugar, that is threatened by a shortfall of water and/or nutrients.

However land posses one additional problem to the supply chain. Because there is no water, plants need to support themselves. If you have been to a rocky shore when the tide is out, you see the seaweeds lying, sprawled over the rocks, like some scene from the-morning-after-the-night-before! Yet at high tide, if you used a snorkel, or dived in the same place where you had previously stood, you would see a completely different vista – fronds of algae standing upright, like a forest, transitioned from a two-dimensional diorama of desolation, to a cosmopolitan, three-dimensional panoply of marine life. The water provides buoyancy, and the algae rise from the rocks to which they are anchored, like kites in the wind.

On land, it is a different story. Support must come from the structure of the organism, not from the medium in which they exist. This is because air offers little in physical assistance. And so land plants use a special polymer called *lignin*. It is made of sugar and amino acids, and is a very strange structure — randomly organized. Because of this, it acts as a code, making it very difficult for animals to digest it. Our digestive systems prefer nice regular structures, not highly complicated ones. Starch, for example, is just a long chain of glucose sugars. In fact, no animal can break lignin down. They rely on bacteria and fungi living in their guts to do this job.

It was this Rubik's cube of digestion that provided the mechanical strength for land plants. It was one of the key innovations that allowed plants to exist on land (the others being the control of water loss and the tricky subject of sex without water). The earliest land plants, the mosses, were restricted because they didn't have any of these innovations and so relied (and still do) mostly on moist environments for their survival.

Once we have plants, then surely the development of an all-singing, all-dancing food web seems fairly straightforward. It would seem likely that as soon as plants invaded the terrestrial world, animals could follow, because there was now an energy supply to support life. However this is not what we find. It would be a long time before plant eaters would evolve. All of the early animals on land were unable to tackle this lignin.

It has been shown that aquatic food webs are structured differently from terrestrial food webs because in aquatic systems, there is no structural support material, and so the lignin problem doesn't exist (Shurin *et al.*, 2006). This allows, even today, for a much more efficient transfer of energy from the photosynthetic organisms to those further along the chain. Back in the early days of living on land, around four hundred and fifty million years ago, the Animal Kingdom consisted of decomposers (feeding on dead bodies) or detritivores (feeding on the left-overs after the decomposers have had a go). The salad bar was well and truly closed!

Indeed the earliest land animal so far discovered (as of 2011) was a creature called *Pneumodesmus neumani*, a millipede and a detritivore. It was found just a few miles from my home, on a beach near Stonehaven on the East coast of Scotland, by Mike Newman, a bus driver and amateur fossil hunter (Wilson and Anderson, 2004). Next came the carnivores, such as early forms of harvestmen (a spider-like creature). The oldest of these was discovered in the world-famous Rhynie Chert in Aberdeenshire, Scotland, home to some of the oldest plants ever found. This specimen also has the dubious honour of possessing the oldest set of fossilized terrestrial genitalia ever found (Dunlop *et al.*, 2003)!

By three hundred and fifty million years ago, there is some evidence of spore-eating and piercing and sucking (akin to modern aphids), but proper leaf-munching only is recorded from three hundred million years ago (see Labandeira (1998) for an excellent review of this). It probably took animals about one hundred and twenty million years to learn how to eat plants properly!

So we see that all the way along the energy chain, there were challenges. The story of evolution is, in many ways, tied to exploring the solution space for these challenges. The difficulties were many: from a shortage of energy-rich compounds around the black smokers, to light energy scattering at depth to thermoclines limiting nutrient supply, to sugar production, to being able to eat the plants, particularly on land. These problems were not solved using a selective, competitive dogma, but by an expansive, diffusional, inclusive approach.

Chapter Seventy-Three
Maximum Diversity at Less Than Maximum Energy Flow

What is interesting is that the greatest diversity we see today is in situations of intermediate energy flow. At very low levels of available energy, not much can live, but the same is true for high levels of energy flow. This is what this section's curve shows (Fig. V.1).

If we look at the most diverse ecosystems, they are not found in high nutrient areas. The Fynbos of South Africa, and the flora of Western Australia are among the most diverse on the planet, yet both are based on relatively low-nutrient soil. The soil in a rainforest is rarely deeper than about twenty centimetres. Coral reefs represent the most diverse habitats in the marine world, but, again, are found on the edge of the blue desert and are destroyed by nutrient-rich coastal water.

So diversity thrives in this intermediate world, where energy flow is sufficient but not excessive. Nutrients act as the doorkeepers of energy flow, and so their levels have a hugely significant impact. Given that energy is the architect of the Biosphere, then anything that changes energy flow can be expected to greatly destabilize the natural world.

We must ask what the basis of this diversity-energy relationship is. Why is it shaped like an upside-down bell? To find the answer we need to return to our see-saw analogy from Section IV. The overall balance in the Biosphere is reached by the system as a whole generating the maximum entropy possible. However no single level of organization can independently maximize its production of chaos. And so we find that there is a solution to this balancing act, and this results in diversity positioning itself at the right distance from the centre of the see-saw, not too far out and not too close in.

Of course, increased energy flow generates more entropy, but because all the components of the Biosphere are tied together, then compromise is reached. You may want to fly high, burn lots of energy and produce huge amounts of entropy, but you need to remember that you are not on a swing; you are on a see-saw.

Thus, as life has evolved, each new species is in conversation with the entire system, not tested against its nearest competitor, as Darwin would have it. It engages in a conversation with the rest of the Biosphere, and with each level, from the chemical reactions within it, to the ecosystem of which it is a part. Tempered by all of these conversations, it reaches a conclusion. This is not selection, but participation, as we have stressed before.

Such delicate engineering has led to a finely tuned outcome, with a diverse, energy-based and energy-driven totality. The supply of nutrients has remained fairly constant over most of evolutionary time. Radiation levels from the Sun, although gradually increasing from the early days of Earth's existence, again have remained fairly constant over the last billion years or so. However, if we perturb this totality, by altering the flow of energy through it, at any point in the chain from Sun to organism, we risk everything. And the record of life on Earth points clearly to this reality.

Chapter Seventy-Four
Mass Extinctions: Snapping Links in Chains

We take the Sun for granted. Of course, clouds can get in the way, but the Sun keeps shining and plenty of radiation reaches the Earth, to warm it and to provide the energy that flows through the Biosphere and maintains life.

Throughout the history of life on Earth, energy levels have risen and fallen. Some of these changes have been subtle. For example, the sunspots on the Sun go through a cycle of changing intensity, when the surface becomes slightly cooler or warmer. It's a very small change, amounting to 0.14%. That is unlikely to drive anything very far at all.

The Earth's orbit around the Sun also changes over time, a bit like a stretched elastic band, narrowing then returning to more of a circular orbit. When stretched, the orbit leads to big differences in the distance between the Sun and the Earth during a year, intensifying seasonality. This cycle takes one hundred thousand years to complete. The Earth's axis sketches out a circle in the sky, every twenty-six thousand years, and also changes its angle towards or away from the Sun, and this cycle takes forty-four thousand years. Both of these alter seasonality. All three different cycles alter the amount of radiation reaching the planet.

Every so often, these cycles come together, each at its maximum disruption, leading to a dramatic drop in temperatures on the surface of our planet. This is what causes ice ages to occur. Now ice ages are quite significant! The last one wiped out almost all life in Northern Europe, and many other regions. Ocean levels dropped over one hundred metres in depth, exposing the continental shelves and thus removing the coastal seas. The

North Sea, for example, disappeared. Ice ages re-sculpture the land, and the Biosphere.

Tectonic plate movement and concomitant changes in ocean circulation have also led to dramatic changes in rainfall patterns over the last fifty million years, leading to the shrinkage of forests and the spread of savannah in sub-tropical regions. Savannah thrives on drier conditions. This in turn led to the spread of grain-eating bird species and to the evolution of one branch of the primates, who came down from the trees and started to walk in the savannah. So here we see whole biomes changing, and having repercussions for other levels of organization.

Combinations of tectonic plate position and the great cycles of Sun-Earth proximity can bring extremely dramatic consequences.

Around four hundred and fifty million years ago, most of the land on the planet, which was still devoid of most, if not all, life, was clumped together in one giant continent, and the rest of the planet was made up of a huge sea, called, quite beautifully, the *Panthalassic Ocean*. Gradually, the supercontinent moved south, and began to accumulate ice. Because all the land was together, the effect was massive, with vast volumes of water being frozen and trapped on top of the huge island.

The sea-level fell dramatically, exposing the continental shelf and so removing the shallow coastal seas. Since all life was in the sea at the time, and most of it would have been in the coastal seas, the removal of these seas would have been devastating. The Ordovician mass extinction led to the loss of eighty-five percent of marine species (Sheehan, 2001) and was the second greatest extinction in history. And the energy chain was broken. Photosynthesis ground to a halt, as the nutrient-rich coastal waters disappeared.

As the ice spread, the Earth became white and acted as a mirror, bouncing the Sun's radiation back into space. This is called the *albedo effect*, and magnifies the impact of a serious glaciation event. One interesting point to note is that if life had already evolved on the land by this stage, it all would have been wiped out, so the only reason the extinction wasn't even more deadly is because of when it happened.

There have been another four mass extinction events. These tended to target the first chain – the transfer of energy from the Sun to the Earth. There have been many theories for how some of these extinctions have been caused, everything from gamma radiation bursts from elsewhere in our galaxy (Melott and Thomas, 2009) through to volcanoes and asteroids.

The Devonian extinction occurred around three hundred and sixty million years ago, and has been blamed on an asteroid (Claeys *et al.* 1992) or multiple asteroids (McGhee, 2002), leading to a dramatic drop in incoming radiation and a collapse in temperature (Joachimski and Buggisch, 2002). The collision(s) would have produced a vast amount of dust and this would have been ejected into the atmosphere, blocking the flow of that all-important energy.

The darkness produced by this dust creates what is called an *impact winter*. At the end of the Cretaceous, in the extinction event that removed the dinosaurs and flying reptiles, it is estimated that the sunlight was reduced by ninety percent and this darkness may have lasted for up to ten years (Galeotti *et al.*, 2004). It would take a further two thousand years for light levels to recover to pre-impact levels. That is a lot of dust! Put any plant in a dark cupboard for more than a month or two and it will be dead.

The Permian mass extinction, two hundred and fifty-two million years ago, is known as the *Great Dying* and was the most significant extinction event in Earth's history. The Permian disaster was likely caused either by a huge asteroid impact, or vast volcanic activity in present-day Siberia, with subsequent repercussions such as methane release from the sea.

The debate about the cause of the Permian event has been huge, but one thing is clear. Vegetation was wiped out. The annihilation of vegetation was so complete that it led to a cessation of coal formation anywhere on the planet. This is called the *coal gap*, and represents the annihilation of plant life from the planet's surface. It would take thirty million years for coal formation to recover (Retallack *et al.*, 1996).

Further evidence of the destruction of almost all vegetation was the change in river morphology. Vegetation alters river paths, and in South Africa, rivers all changed course to a vegetation-free pattern of flow at this time (Ward *et al.*, 2000). No vegetation means no food, which means mass starvation and extinction. Indeed it is possible that the planet returned to a very primitive early terrestrial foodchain of detritivores for a considerable period of time.

The Permian represented the almost complete severance of the energy chain, between incoming radiation and sugar production. Whether it was caused by drought, darkness (from volcanic or asteroid created dust in the atmosphere) or soaring temperatures, it meant that the energy flow was cut off dramatically with awful consequences.

The Triassic mass extinction, two hundred million years ago, is perhaps the most mysterious. Huge volcanic activity in the Atlantic Ocean, or a massive asteroid have been blamed (Tanner *et al.*, 2004) as has the ever more popular multiple event combination (Sephton *et al.*, 2002), but all are agreed that the final outcome was a dramatic drop in photosynthesis (Ward *et al.*, 2001; McRoberts and Newton, 1995; Tomašových, 2006). Again the crucial chain was snapped and starvation claimed a multitude of creatures, great and small.

Finally, the K/T event at the end of the Cretaceous (sixty-five million years ago) is perhaps the best known, due to its removal of the dinosaurs from the planet. Debate still rages over whether it was an asteroid or a giant volcanic event in India called the *Deccan Traps*. Whichever was the cause, it is fairly certain that the Sun's radiation was blocked by atmospheric dust, leading to the collapse of photosynthesis, and the snapping of the energy chain once again.

Chapter Seventy-Five
Starvation: a Driving Force of Human Civilization

Overall, then, we see that a decrease in energy flow has a disastrous impact on the Biosphere. In the last section, we explained why this is. Remember the duck in the barrel? If we don't replace the energy that leaks into the Universe, the barrel runs dry and we die. It is that simple.

Starvation has had massive implications for life. It is the end product of the collapse of the energy chain, because it is, by definition, the consequence of not getting enough energy. Ultimately, much of the destruction from the big five extinctions has been carried out by this particular horseman of the apocalypse. It is the wolf at the door, the grim reaper, unpredictable, but savage. Whole civilizations of humans have also been devastated by starvation, resulting from drought, as we have mentioned earlier. Indeed, in the early history of the human race, as hunter gatherers, significant volcanic or asteroid dust would have been devastating. For Maynard Smith to dismiss the horseman of famine (Smith, 1958) was, surely, a highly questionable position to take.

And so it should not surprise us that the history of the human race has been governed by food supply. Even today, *food security* is a huge topic for inter-governmental summits. Do we have enough food? How can we ensure this? Malthus was obsessed by it. In 1898, Sir William Crookes, the president of the British Association, said, in his presidential address, that by 1931 there would be insufficient food to feed us and that mankind faced starvation (quoted in Russell, 1954).

Sir John Russell writing in 1954 (Russell, 1954), declared *"world food production since 1939 has not even kept pace with the growth of the world population"*. And as recently as 2011, the British Government warned of a significant food crisis ahead. The contents of this report make extremely uncomfortable and disturbing reading, and yet were hardly mentioned in the national press in the UK. Here is their summary of what we are facing, taken directly from the report. It doesn't paint a pleasant picture.

"The lack of sustainability in the global food system is already causing significant environmental harm, for example, through nitrogen pollution, food production's contribution to greenhouse gas emissions, and the drying up of rivers and lakes. Many marine ecosystems are damaged by unsustainable fishing.

There is increased competition for, and scarcity of, inputs into food production. Of these, as discussed above, water is the most pressing, with significant effects on regional productivity likely to occur by 2030.

Competition for land has also emerged as a significant factor in many countries.

Some effects of climate change are now inevitable and the food system must prepare for them and adapt.

The food system is a significant producer of greenhouse gases and must contribute to global mitigation efforts.

There is the risk of negative irreversible events if action is not taken; this includes the loss of biodiversity, the collapse of fisheries, and the loss of some ecosystem services (for example, the destruction of soils).

There is substantial evidence for increasing global demand for food (which probably contributed to the recent food price spike).

There is evidence of a slowdown in productivity gains today correlated with a reduction in R&D investment in many countries over the last two decades.

The absence of food security will also make it much harder or impossible to pursue a broad range of other policy goals. It may also contribute to civil unrest or to failed states; it may stimulate economic migration or fuel international tensions." (Foresight, The Future of Food and Farming (2011) Final Project Report, The Government Office for Science, London, p 165.)

The report also states that nine hundred and twenty-five million people have diets that contain insufficient calories and that a further one billion people are deficient in one or more essential micronutrient. They record that by 2030, a forty percent increase in food production will be needed, and by 2050, this rises to seventy percent. This is serious stuff.

Huge industries promise to solve these problems, while making billions doing it. Also, things that we would not have otherwise accepted because of the risk, or lack of knowledge, are suddenly ushered through because *"desperate times require desperate measures"*. Feed me, even with genetically modified crops. Drain the previously protected wetlands, cut down the trees for grazing, drill for oil in the Arctic and transform diversity into monoculture. We need to wake up here. All of these approaches only take us further away from long-term survival, not closer to it. Is this the legacy you want to leave for your children and grand-children?

Chapter Seventy-Six
The Chain Gang: How We Enslaved Our Planet

Perhaps the greatest crime that we have committed against the Biosphere is the enslavement of the land for our own ends, and the pollution of the planet by the application of fertilizers. We may never know what led us to give up the nomadic hunter-gatherer lifestyle, but give it up we did, forming settlements and needing food to sustain ourselves. Agriculture provided this escape from a life on the hop, allowing us to produce our own food, both plant and animal.

At first agriculture was of a basic form, what we would now call *subsistence agriculture*, where we grew what the land could support, having years of fallow to give the soil a chance to recharge. The productivity and energy flux through such a farm, like the *shamba* of Kenya, was basically no different than a natural ecosystem, merely changing the emphasis, towards food production.

However, we needed to force more energy through the chain, and so developed and added fertilizers to allow the soil to produce more. The fertilizers had to be soluble, so that the plant could uptake them from the soil solution. But this is where the problem came. Because they were soluble, fertilizers could move wherever the water went: into the streams, the rivers, the wetlands, the lakes and, ultimately, the oceans. The effect of adding fertilizers has been dramatic. Diversity has collapsed and whole ecosystems have been destroyed. The scale is unprecedented, and this pollution event, perhaps the biggest and most deadly in the history of the Earth, is wreaking havoc across the planet.

For, as we have seen, ecosystems are tightly balanced, working optimally at intermediate energy levels. Adding nitrogen, phosphorus, iron and potassium, we open the flood gates and this allows huge amounts of energy to flow through the system. Dumping large amounts of iron, one of the most limiting elements, into the oceans, in order to draw down carbon dioxide, is another example of such compartmentalized thinking. The idea was that the iron would stimulate photosynthetic bacteria, algae and protists in the ocean, leading them to absorb carbon dioxide and converting it into biomass. However this fertilizing of the ocean is more likely to destabilize the ecosystem, leading to even greater problems.

This poisoning of natural systems by fertilizers is called *eutrophication*. It is one of the three modern horsemen of the apocalypse, which we identified in Section II, and is the signature of the Sixth Mass Extinction.

Instead of a break in the energy chain, as in previous extinctions, we have released a surge of energy throughout the Biosphere. However, as our curve for this section indicates, too much energy is just as damaging as too little. Never in the history of the planet has such a surge occurred, and so Nature is not prepared for the consequences.

With the balance disturbed, a small number of species grow far beyond their sustainable numbers, decimating the finely tuned structure of the ecosystems within which they dwell. You only have to look at a lake where agricultural run-off has poured in. Thick layers of algae grow at the surface, known as algal blooms. Many of these algae produce serious toxins.

The thick mat of algae also blocks out the Sun from deeper in the lake, where submerged plant communities are lost. This destroys the habitat structure, as many organisms attach themselves to these big underwater plants. Other invertebrates hide from predatory fish, and with the disappearance of their hidey-holes, their populations collapse. This is disastrous, as many of these little beasts would normally eat the algae that are forming the thick rotting mats, and so there is a runaway escalation of the problem.

There is a final terrible outcome. Now that the large plants are dead, and the mat is starting to die, bacteria move in to feast on the remains. These bacteria use up huge amounts of oxygen in the process, and the remaining life in the lake literally suffocates, as dissolved oxygen disappears. This stage is often visualized by the appearance of hundreds of dead fish floating on the surface, whose rotting bodies absorb even more oxygen.

It's a spiral of death, a consequence of imbalance, and an outcome of our attempts to engineer the flow of energy for our species. By releasing our crops from their negotiations with the natural ecosystem, we create imbalance. Like a cancerous cell, individual species multiply and destroy the greater organism. And it is happening around the globe as we speak. Yet the drive is to transform more natural habitat into this pollution source, and to apply more chemicals. I haven't even mentioned the impacts of pesticides and herbicides on natural communities.

Eutrophication has had huge impacts across the planet (Scheffer *et al.*, 2001; Smith, 2003; Fabricius, 2005). Tropical lakes have been devastated (Seehausen *et al.*, 2006), as have tropical forests (Lu *et al.*, 2010). My own team discovered significant impacts on temperate forest function (Carfrae *et al.*, 2006). Coral reefs have collapsed, by a combination of dissolved inorganic nutrients, particulate organic matter, turbidity and sedimentation (Golbuu *et al.*, 2011). Waste from fish farming in the Red Sea has led to the destruction of fifty percent of the coral (Loya, 2004). Rocky shores have seen diversity decrease by up to forty-six percent (Worm and Lotze, 2006). For every ten percent increase in farm land, there is a six percent decrease in fish and invertebrate numbers in associated rivers and streams (Weijters, 2009).

Reflecting on this last paragraph, these are big impacts, not trivial perturbations. Fifty percent, forty-six percent – we cannot ignore this scale of damage. As I said earlier, we are not heading for a crisis, we are already there.

Eutrophication has also been discovered to increase the severity of coral diseases such as aspergillosis and yellow band disease (Bruno *et al.*, 2008). Of equal concern is the discovery that eutrophication plays a significant role in amphibian disease, death and extinction. Excess nutrients lead to algae growing. This, in turn, leads to populations of snails that feed on the algae to explode, and these snails act as the vector of the pathogen (Johnson *et al.*, 2007). These pathogens are thought to be responsible for a number of amphibian extinctions recently. It is likely that similar links will lead to an increase in the occurrence of a number of very nasty human parasites as well. So the monstrous transformation of the Biosphere that we have orchestrated is very likely to attack us in ways that we may not have suspected.

It has recently been discovered that global warming is expected to exacerbate the impact of eutrophication (Matzinger, 2007), and so these two man-made horsemen of the apocalypse will ride together. And there are other more subtle impacts being discovered. For example, it has been found that biochemical diversity within species of lichens is severely reduced by eutrophication (Hauck, 2011). So here we have a change in energy flow impacting on a level below the organism (biochemistry) and at a population level (population diversity).

By altering the flow of energy through the Biosphere, we impact on every aspect of it, from biochemistry to ecosystem function, and from biome to population. Imbalance reaches deep into every aspect of diversity. This is no reductionist outcome, but rather operates across every level of organization – a truly *transductionist* process (see Appendix III), and further evidence for the energetic theory of evolution and the role of energy as the architect of the structure of our Biosphere.

If we continue on this path, all that will remain will be a few dominant species who require huge amounts of energy to function. When this will become even more serious is if another traditional mass extinction occurs, breaking the energy chain. If and when this happens, we will have no species that can survive the massively reduced energy flow, and so that extinction is likely to be much more deadly than anything before.

We have also cleared many natural habitats, in order to increase the surface area of the planet that we can use to grow crops and feed livestock. Thus we take soils that were in balance, energetically, and pour nutrients on them, destroying this balance. So not only do we have the problem of nutrient pollution, but we are increasing the problem by ongoing habitat conversion. And that is the point. It would be bad enough that we destroy habitats, but we go much further, converting them into areas whose toxic juices flow from them and poison what remains.

Chapter Seventy-Seven
Form, Function and the Theatre of Extinction

Mass extinctions resemble a play by William Shakespeare. In all of the performances of this play, the text has remained the same, but the actors have changed. Each actor brings his or her own flair to the part, but the script ultimately determines their role. After each mass extinction event, new organisms take on the roles of carnivores, herbivores, detritivores and producers. However the overall script is the same. This is because the levels of organization are functional, and forms diffuse into the functional space, acting out their parts. If you don't say your lines, you won't be in the production. Thus the tight functional play resumes after each interruption, and is always the same. Individuals, populations, ecosystems and biomes re-establish as before, and are functionally identical. Thermodynamics writes the script.

Ultimately, the laws of thermodynamics determine that functional reality is restored to how it was before. The lessons of mass extinction are to do with the restoration of functional types, not the diversification of forms. Unfortunately, due to the dominance of form over function in biology, this has been, generally, missed. So when we try to understand evolution, we need to talk to the playwright, not the actor. In other words, it is thermodynamics that gives us the answers, not the phylogeny and taxonomy of form.

Simon Conway Morris, the renowned palaeontologist, has compared evolution to an oil painting, writing, in *The Crucible of Creation* (Conway Morris, 1998), "*It* [Darwinian Theory] *has explained the nature and range of pigments, how extraordinary azure colour was obtained, what effect cobalt has and so on. But the description is quite unable to account for the picture itself.*"

So we can look at life on Earth as a single functional unit, expressing itself, through form, in a myriad of ways. This also helps explain why there are so many morphological expressions of so few functional types. Finally, by viewing mass extinctions from a thermodynamic, functional approach, we replace contingency of form, as put forward by Stephen Jay Gould, with what I would call *functional continuity*.

Let me explain this last point. Gould focussed on forms, and wondered if lady luck had as much to do with the direction of evolution as anything else, or, maybe, more than anything else. He suggested that there was not a ladder of progress from start to finish in evolution through time, but rather, because of the intermittent wipe-outs, there was at least a degree of luck as to what survived. The destruction was so cataclysmic, that it couldn't be adapted for, and so the survivors couldn't be predicted. He claimed that if we re-ran the film of life again, we would likely end up in a very different biology than we are in today.

With function, no such contingency is needed. Function is restored each time, with no luck or unpredictability involved. The director of operations is the second law, and no detail evades notice. Form is merely the outcome of diffusional exploration of space. The exploration is a certain thing. If there is space, then there is exploration. But the outcomes are always tightly intermeshed with the Biosphere as a whole, and with the maximum output of chaos at the overall planetary level.

In terms of the detailed forms that will replenish the vacated planet after the next mass extinction, the functionalist and formist would agree that we cannot predict exactly what they will look like. However the functionalist can say a lot more than the formist. We would predict that the laws of thermodynamics would still hold, and thus we would expect that the Biosphere would function in the same way as it always has done, with primary producers, primary consumers, secondary consumers and detritivores all present. Their forms will result from an exploration of energetic space by morphological diffusion. As Keith Farnsworth and Karl Niklas wrote, *"We see evolution of design more as a process of diffusion into a space of possible solutions, than as a process of scalar optimization"* (Farnsworth and Niklas, 1995).

Evolution shares this diffusion with developmental biology, physiology and indeed with the rest of the Cosmos. Not only are we stardust, as Joni Mitchell famously sang at Big Sur, California, but we are under the same rules as all the other stardust out there. Evolution is merely part of the greater cosmic dance of matter to the tune of thermodynamics.

D'Arcy Wentworth Thompson (1860-1948), the great polymath, often viewed by formists as one of their own, stated in his fascinating book, *On Growth and Form* (1917), *"We rise from the conception of form to an understanding of the forces which gave rise to it; and in the representation of form and in the comparison of kindred forms, we see in the one case a diagram of forces in equilibrium, and in the other case we discern the magnitude and the direction of the forces which have sufficed to convert the one form into the other."* Here, quite clearly, Thompson shows his true colours as a functionalist, *"rising from the conception of form"* referring to the *"representation of form"* and discussing the *forces* that convert one form to another.

Reductionist, formist thinking cannot perceive this. It is an appreciation of the functional, thermodynamic ecology that allows us to understand how these systems work. We have become separated, scientifically, technologically, intellectually, physically and philosophically, from our context. We now manipulate our planet, rather than work within its energetic rules. We view nature as a building, reducible to pieces that we can alter and restructure.

Yet because we have developed a reductionist, form-based ethos, we fail to understand the functional complexity of the system. Optimizing our own existence will not produce a sustainable system. Our actions make sense to us within the narrow lens of human self-focus. Looking down at our feet, we fail to see the destruction around us.

Chapter Seventy-Eight
Lessons from the Curve

So what can we learn from the curve describing the relationship between energy and diversity? Firstly, our attempt at increasing productivity by increasing fertilization of a larger and larger portion of our planet, both terrestrial and aquatic, is disastrous for the Biosphere. The consequences will be another mass extinction, but of a nature that will make recovery more difficult, due to the demise of creatures who can survive low energy environments.

We need to stop this transformation of the planet. This will require a significant change in farming methodology. The signs so far are not promising. Recovery in freshwater systems, where sediment forms a repository for the nutrients, is extremely slow (Schindler *et al*, 2008). However we must stop this process now, otherwise things will be even worse. Eutrophication, habitat destruction and climate change are all symptoms of one thing, our need and lust for energy. These three horsemen are of our own making, but also promise significant, negative repercussions for us.

Energy is central to it all, and we need to reduce our abuse of it. There is a direct link between our abuse of energy and the destruction that we seem to be ignoring all around us. It is our relationship with energy that lies at the heart of the matter. And it is our almost hypnotic attraction to form rather than to function that has blinded us. The consequences have been grave, but it is not too late to change our ways.

Let me finish with a quote from Walter Teague (1883-1960), one of the world's leading industrial designers, taken from his book *Design This Day*, who summed things up rather well:

"The function of a thing is its reason for existence, its justification and its end, by which all its possible variations may be tested and accepted or rejected. It is a sort of life-urge thrusting through a thing and determining its development. It is only by realizing its destiny, and revealing that destiny with candor and exactness, that a thing acquires significance and validity of form. This means much more than utility, or even efficiency: it means a kind of perfected order we find in natural organisms, bound together in such rhythms that no part can be changed without wounding the whole."

REFERENCES

Bruno, J. F., Petes, L. E., Drew-Harvell, C. and Hettinger, A. (2003) Nutrient enrichment can increase the severity of coral diseases. *Ecology Letters* 6: 1056–106.

Carfrae, J.A., Skene, K.R., Sheppard, L.J., Ingleby, K. and Crossley, A. (2006) Effects of nitrogen with and without acidified sulphur on an ectomycorrhizal community in a Sitka spruce (*Picea sitchensis* Bong. Carr) forest. *Environmental Pollution* 141: 131-138.

Christner, B.C., Morris, C.E., Foreman, C.M., Cai, R.M. and Sands, D.C. (2008) Ubiquity of biological ice nucleators in snowfall. *Science* 319: 1214.

Claeys, P., Casier, J-G. and Margolis, S.V. (1992) Microtektites and mass extinctions: evidence for a Late Devonian asteroid impact. *Science* 257: 1102-1104.

Conway Morris, S. (1998) *The Crucible of Creation: The Burgess Shale and the Rise of Animals.* Oxford University Press, Oxford.

Crossland, M.R. and Alford, R.A. (1998) Evaluation of the toxicity of eggs, hatchlings and tadpoles of the introduced toad *Bufo marinus* (Anura: Bufonidae) to native Australian aquatic predators. *Australian Journal of Ecology* 23: 129–137.

Dunlop, J. A., Anderson, L. I., Kerp, H. and Hass, H. (2003) Preserved organs of Devonian harvestmen. *Nature*, 425: 916.

Fabricius, K.E. (2005) Effects of terrestrial runoff on the ecology of corals and coral reefs: review and synthesis. *Marine Pollution Bulletin* 50: 125-146.

Farnsworth, K. D. and Niklas, K.J. (1995) Theories of optimization, form and function in branching architecture in plants. *Functional Ecology* 9: 355–363.

Foresight. The Future of Food and Farming (2011) Final Project Report. The Government Office for Science, London.

Galeotti, S., Brinkhuis, H. and Huber, M. (2004) Records of post Cretaceous-Tertiary boundary millennial-scale cooling from the western Tethys: a smoking gun for the impact-winter hypothesis. *Geology 32*: 529-532.

Golbuu, Y., van Woesik, R., Richmond, R.H., Harrison, P. and Fabricius, K.E. (2011) River discharge reduces reef coral diversity in Palau. *Marine Pollution Bulletin* 62: 824-831.

Greenough, H. (1947) *Form and Function: Remarks on Art* (ed. Small, H.A.). University of California Press, Berkeley, California.

Johnson, P.T.J., Chase, J.M., Dosch, K.L., Hartson, R.B., Gross, J.A., Larson, D.J., Sutherland, D.R. and Carpenter, S.R. (2007) Aquatic eutrophication promotes pathogenic infection in amphibians.

Proceedings of the National Academy of Sciences, USA 104: 15781-15786.

Hauck, M. (2011) Eutrophication threatens the biochemical diversity in lichens. *The Lichenologist* 43: 147-154.

Honzik K. (1947) Tvorba životního slohu. Vydal Václav Petr, Praha.

Joachimski, M.M. and Buggisch, W. (2002) Conodont apatite δ^{18} signatures indicate climatic cooling as a trigger of the Late Devonian mass extinction. *Geology* 30: 711-714.

Kaufmann, E. (1955) *Architecture in the Age of Reason: Baroque and Post-Baroque in England, Italy, and France.* Harvard University Press, Cambridge, Massachusetts.

Labandeira, C.C. (1998) Early history of arthropod and vascular plant associations. *Annual Review of Earth and Planetary Science* 26: 329-377.

Lampo, M., and Giulio A. L. (1998) The invasion ecology of the toad *Bufo marinus*: from South America to Australia. *Ecological Applications* 8:388–396.

Littler, M.M., Littler, D.S., Blair, S.M. and Norris, J.N. (1985) Deepest known plant life discovered on an uncharted seamount. *Science* 227: 57-59.

Loya, Y. 2004. The coral reefs of Eilat—past, present and future: three decades of coral community structure studies. In: Rosenberg, E., Loya, Y. (eds.), *Coral Reef Health and Disease.* Springer, Berlin.

Lu, X., Mo, J., Gilliam, F.S., Zhou, G. and Fang, Y. (2010) Effects of experimental nitrogen additions on plant diversity in an old-growth tropical forest. *Global Change Biology* 16: 2688–2700.

Matzinger, A., Schmid, M., Veljanoska-Sarafiloska, E., Patceva, S., Guseska, D., Wagner, B., Müller, B., Sturm, M. and Wüest, A. (2007) Eutrophication of ancient Lake Ohrid: global warming amplifies detrimental effects of increased nutrient inputs. *Limnology and Oceanography* 52: 338-353.

McGhee, Jr., G.R. (2001) The 'multiple impacts hypothesis' for mass extinction: a comparison of the Late Devonian and the late Eocene. *Palaeogeography, Palaeoclimatology and Palaeoecology* 176: 47-58.

McRoberts, C.A. and Newton, C.R. (1995) Selective extinction among end-Triassic European bivalves. *Geology* 23: 102-104.

Melott, A.L. and Thomas, B.C. (2009) Ordovician geographic patterns of extinction compared with simulations of astrophysical ionizing radiation damage. *Paleobiology* 35: 311-320.

Memmo, A. (1973) *Elementi d'architettura Lodoliana*. Mazzotta, Milan.

Pearson, D. (2001) *The Breaking Wave: New Organic Architecture.* Gaia, Stroud, UK.

Retallack, G.J., Veevers, J.J. and Morante, R. (1996) Global coal gap between Permian-Triassic extinction and Middle Triassic recovery of peat-forming plants. *Geological Society of America Bulletin* 108: 195-207.

Russell, E.S. (1916) *Form and Function: A Contribution to the History of Animal Morphology.* John Murray, London.

Russell, E.J. (1954) *World Population and World Food Supplies.* George Allen and Unwin Ltd, London.

Scheffer, M., Carpenter, S., Foley, J.A., Folke, C. and Walker, B. (2001) Catastrophic shifts in ecosystems. *Nature* 413: 591–599.

Schindler, D.W., Hecky, R.E., Findlay, D.L., Stainton, M.P., Parker, B.R., Paterson, M.J., Beaty, K.G., Lyng, M. and Kasian, S.E.M. (2008) Eutrophication of lakes cannot be controlled by reducing nitrogen input: results of a 37-year whole ecosystem experiment. *Proceedings of the National Academy of Sciences, USA* 105: 11254–1125.

Seehausen, O., van Alphen, J.J.M. and Witte, F. (1997) Cichlid fish diversity threatened by eutrophication that curbs sexual selection. *Science* 277: 1808-1811.

Sephton, M.A., Amor, K., Franchi, I.A., Wignall, P.B., Newton, R. and Zonneveld, J.-P. (2002) Carbon and nitrogen isotope disturbances and an end-Norian (Late Triassic) extinction event. *Geology* 30: 1119-1122.

Sheehan, P.M. (2001) The Late Ordovician mass extinction. *Annual Review of Earth and Planetary Sciences* 29: 331-364.

Shurin, J.B., Gruner, D.S. and Hillebrand, H. (2006) All wet or dried up? Real differences between aquatic and terrestrial food webs. *Proceedings of the Royal Society B.* 273: 1-9.

Skene, K.R. (2011) Form, function, forests and fossils: sustainability revisited. *Contemporary Review*. In press.

Smith, J.M. (1958) *The Theory Of Evolution*. Cambridge University Press, Cambridge.

Smith, V.H. (2003) Eutrophication of freshwater and marine ecosystems: a global problem. *Environmental Science and Pollution Research International* 10: 126–136.

Sullivan, L.H. (1896)*The Tall Office Building Artistically Considered*. Lippincott's Magazine, March 1896.

Tanner, L.H., Lucas, S.G. and Chapman, M.G. (2004) Assessing the record and causes of Late Triassic extinctions. *Earth-Science Reviews* 65: 103-139.

Teague, W.D. (1940) *Design this Day: the Technique of Order in the Machine Age.* The Studio, London.

Thompson, D.W. (1917) *On Growth and Form.* Cambridge University Press, Cambridge, UK.

Tomašových, A. (2006) Brachiopod and bivalve ecology in the Late Triassic (Alps, Austria): onshore-offshore replacements caused by variations in sediment and nutrient supply. *Palaios* 21: 344-368.

Ward, P.D., Montgomery, D.R. and Smith, R. (2000) Altered river morphology in South Africa related to the Permian-Triassic extinction. *Science* 289: 1740-1743.

Ward, P.D., Haggart, J.W., Carter, E.S., Wilbur, D., Tipper, H.W. and Evans, T. (2001) Sudden productivity collapse associated with the Triassic-Jurassic boundary mass extinction. *Science* 292: 1148-1151.

Weijters, M.J., Janse, J.H., Alkemade, R. and Verhoeven, J.T.A. (2009) Quantifying the effect of catchment land use and water nutrient concentrations on freshwater river and stream biodiversity. *Aquatic Conservation: Marine and Freshwater Ecosystems* 19: 104–112.

Wilson, H.M. and Anderson, L.I. (2004) Morphology and taxonomy of Paleozoic millipedes (Diplopoda: Chilognatha: Archipolypoda) from Scotland. *Journal of Paleontology* 78: 169–184.

Wittkower, R. (1999) *Art and Architecture in Italy 1600-1750.* Yale University Press, London.

Worm, B. and Lotze, H.K. (2006) Effects of eutrophication, grazing and algal blooms on rocky shores. *Limnology and Oceanography* 51: 569-579.

SECTION VI
THE DIVERSITY-DISTURBANCE CURVE: FIRE, ELEPHANTS AND NOISY INFORMATION

Figure VI-1 is an important curve for the human race to understand. It shows the relationship between diversity and disturbance. Disturbance can be anything from fire to floods, and from predators to disease. We are significant disturbers. And this is why this curve is important. What level of disturbance is too much? If we are to cut back on our impact on the planet, should we become invisible, or is there some way in which our activities can contribute to the sustainability and resilience of the Biosphere? Another area where this relationship is central relates to our efforts to conserve nature. We discover that disturbance is actually essential for ecosystem function, and that by silencing it, we are more likely to damage the Biosphere than help it. Finally we examine the relationship between disturbance and resilience, and learn how noise fundamentally contributes to sustainability.

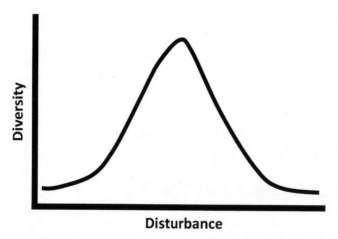

Figure VI.1 The relationship between diversity and disturbance (Increasing from left to right).

Chapter Seventy-Nine
When in Doubt, Wave your False Teeth in the Air

So the day he had dreaded, but had been warned about by so many, had finally arrived. Joseph Thomson found himself face-to-face with the Maasai tribe. He realized that the next few minutes would be crucial. The whole expedition was designed to find a safe route through Maasai territory, and now it was the moment that would define his mission, and quite possibly, his life.

The Maasai were the most feared tribe in East Africa, with a reputation as superb hunters and warriors. Indeed, this tribe had avoided being taken into slavery because the slave traders were so afraid of them. They were cattle herders, and frowned upon agriculture, believing that the cultivation of the soil was a crime against the gods (Kenyatta, 1965).

I spent part of my PhD research in East Africa. It was an amazing experience for a young man, my first time in Africa, and I remember it as a beautiful region with wonderful, deep-thinking people. I noticed that all the private security guards were Maasai, their tall stature, chiselled faces, deep-set narrow eyes and unreadable stare unmistakable. Lions and elephants are rumoured to fear these people. I still recall vividly an event that occurred when my wife, Marion, and I were camping in an organized group on the edge of the Maasai-Mara National Reserve. The camp was, naturally, guarded by Maasai.

We emerged from the tent on the first morning to be greeted with the remains of a young lion which had apparently been stalking our camp the previous night and had been killed with a Maasai spear. We certainly hadn't heard gunfire, and there was no evidence of guns before or after the incident. From what I could tell, the wounds were spear-like. Man against beast, armed only with a pointed stick, the human warrior had won. The following night, this experience had mixed blessings. There were Maasai capable of killing lions with their own bare hands and this was comforting. However there were lions, and we were in a tent, with millimetres of canvas between us and the top predator in the African continent. What if the guards fell asleep?

It was a god-forsaken place, where Thomson and the Maasai came face to face. They called it *Empusel*, literally *a salty dusty place*. You didn't have to look far to see the source of the dust. For just twenty-five kilometres further south towered the largest mountain in Africa, and the largest isolated mountain (i.e. not part of a range) in the world, *Kilimanjaro*. Created from volcanic eruptions across a million years, the dust of *Empusel* bore testament to this sleeping giant.

Dominated by a huge dry lake dating back many thousands of years, the landscape was almost pre-historic. Yet green oases were scattered around, swamps and springs, which also owed their existence to the mighty mountain. This is because *Kilimanjaro*, although only three hundred and seventy kilometres south of the equator, has glaciers on its highest peak. As we noted at the end of Section I, it gets colder with altitude, and, at five thousand eight hundred and ninety-five metres, an ice cap has remained in place since the last ice age. The melt water from the mountain provides much needed moisture. Unfortunately, due to glacial retreat it is predicted that this ice cap will be lost by 2020 (Thompson *et al.*, 2009). Eventually this will mean an end to the life-giving water from the mountain, but at present the problem is the opposite of that. Increased melting means that the swamps are expanding and woodland is being killed off, threatening diversity.

Thompson was still only twenty-five years old, but his leadership skills had been noted by the Royal Geographical Society, when, five years earlier, in 1878, and straight after graduating from the University of Edinburgh, he was forced to assume leadership of a difficult expedition across what is now Tanzania, following the sudden death of the original leader. And so he had been chosen for what was viewed as an even more difficult challenge: establishing a route through Maasai country to Lake Victoria.

Faced with these ferocious tribesmen, what he decided to do has gone down in expedition folklore. He pulled out his false teeth and waved them in the air, convincing the warriors that he was a magician! Peace was made, and the expedition carried on to Lake Victoria. The return trip was marred by him being gored by a buffalo, but he survived to tell the tale. Indeed, inspired by Thomson's story, the young H. Rider Haggard wrote of the teeth-waving display in his fictional classic, *King Solomon's Mines*. Thomson would later be immortalized by having a species of herbivore named after him: *Thomson's gazelle*.

But it was this dry and dusty place, *Empusel*, or, as it is known today, *Amboseli*, that would become important to ecologists more than a century later. For *Amboseli* is rich in diversity, with over four hundred different species of birds, almost all the significant vertebrate species in Africa, and a large herd of the biggest of all, the elephant. Indeed both species of African elephant can be found here, the forest elephant and the savannah elephant.

There are now around one thousand three hundred elephants, and concern has grown relating to their impact on this already fragile landscape. David Western, winner of the 2010 World Ecology Award, published results of a study on the relationship of diversity and elephant population density (Western, 1989). He wanted to discover what effects elephants had on the ecosystem as a whole. His results are summarized in Figure VI.2, below.

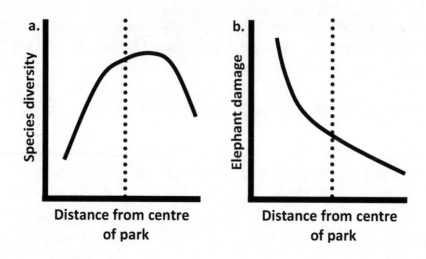

Figure VI.2 a. Species diversity with increasing distance from the centre of Amboseli Park; b. Elephant damage (proportional to elephant density) with increasing distance from centre of Amboseli Park. The boundary of the park is indicated by the dashed line in both graphs, with the area to the right of the line representing unprotected land.

Figure VI.2a shows how the diversity changes as we walk from the centre of *Amboseli National Park*. The Park boundary is at six kilometres from the centre (marked by the vertical dotted line). Interestingly, diversity is at its highest just outside the park. Change in elephant population density, measured by damage to the acacia trees, is shown in Fig VI.2b.

What we see is that elephant numbers are highest deep in the park, and decrease as we move outwards, due to poaching. Their impact on the habitat declines, as can be seen. Diversity is low, both at the highest density and the lowest, peaking at an intermediate level of disturbance. This is in agreement with our curve for this section. So diversity peaks when there is some disturbance.

It was Joseph Connell (Connell 1975; 1978) who suggested that this relationship between diversity and disturbance may be important. He said that low disturbance levels allowed competition to reduce diversity while high levels of disturbance led to a destructive reduction in diversity. At intermediate levels, opportunities would open up, and this allowed a greater diversity of species to develop without being outcompeted nor destroyed. This is known as the *Intermediate Disturbance Hypothesis*.

Although some communities differ, a huge range of important natural ecosystems follow the Intermediate Disturbance Hypothesis. These include coral reefs (Connell, 1978), Mediterranean salt marshes (Quintana, 2002), intertidal pools (Lubchenco, 1978) and tropical rain forests (Molino and Sabatier, 2001).

So disturbance has a significant impact on diversity. However the reverse is also true. The more diverse an ecosystem, the more resilient it is to disturbance. Let's visit a honey bee hive to learn more.

Chapter Eighty
Honey Bees, Royal Jelly and Sex: the Basis of a Good Air-conditioning Unit

Honey bee colonies depend entirely on the queen bee and her sex life. They consist of a small number of male drones, a huge number of female workers, and a single queen, whose sole purpose is to produce around two thousand eggs each day. Unfertilized eggs develop into male drones while fertilized eggs become female workers.

All baby bees are fed royal jelly for a few days. This special food is made in a gland located in the head of the worker bee. However, if the queen is terminally ill or dies (queens live for around eighteen months), the female worker bees will keep feeding one little female larva extra amounts of this special baby food, and for much longer. This has an amazing effect. Instead of developing into another female worker bee, the larva becomes a queen, replete with functional ovaries. In 2011, Professor Masaki Kamakura revealed, in the journal *Nature*, that one particular protein, *royalactin*, present in the royal jelly, was responsible for all of the developmental changes required to produce a queen (Kamakura, 2011).

The new queen heads off on what is known as her *nuptial flight*. In my mind, this term always conjures up an image of her clutching her bouquet, enrobed in Chantilly lace with a '*Just Married*' notice stuck to her abdomen, confetti strewn around the decorated hive! During this flight she produces a special pheromone that attracts all the male drone honey-bees from a wide area to come to her and mate with her (the power of perfume once more, through the workings of the second law, of course!). On mating, the males die. She may mate with as many as twenty males during this time, and the number of different mates is very important. It is the only time that she mates, and so this supply of sperm cells will last her entire reproductive life. Thus the genetic variation of her future hive will be determined by how many different males she mates with.

This genetic diversity has an important implication for the hive. The workers can sense when the hive temperature is getting too hot, and create air currents to fan the hot air out by beating their wings. If it gets too cold, they crowd together, increasing their metabolism to generate heat. In hives where the queen has mated with only one or a few males, the female workers are all very similar and so control is not very smooth — a sort of all-or-nothing effect. However in hives with a queen who has mated with many males, there is a much broader response, and so temperature is more subtly controlled, with different workers responding at slightly different temperatures, leading to a more constant environment (Jones, *et al.*, 2004).

So we see that diversity in bees leads to a much greater resilience in the face of environmental disturbance (temperature change). The same results (greater resilience from greater genetic diversity) emerge for sockeye salmon (Schindler *et al*, 2010). This is resilience at the population level. At the ecosystem level we also find increased resilience with increased diversity in a wide range of situations including rock pools (Souza, 1979; Allison, 2004), sea grass communities (Hughes and Stachowicz, 2004), bryophyte communities (Mulder, 2001), grassland (Tilman, 1996) and coastal sub-tropical forest (Virah-Sawmy *et al.*, 2009).

This has been called a chicken and egg situation (Hughes, 2010). Diversity helps ecosystems survive disturbance, yet disturbance promotes diversity. There is a further underlying pattern. Entropy is at its highest within intermediate disturbance situations

(Naveh and Whittaker, 1979; Kratochwil, 1999). Once again, it is the second law of thermodynamics that drives this relationship.

Of course disturbance represents the introduction of chaos into the system, and so, as we have seen for other relationships so far, too little or too much chaos has negative impacts on any level of the Biosphere. There is a maximum amount of chaos (the Maximum Entropy Principle again), and this represents the point towards which the system will move. It is like a small ball in a soup bowl, where the sides represent an unbalanced system and the base represents balance. It will always roll to the bottom of the bowl, wherever you start it from. And so the Biosphere operates in this way. This is why, as we have discussed, your garden always attempts to *roll* back to a natural succession.

If we destabilize the Biosphere, we will expect it to roll back and forwards, but eventually settle. However, if we force it to remain away from where it wants to be, two things can happen. We will have to continue to exert effort to keep it from returning, and if we push it too far, the ball might roll out of the bowl altogether. This is always a concern. Have we pushed the Biosphere too far already, or can it recover? One thing we know is that for it to recover, we must let it swing freely and allow it to find the balance that we have stolen from it.

Chapter Eighty-One
Conversing with the Curve

So let's return to the curve (Fig. VI.1) and examine its repercussions for the human race. What we learn from it is that diversity increases if we introduce disturbance into the pot. So if we are trying to conserve a habitat, we don't want to exclude all noise. For example, fire is an important part of ecosystem functioning. If we stop all fires from happening, the outcome can be disastrous. Not only will we see a drop in diversity, and thus resilience, but litter will build up on the ground, eventually leading to a much greater fire, that will burn deeply and destroy the seeds that form the bridge to a regenerated ecosystem.

Also, many species are designed to respond positively to fire, needing heat or smoke for their seeds to germinate. Preventing fires from occurring allows fire-sensitive species to thrive, and thus when a fire eventually happens, there may not be the resistant species left to form the road to recovery.

In fact, many species, such as eucalyptus trees, are fire starters! Eucalyptus bark naturally peels off trees annually and builds up on the ground. Along with the leaves, the branches and the seed pods, the bark is full of eucalyptus oil. The oil plays two roles. Firstly, it prevents decomposition, and so the litter layer builds and builds. Secondly, eucalyptus oils are extremely flammable. And so we have a tree whose litter doesn't rot, and therefore accumulates, while also being a significant fire hazard.

There have been many tragedies where people have lost their lives in forest fires. However, it must be said that if I was going to buy a house somewhere, I would first check the reproductive strategies of the plants in the vicinity. If they require smoke or fire as part of their life cycle, then don't buy a house there. Most estate agents and house buyers do not consult a plant ecologist when looking at a property, because, like so many others, they live in *Bubbleworld*, and engaging in any sort of conversation with the natural world seems irrelevant and stupid. However if they had done this, many lives could have been spared, because they wouldn't have been living in the middle of an ecosystem that relies on fire and is designed to combust at the drop of a match.

And this brings us to an important point. Ecosystems evolve in such a way as to achieve a balance with everything else. There will be a natural level of disturbance surrounding any level of organization, and we would expect that level to work best at that level of disturbance.

As a student, I always revised for examinations with some background music. However, when I went to the University library to study, the silence was distracting! I discovered that a little tape recorder (shows my age!!) and headphones helped. The point is that I was used to some disturbance, and found it hard to focus without this. So nature has evolved with a certain background noise, and has found its balance with this noise as part of the equation. Less noise or more noise, and the balance will be perturbed.

So when we try to discover what level of noise we should be inputting into the Biosphere, we need to think in terms of what our role used to be when we first emerged onto the stage that is the living world. We have a huge clue as to how much noise to make in our curve, because diversity is likely to be maximised at the point where disturbance is at the right level. So if we adjust our behaviour and monitor its impact, we can gradually move towards that point. It is all about listening, participating and listening some more. The same applies to our approach to conservation. The better we do, the less we have to do, as a balanced see-saw doesn't need constant correcting.

The right amount of disturbance, from us and from all the other contributors of noise, provides resilience and contributes to sustainability. So we have a role to play here, as one of these contributors. We won't achieve sustainability by creating museums of diversity, by preventing change or by surrounding our wildlife in protective bubble wrap. We won't achieve sustainability by trying to stop the sand dunes from changing. Sustainability doesn't mean silence. It means the right amount of noise!

In the next section, we are going to look at a very special kind of disturbance, genetic mutation. The code of life, as it is called, presents some very useful lessons for our survival.

REFERENCES

Allison, G. 2004. The influence of species diversity and stress intensity on community resistance and resilience. *Ecological Monographs* 74:117–134.

Connell, J.H. (1975) Some mechanisms producing structure in natural communities: a model and evidence from field experiments. In: Cody, M.L. and Diamond, J. (eds) *Ecology and Evolution of Communities.* Harvard University Press, Cambridge, Massachusetts.

Connell, J.H. (1978) Diversity in tropical rainforests and coral reefs. *Science* 199: 1302-1310.

Hughes, A.R. (2010) Disturbance and Diversity: An Ecological Chicken and Egg Problem. *Nature Education Knowledge* 1: 26.

Hughes, A. R. and Stachowicz, J. J. (2004) Genetic diversity enhances the resistance of a seagrass ecosystem to disturbance. *Proceedings of the National Academy of Sciences USA* 101, 8998-9002.

Jones, J.C., Myerscough, M.R., Graham, S. and Oldroyd, B.P. (2004) Honey bee nest thermoregulation: diversity promotes stability. *Science* 305: 402-404.

Kamakura, M. (2011) Royalactin induces queen differentiation in honeybees. *Nature* 473: 478-483.

Kratocheil, A. (1999) *Biodiversity in Ecosystems: Principles and Case Studies of Different Complexity Levels.* Kluwer Academic Publishers, Dordrecht, The Netherlands.

Lubchenco, J. (1978) Plant species diversity in a marine intertidal community: importance of herbivore food preference and algal competitive abilities. *American Naturalist* 112: 23-39.

Molino, J.-F. and Sabatier, D. (2001) Tree diversity in tropical rain forests: a validation of the intermediate disturbance hypothesis. *Science* 294: 1702-1704.

Mulder, C. P. H., Uliassi, D. D. and Doak, D.F. (2001) Physical stress and diversity-productivity relationships: the role of positive interactions. *Proceedings of the National Academy of Sciences USA* 98: 6704-6708.

Naveh, Z. and R. H. Whittaker. (1979) Structural and floristic diversity of shrublands and wood-lands in Northern Israel and other Mediterranean areas. *Vegetatio* 441: 171-190.

Quintana, X.D. (2002) Measuring the intensity of disturbance in zooplankton communities of Mediterranean salt marshes using multivariate analysis. *Journal of Plankton Research* 24: 255–265.

Schindler, D.E., Hilborn, R., Chasco, B., Boatright, C.P., Quinn, T.P., Rogers, L.A. and Webster, M.S. (2010) Population diversity and the portfolio effect in an exploited species. *Nature* 465: 609–612.

Souza, W.P. (1979) Disturbance in marine intertidal boulder fields: the non-equilibrium maintenance of species diversity. *Ecology* 60: 1225-1239.

Thompson, L.G., Brecher, H.H., Mosley-Thompson, E., Hardy, D.R. and Mark, B.G. (2009) Glacier loss on Kilimanjaro continues unabated. *Proceedings of the National Academy of Sciences USA* 106: 19770–19775.

Tilman, D. (1996) Biodiversity: population versus ecosystem stability. *Ecology* 77: 350-363.

Virah-Sawmy, M., Gillson, G., and Willis, K.J. (2009) How does spatial heterogeneity influence resilience to climatic changes? Ecological dynamics in southeast Madagascar. *Ecological Monographs* 79: 557–574.

Western, D. (1989) The ecological value of elephants: a keystone role in Africa's ecosystems. In: *The Ivory Trade and the Future of the African Elephant.* Ivory Trade Review Group, Queen Elizabeth House, Oxford, UK.

SECTION VII
THE ULTRAVIOLET-SURVIVAL CURVE: THE VULNERABILITY OF HUMANKIND

This set of curves (Fig. VII-1) shows the relationship between the intensity of ultraviolet radiation and the survival of three organisms: a bacterium (McCready and Marcello, 2003)), yeast (Tuite and Cox, 1980) and humans (Bohr, *et al.*, 1996). These creatures are very different from each other, from extremely primitive to extremely complex. Many would see the human as the crowning achievement of evolution, an example of progress.

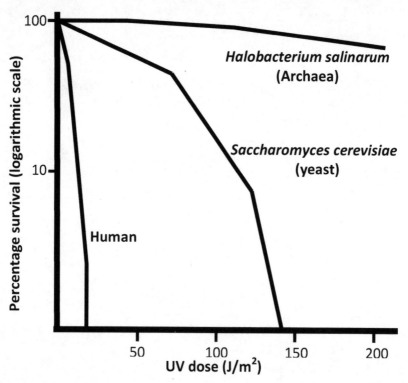

Figure VII.1 Survival of three different organisms in increasingly powerful UV radiation.

Darwin himself, at the end of *Origin*, claimed that higher animals were *"the most exhalted object that we are Capable of conceiving"*. Yet the tiny little bacterium, a member of a primitive, ancient group of organisms called the *Archaea*, is far more resilient than the more sophisticated yeast cell, while the yeast cell is far more tolerant than we are. This tells us a huge amount about how the Biosphere works, how complexity and division of labour do not equate to resilience, why sexual reproduction may not be all that it is cracked up to be and why we are the most vulnerable life forms on the planet. It is a lesson of humility and a lesson of awe, as we uncover an invisible force that is responsible for diversity, cell divisions, energy flow and visual reality itself. We uncover an important message for economists (both *macro-* and *micro-*) too. Ultimately, our curves provide a strong reminder of how confused we have become when considering what progress really means.

Chapter Eighty-Two
Mutation, Mutation, Mutation

Ultraviolet radiation comes from the Sun, and is part of a broad spectrum of energy released by our neighbouring star. It has a wavelength that is shorter than violet light, hence, *ultra-violet* (UV). Because ultraviolet has a short wavelength, it can impact strongly with molecules. One of the molecules with which it interacts is DNA.

The energy of UV is strong enough to break the bonds between some of the atoms in the DNA. Basically, when UV strikes a molecule, the energy causes the electrons in a molecule to become *excited*. This is the scientific term, but it is a very visual word! You can imagine the electron jumping up and down, waving its arms in the air and laughing. As we all know, though, it can be dangerous to become too excited. How many of us have injured ourselves as children when playing a game with friends. My father used to recite a very silly rhyme to me. Its context was a small boy riding along on his bicycle and it went something like this:
"Look Mummy, no hands Mummy!
Look Mummy, no feet Mummy!
[changing to a sobbing voice] *Look Mummy... no... teeth... Mummy!"*

And in a way, that is what can happen when UV interacts with our genetic material. We often imagine our cells as very static places, like the little plastic models with balls and sticks that we see in school. This is anything but the case. Long molecules such as DNA are in constant movement, like snakes with itchy backs. The double helix flexes and bends in this turbulent environment.

We know that DNA is made of four types of base: adenine (A), guanine (G), cytosine (C) and thymine (T). The order that these four letters take determines the code. This code then is translated into a protein. UV particularly causes damage where two thiamine bases sit beside each other. It causes them to become stuck together. However this doesn't always happen. When a pulse of ultraviolet radiation hits the coil, it has to hit it in the right place and at the right time. The two thymines must be closer together than usual, caused by a flex in the DNA during all of its sinuous curving. Imagine two thymines sitting on a bench made of rubber. If we bend the ends of the bench up, then the two bases will be thrust together. If the UV hits at just the right moment, in just the right place, where two such thymines are closer together than usual, they will become glued (Schreier *et al.*, 2007).

This explains a lot about the process. Before this discovery, we had wondered why UV sometimes caused a mutation and sometimes didn't, even though everything seemed the same. The mutation is basically random, and only takes a fraction of a second. This is also worrying, as previously it had been thought that it was a consequence of long-term exposure. Thymine and cytosine can also become glued together in a similar way.

In terms of repair, humans only have one method, the Nucleotide Excision Repair (NER). Here, the faulty DNA is cut out (excised) and replaced. However this repair mechanism itself can become damaged. NER is a complicated process and involves some thirty different proteins. Damage to any one of these proteins leaves the human without a hope. We and the other placental mammals are in the same wagon (the one without a spare tyre). We really are the least protected organisms on Earth.

Everything else has back-up plans. These include using a special enzyme to break the glued bases, powered by light from the Sun, called *photoreactivation* (Lindahl and Wood, 1999). Without any backup, then UV can destroy our DNA. People with a damaged NER programme suffer from what is called *Xeroderma pigmentosum,* leading, often, to death before the age of twenty years. That is how important the NER correction system is. It is not that we are unlucky to experience a mutation. Thousands occur in each of us every day. We're just unlucky if it doesn't get fixed.

So we see that UV alters the genetic code. In fact it is a key driver of code change. This consists of the introduction of chaos into the code. The ultraviolet radiation randomly targets the DNA and changes the order of the bases. This then leads to proteins of different shapes. In other words, the proteins start to explore different spatial orientations. This is a diffusive process, just like the perfume spreading in a room. In the case of the perfume particles, random vibration of the even smaller gas particles means the larger particles are bombarded and bounce around. This random movement eventually leads to all of the particles being spread out evenly within the space.

However, with DNA, it isn't so much that the particles are vibrating randomly in space, becoming more and more disorganized. Rather it is the code that is becoming increasingly chaotic. That change in code leads to a change in the shape of a protein. So we have random shape shifting as a result of random code changing. Imagine a protein continuously changing shape as the result of thermodynamics working at the level of an increasingly chaotic code. The driver is the second law of thermodynamics. The outcome is protein structure exploring space. Every so often, the form produced will be able to do something useful, opening up a whole new set of opportunities.

Imagine if one of the shapes turned out to be a toasted sandwich maker, for example! Suddenly the aroma of melting cheese and sun-dried tomatoes would waft across the Universe! An entirely new future would lie ahead!

These proteins then become functional facilitators, and contribute to the flow of energy through the cell, the organism and beyond. However, unlike the perfume, or the juice in a jar, there is a maximum amount of entropy that can be generated within the DNA code, with the letters changing randomly, in order to maintain the overall generation of entropy by the Biosphere at a maximum level. There is a control upon the process, and it will not be free to work to equilibrium, because energy flowing through all the other levels of organization will counteract this slide. In other words, there is an intermediate disturbance level, above or below which the Biosphere would not be able to operate maximally.

Overall, of course, the entire Biosphere is working to produce the maximum amount of chaos that it can. But a balance must be achieved, and so code chaos is also sitting on the see-saw, finding its place within the greater scheme of things. This optimal level of code chaos finds its context within protein space, species space, population space and ecosystem space. All of these spaces are defined by thermodynamics, and each one is counter-balanced by each other one. The conversations and interactions between these levels represent the Biosphere.

Indeed, it is this character, this equity and this interdependence that led me to define life as follows: *"Life is the interactive outcome of energetic conversations across all levels of the Biosphere"*. By this, I mean that to interact, to converse and to find balance is to truly live.

So we see that the generation of variation itself is under the control of the Second Law of Thermodynamics, with the code becoming more chaotic with every mutation. In other words, the natural direction for DNA sequence to follow is one of increasing chaos. Along the way, the code will come to represent a range of proteins and some of these will find meaning within other levels of organization.

Repair mechanisms help control this, but require energy, as does any process that wishes to stand against entropy. Without these repair mechanisms, organisms die earlier. Mutation rate is part of this balance within which the Biosphere lives, and we have massively disrupted this balance, by destroying the ozone layer, as we have so many other things.

Chapter Eighty-Three
UV: the Storyteller and the Biosphere

The story of UV and its interaction with the Biosphere is both fascinating and intricate, intertwining the major strands that define the history of life on Earth.

It all started 3.5 billion years ago. At this stage life was deep under water. It had to be this way, because early Earth was completely exposed to extremely high levels of UV from the Sun. There was no ozone shield in the atmosphere. As this early experiment of life really took off, gathered around hydrothermal vents (Wächtershäuser, 1990) with their supply of sulphur and iron, there was the problem that would later confront humankind: diminishing resources. The material that life was relying on to provide energy was limited. Further up on the ocean floor, there would be un-exploited minerals.

But these were only accessible if the cell could avoid UV damage. It was a classic *catch-22* situation. Starve to death below, or fry your genes above. Competition for a diminishing resource is never a solution, as a population will always expand to fill the resource space available. Indeed, competition is merely evidence of the filling of this space. Rather it is creativity, variation and innovation which allow life to explore new space. It is the equivalent of creating a hole in the ceiling, allowing you to squeeze through into the attic for the first time.

Even with the water acting as a shield, organisms still needed to protect themselves further, and the exploration of radiation-absorbing molecules proved crucial. These molecules specialized in absorbing radiation and then releasing it, as heat or fluorescent light. Faint glimmers began to appear in the dark ocean. This stopped the energy from damaging the delicate genetic material. Such protection allowed the organisms to move a little closer to the surface.

And, of course, these molecules were about to usher in a huge revolution on this planet. For, as we have said, their special characteristic was that they absorbed radiation, releasing it in a different form. They originally acted a bit like an umbrella, protecting you from the rain, which harmlessly drips off the surface of the umbrella, safely around you. Then some of these organisms, instead of releasing the energy to the sea, used it to do some work. That work was to split water into hydrogen and oxygen. Now the Biosphere started to take its energy from the Sun instead of the Earth, and used water, which was certainly not in short supply. Photosynthesis had begun and the blue-green machines of energy transformation had arrived. The umbrellas were turned upside down, no longer deflecting the energy, but gathering it in (Mulkidjanian and Jung, 1999). They had changed their role from *protection* to *provision*. For more detail on this, see the excellent review by V.D.Samuilov (Samuilov, 2005).

The original protective molecules weaved their way back and forth across the membranes of early organisms ten times, like a giant serpent whose scales could absorb energy and release it in different forms. Over evolutionary time, the snake split into smaller snakes that now represent the bits of the modern photosynthetic machine. All the key components of the photosynthetic system today, the three antennae that pick up the light energy, just like a satellite dish, and the three centres, where this energy is used to excite electrons (*Yipee!*), split water and prepare the way for making sugar, are thought to have come from this one huge ancient protein. It has been discovered that modern-day photosynthetic proteins are particularly high in UV-absorbing amino acids, reflecting this earlier role.

One particular form of this *"snake"* is particularly interesting. It is found in the *Archaea*, the prokaryotic kingdom to which animals are most closely linked (Matsumi *et al.*, 2011), and to which the star organism of Figure VII-1 belongs. This protective molecule is called *retinal*. Many of these organisms also possess a photosynthetic pigment that contains the same molecule (Ebray, 2002). Yes, that's right, the same retinal that is *also* the crucial bridge between light and a nerve signal in your eyes. In these ancient organisms, this photosynthetic molecule lies at the surface of the cells, covering up to fifty percent of them. This pigment absorbs light.

It is now thought that retinal originally evolved as a UV absorber in the early oceans. It makes sense too. A structure whose role is to absorb light and report on it to the brain must be able to absorb light energy in the first place. It can absorb UV just as well, and on the early Earth, that would be essential. However as oxygen saturated the oceans, it began to leak out into the air.

High in the atmosphere, something unusual happened to this oxygen. Ultraviolet radiation converted the oxygen gas (O_2) into ozone (O_3) and *vice versa* (UV breaks down ozone as well as building it up), and in doing so, the UV was converted into heat, generating entropy. A sort of equilibrium is formed between ozone destruction and production. So this process of ozone formation converted the UV into a harmless form of radiation. It is often said that ozone blocks UV, but it actually absorbs it during its synthesis.

The ozone increased over time as oxygen levels built up, providing greater and greater protection. Eventually, UV was sufficiently reduced to allow life to move on to land. And so ozone played an important role in this aspect of evolution. Amazingly, this change in role, by the snake-like protein, from protector to provider, led to a greater protection for the entire planet. As provider, the protein helped split water, producing oxygen. And it was this oxygen that would interact with ultraviolet radiation itself and absorb it. You couldn't script it any better — a classic medieval morality tale or one of those spaghetti westerns where the bad guy always dies!

So the UV problem appeared to have become fixed once and for all, freeing up organisms, that hadn't got protective molecules, to head for the surface and, eventually, make it onto land. Those who possessed the protective molecules were now free to transform them into something else without the fear of annihilation by the killer UV rays from outer space! They could, literally, beat their swords into ploughshares, and their spears into pruning forks. It was a peace dividend. This would lead one lineage, from which humankind would ultimately emerge, to being lured into a false sense of security. They would relinquish most of their DNA protection and correction mechanisms, only to suffer at their own hands, so to speak, when they invited the auld enemy, ultraviolet radiation, back into their living rooms to hunt them down, as they sipped on a refrigerated glass of chardonnay.

Chapter Eighty-Four
The Eyes Have It: Perception Dawns

Meanwhile, the retinal was to become the central molecule of the eye, gathering in light information to inform the brain, and allowing the visual reconstruction of the world around us. We see ultraviolet radiation as the challenge creating the solution space that retinal filled, functioning to protect the genetic material from too much mutation, by absorbing and releasing the potentially harmful energy. Then, this molecule was used to harvest energy, transferring the power supply of the Biosphere from chemicals found around hydrothermal vents to the Sun, which represented an almost limitless source.

This energy was used to split water, releasing oxygen. The oxygen became central to burning the sugars made in photosynthesis, and so aerobic respiration was born. Excess oxygen formed the protective layer of ozone. This is a beautiful transfer, as the original protective molecules became used to produce oxygen, which itself became the protective molecule of the Biosphere. Finally, this molecule was used to gather energy for a new use, as information, and visual reality was born!

It is interesting to note that many species can see ultraviolet radiation. Our eyes prevent the UV from reaching our retina, but in a wide range of species, from bees to birds, the retinal molecule can absorb the UV just like all of the other wavelengths of visible light. Many flowers have patterns that can only be seen in UV. Birds of prey, such as the common kestrel (Viitala *et al.*, 1995), the rough-legged buzzard (Koivula *et al.*, 1995) and the great grey shrike (Probst *et al.*, 2002), can see scent trails of voles. The trail is made from urine, which has a high ultraviolet reflectance. Fruit-eating birds use UV to tell them if fruit is ready to eat. Mature fruit reflects UV, whereas unripe fruit does not (Altshuler, 2001). Many birds use UV-reflecting plumage and beaks to attract mates or to identify themselves (Muellen and Pollard, 2008). Another interesting example is in egg recognition. Song thrushes (*Turdus philoomelos*) recognize their eggs using UV and green parts of the spectrum (Honza *et al.*, 2007). This is important in detecting imposter eggs from parasitic birds such as cuckoos. Here, the UV acts as a security code.

So we see that the story of UV has gone full circle, from disrupting the information held in DNA, to the production of ozone through to its use as information itself. Along the way, we have discovered its role in the production of oxygen, of ozone, of photosynthesis, of multicellularity, of aerobic respiration, of terrestrial life and of sight. So, as I said, the story of UV and its interactions with the Biosphere is really the story of life.

Chapter Eighty-Five
Tipping the Balance

Life found a way of working with ultraviolet radiation, and has often been inspired by it. The ozone layer became an important protective shield, created by UV and yet protecting us from ninety percent of this radiation by absorbing it. But if we look at the ozone layer today, we find a disturbing picture.

The bad news first emerged in a *Nature* article in 1985 (Farman *et al.*, 1985) when three scientists (Joseph Farman, Brian Gardiner and Jonathan Shanklin), reported a dramatic destruction of the ozone layer. The destruction has continued ever since.

The World Meteorological Organization announced, in April, 2011, that the ozone level has been depleted to an unprecedented level over the Arctic in the spring of 2011, representing a forty percent loss. This is nothing compared to Antarctica, where a huge ozone hole develops annually, representing a fifty percent depletion, covering an area equal to three times that of the USA. These ozone holes occur annually, during winter months. The holes recede during the summer months. This saves us from the stronger summer radiation. Recent reports say that although the Antarctic hole is shrinking slightly, it is staying around for longer each year, which is very worrying, given that this will leave the region exposed to the stronger summer radiation.

So what has led to this destruction? One word covers it: chlorofluorocarbons, or CFCs. These are compounds that contain carbon, fluorine and chlorine. Where did they come from? They are man-made gases, used for refrigerators and for aerosols. In other words they are the tools of comfort, not of necessity. We would and did survive without them quite happily, but they are part of the modern world.

It was James Lovelock who first discovered that levels of CFCs were rising in the atmosphere, but failed to recognize them as hazardous (Lovelock, 1971; Lovelock *et al.*, 1973). The damage that CFCs do to ozone was uncovered by two groups at the same time (Stolarski and Cicerone, 1974; Molina and Rowland, 1974). CFCs do not break down easily, and can spread high into the atmosphere, penetrating the ozone layer. This journey can take several years.

In the upper atmosphere, the ultraviolet radiation splits the CFCs, releasing chlorine. It is the chlorine that then converts the ozone to oxygen gas (O_2). It does this by grabbing one of the three oxygen ions, leaving an O_2 and a single O. This single oxygen then combines with another single one, making another O_2. The chlorine detaches and heads off to find another ozone molecule to attack. One chlorine atom can destroy one hundred thousand ozone molecules.

CFCs can last in the air for one hundred years, and so although we have now largely stopped using them, they will persist in our atmosphere for a long time.

We are all aware that there has been a significant increase in cancers of the skin as a result of ozone depletion. Australia, because of its proximity to the Antarctic ozone hole, has the highest rates of skin cancer in the world. For example, Australia is exposed to fifteen percent more UV than Europe. Two-thirds of Australians will have suffered skin cancer by the time they reach seventy years of age. You might want to read that last sentence again. It is another reminder that the changes we are producing on the planet are not trivial. A further ten percent depletion of the ozone layer is estimated to produce a twenty-five percent increase in the most common kinds of skin cancer.

It is not only humans that are affected by rising UV levels. If only this were so. Antarctic sea urchin embryos, which are important parts of the food chain, experience developmental abnormalities. They would normally be protected by sea ice, but this is also disappearing. It is thought that this combination of disappearing ozone and sea ice spell serious problems for the Antarctic marine ecosystem (Lister *et al.*, 2010*a*).

The same results have been found for tropical marine ecosystems (Lister *et al.*, 2010*b*). Coral reefs are also damaged by UV (Banaszak and Lesser, 2009) as are phytoplankton (Gieskes and Buma, 1997; Häder, 1997). On land, crop plants show reduced growth and seed production (Surahbi *et al.*, 2009; Jansen *et al.*, 1998). None of this is good.

Once again we have perturbed the energetic context of the Biosphere, this time altering the type of radiation reaching the surface of the planet. And this particular perturbation has a direct impact upon us, exploiting our lack of back up in terms of correcting mutations. Perhaps the UV disaster is the one that we are most aware of, as we book in for treatment at our local cancer centre. Yet it is only a relatively minor perturbation compared to the other apocalyptic horsemen that we have unleashed upon the Biosphere, merely the icing on a cake of planetary destruction, if you will.

Chapter Eighty-Six
The Vulnerable Ones

Figure VII-1 demonstrates our place in the world. We truly are the vulnerable ones, extremely susceptible to change, with little resilience. We require a huge support network for our survival which is energy-expensive and damaging to the planet. Indeed, the price of our continued existence is extreme. Figure VII.1 shows that as life has become more complex, it has become less resilient. The most resistant organisms are the *Archaea*, simple, single-celled, bacterial organisms with no internal membranes, no nucleus, no organelles and no sexual reproduction. These creatures can swap DNA with lots of different organisms. They do not exist as species, because there is no sexual separation. They can swap genes with just about anything.

The yeast is intermediate, in terms of complexity and survivability, showing some resilience amid increasing radiation levels. Yeast are also single-celled organisms, but are much more complex than the Archaea. Yeast have nuclei, lots of internal organelles, and can reproduce sexually. Yet all of this complexity does not make them more resilient.

Finally, humans are the least resilient. Based on the cell plan of yeast, but multi-cellular with organs, humans possess an elaborate immune system. However they fall far below the little Archaea in terms of survivability.

The lesson from this curve is straight-forward: simplicity is best. Why is this? Surely division of labour and specialization, principles that lie at the core of Adam Smith's economics, are the most productive, efficient, advanced and progressive ways to operate? Possibly, in terms of raw economics this may be the case, but certainly not in terms of resilience. Lots of small units, communicating with each other and freely exchanging (genetic) information are far superior to huge multi-cellular organizations. Why is this the case?

Firstly it's to do with reproduction. Sexual reproduction brings with it a very major barrier: speciation. Once you become a species, you can no longer swap genes with other species. You are cut off, isolated genetically. The more primitive bacteria and Archaea do not have this barrier and can swap genes with just about anything. This is hugely advantageous in terms of sharing solutions. This is why bacteria are such a threat. They can quickly acquire resistance to antibiotics, for example, from a completely different type of bacterium. Sexual reproduction increases our vulnerability to change, making us less resilient.

Secondly, the more complex we are, the more complex are our needs. Large species need large niches. We can think of this in terms of a printed colour photograph. If you look at a photograph under a microscope, you will discover that it is made of thousands and thousands of tiny squares, called pixels. There are lots of different colours. These combine to give the impression of a smoothly changing picture. You can increase or decrease the resolution of the photograph by decreasing or increasing the size of the pixels, respectively.

Now imagine that there is a picture of an apple. A large organism, such as an apple strudel monster, needs the entire apple to live on. It cannot see the tiny pixels that make up the apple. However a small bacterium can live on one of these pixels. There might be twenty different colours making up the apple, and indeed some of these pixels can be used to make other pictures, of tomatoes, strawberries and roses. However, only a particular arrangement of them in space and time will form an apple.

Thus the number of possible apples is limited, compared to the number of pixels. Now imagine a catastrophe occurring. The picture is shredded up into tiny pieces, each only one pixel in size. The apple has disappeared, but the bacteria can keep living on their little pixels. The bacteria are much more resilient here than the apple strudel monster.

This is why simple organisms are better at surviving. Their niches are smaller and more fundamental and so when instability comes, survival is more likely. Mass extinctions are an example of the breaking up of the picture, leaving fragments that do not form any complex image. The bacteria can survive, as can other simple organisms, and gradually the more complex picture reforms. Also, the bacteria can swap ideas, allowing them to change pixel colour if needed.

The idea that knowledge is power, and therefore knowledge should be guarded, may work in political manoeuvring, and it certainly appears to, but it will matter not a jot in terms of our sustainable continuance on this planet. Sharers will survive, not keepers. Sharing takes trust. However, we are not being asked to trust an enemy, but, rather, the Biosphere from whence we came.

In terms of economics, there is a lesson too for large multinational organizations. Global disruption, as is likely to occur, will greatly threaten such huge creatures, whereas small, local units of industry will have a much better chance of surviving. What we need to do as a species is to reduce our pixel requirements. How can we do this? By reducing division of labour, focusing on generalism, not specialism, opening boundaries in order to share ideas and sharing resources. Resilience will increase with these qualities. Don't take my word for it. Look at Figure VII-1.

Progress was the great battle cry of the Enlightenment. However, if we look at Figure VII-1, and judge how progress shapes up, then our modern concept of what progress is fails dramatically. It is the simplest, cottage industry that survives, not the huge, multi-national multi-cellular creature. Indeed the Enlightenment's concept of progress has been a significant driver of the disaster that we have created, for ourselves and all other life forms on this planet. We have relinquished our options on sustainability and resilience in pursuit of this progress.

Our economic models are all focused on competition, specialism and isolationism, rather than the collective quorum of the bacteria, which shares all and celebrates *Generalism*. We find a celebration of the ideas of Patrick Geddes, that great generalist, in these creatures, rather than Adam Smith, and the biology of thermodynamics, rather than that of natural selection.

The landscape around us is ultimately an energetic one, defined by the availability of free energy and the generation of entropy. The history of life on Earth is super-imposed upon this landscape. In this section we have traced the impact of one form of energy, ultraviolet radiation, upon the Biosphere. The sense of sight and all of the other senses are concerned, fundamentally, with monitoring our energetic context, be it light, sound, chemistry or pressure. And these very senses can trace their origin back to early interactions with energy, often in a very different context.

Ultimately, the conversation of the Biosphere is an energetic conversation. And if we perturb the energetic landscape, we must expect problems. Furthermore, we have recognized that resilience comes from simplicity, and so any move we make towards resilience should be towards simplicity. If someone suggests otherwise, show them the curve.

REFERENCES

Altshuler, D.L. (2001) Ultraviolet reflectance in fruits, ambient light composition and fruit removal in a tropical forest. *Evolutionary Ecology Research* 3: 767–778.

Banaszak, A.T. and Lesser, M.P. (2009) Effects of solar ultraviolet radiation on coral reef organisms. *Photochemical and Photobiological Sciences* 8: 1276-1294.

Bohr, V.A., Okumoto, D.S., and Hanawalt, P.C. (1986) Survival of UV-irradiated mammalian cells correlates with efficient DNA repair in an essential gene. *Proceedings of the National Academy of Sciences, USA* 83: 3830-3833.

Ebray, T.G. (2002) A new type of photoreceptor in algae. Proceedings of the Academy of Sciences, USA 99: 8463-8464.

Farman, J. C., Gardiner, B. G. and Shanklin, J. D. (1985) Large losses of total ozone in Antarctica reveal seasonal ClOx/NOx interaction. *Nature* 315: 207–210.

Gieskes, W.W.C. and Buma, A.G.J. (1997) UV damage to plant life in a photobiologically dynamic environment: the case of marine phytoplankton. *Plant Ecology* 128: 17-25.

Häder D.-P. (1997) Penetration and effects of solar UV-B on phytoplankton and macroalgae. *Plant Ecology* 128: 5-13.

Honza, M., Polacikova, L. and Prochazka, P. (2007) Ultraviolet and green parts of the colour spectrum affect egg rejection in the song thrush (*Turdus philomelos*). *Biological Journal of the Linnean Society* 92: 269–276.

Jansen, M.A.K., Gaba, V. and Greenberg, B.M. (1998) Higher plants and UV-B radiation: balancing damage, repair and acclimation. *Trends in Plant Science* 3: 131-135.

Koivula, M. and Viitala, J. (1999) Rough-legged buzzards use vole scent marks to assess hunting areas. Journal of Avian Biology 30: 329–332.

Lindahl, T. and Wood, R.D. (1999) Quality control by DNA repair. *Science* 286: 1897–1905.

Lister, K.N., Lamare, M.D. and Burritt, D.J. (2010a) Sea ice protects the embryos of the Antarctic sea urchin *Sterechinus neumayeri* from oxidative damage due to naturally enhanced levels of UV-B radiation. *Journal of Experimental Biology* 213: 1967-1975.

Lister, K.N., Lamare, M.D. and Burritt, D.J. (2010b) Oxidative damage in response to natural levels of UV-B radiation in larvae of the tropical sea urchin *Tripneustes gratilla*. *Photochemistry and Photobiology* 86: 1091-1098.

Lovelock, J.E. (1971) Atmospheric fluorine compounds as indicators of air movements. Nature 230: 379.

Lovelock, J.E., Maggs, R.J. and Wade, R.J. (1973) Halogenated hydrocarbons in and over the Atlantic. *Nature* 241: 194-196.

Matsumi, R., Atomi, H., Driessen, A.J.M. and Oost J.V.D. (2011) Isoprenoid biosynthesis in Archaea – biochemical and evolutionary implications. *Research in Microbiology* 162: 39-52.

McCready, S.J. and Marcello, L. (2003). Repair of UV damage in *Halobacterium salinarum*. *Transactions Biochemical Society* 31: 694-698.

Molina, M.J. and Rowland, F.S. (1974) Stratospheric sink for chlorofluoromethanes – chlorine atomic catalysed destruction of ozone. Nature 249: 810-812.

Muellen P. and Pohland G. (2008) Studies on UV reflection in feathers of some 1000 bird species: are UV peaks in feathers correlated with violet-sensitive and ultraviolet-sensitive cones? *Ibis* 150: 59–68.

Mulkidjanian, A.Y. and Junge, W. (1999) Primordial UV-protectors as ancestors of the photosynthetic pigment-proteins. In: Peschek, G.A, Löffelhardt, W. and Schmetterer, G. (eds.) The Phototrophic Prokaryotes. Kluwer Academic/Plenum Publishers, New York, pp. 805-812.

Probst, R., Pavlicev, M. and Viitala, J. (2002) UV-reflecting vole scent marks attract a passerine, the great grey shrike *Lanius excubitor*. *Journal of Avian Biology* 33: 437–440.

Samuilov, V.D. (2005) Energy problems in life evolution. *Biochemistry (Moscow)* 70: 246-250.

Schreier, W.J., Schrader, T.E., Koller, F.O., Gilch, P., Crespo-Hernández, C.E., Swaminathan, V.N., Carell, T., Zinth, W. and Kohler, B. (2007) Thymine dimerization in DNA is an ultrafast photoreaction. *Science* 315: 625-629.

Stolarski, R.S. and Cicerone, R.J. (1974) Stratospheric chlorine: a possible sink for ozone. *Canadian Journal of Chemistry* 52: 1610-1615.

Surabhi, G.-K., Reddy, K.R. and Singh, S.K. (2009) Photosynthesis, fluorescence, shoot biomass and seed weight responses of three cowpea (*Vigna unguiculata* (L.) Walp.) cultivars with contrasting sensitivity to UV-B radiation. *Environmental and Experimental Botany* 66: 160-171.

Tuite, M.F. and Cox, B.S. (1980) Ultraviolet mutagenesis studies of [*psi*], a cytoplasmic determinant of *Saccharomyces cerevisiae*. *Genetics* 95: 611-630.

Wächtershäuser, G. (1999) The case for the chemoautotrophic origin of life in an iron-sulfur world. *Origins of Life and Evolution of Biospheres* 20: 173-176.

Viitala, J., Korpimaki, E., Palokangas, P., and Koivula, M. (1995) Attraction of kestrels to vole scent marks visible in ultraviolet-light. *Nature* 373: 425–427.

SECTION VIII
THE SQUIRREL AMNESIA-OAK TREE SUCCESS CURVE: HOW TO DESIGN A SUSTAINABLE FUTURE BY FORGETTING WHERE YOU HID YOUR NUTS

The seventh and final curve in our exploration of the key relationships within the Biosphere takes us into a forest, in the company of a rather forgetful squirrel. This curve is all about sub-optimization. The human race is typified by one key drive: optimization. We strive for efficiency, and this striving has been measured in terms of progress. It was the Enlightenment that set the agenda, bringing together human-centric reason with technology. This marriage would lead to the optimization of almost all that we do. Yet many relationships display anything but optimization. And the relationship between squirrel amnesia and oak forest success, shown in Figure VIII.1, displays this classic aspect of life.

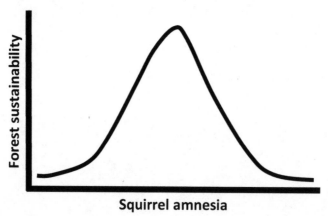

Figure VIII.1 The relationship between squirrel amnesia and forest sustainability.

In this section we explore sub-optimization and see why it lies at the heart of the Biosphere. We then examine the central role that design will play in our hope for a sustainable future, and understand why inefficiency is a crucial component of any design. We look at a new approach to design, based around the Biosphere and its thermodynamic context.

Chapter Eighty-Seven
Sub-optimality in Nature

He'd buried them somewhere around here. Hundreds of acorns carefully gathered and secreted away for the winter, each one chosen with a feast in mind. And now, this snowy morning, waking to the feeling of overwhelming hunger, all Mr Squirrel had to do was remember where he had hidden the damn nuts. This was getting ridiculous. *Squirrel Nutkin* indeed! More like *Squirrel Nothing*, with the *"nothing"* referring to the substance of his memory and the content of his belly.

And this wasn't the first time either. Just a couple of days ago, it had taken him three hours to track down one of his caches. Maybe he was being too cryptic, placing the tasty morsels in more and more obscure hidey-holes. If only he had some way of recording exactly where and when he had hidden these nuts. Maybe some kind of hand-held global positioning system device or...

Then, from nowhere, a magical cloud appeared in front of him, full of sparkles and fireworks, and out of it stepped a rather muscular little wood mouse, oozing attitude and zeal.

"You see," the wood mouse proclaimed with a flourish of his paw, "it's the way it's meant to be!"

Mr Squirrel just stared at this flamboyant little chap, and was about to try to think of something to say when the mouse took a stick from the ground and sketched out a rectangle in the air, which transformed into a flat screen monitor.

"Let's take two scenarios here, Squirrel. First, you remember where all the nuts are. You become the recall rodent himself — not one acorn escapes your crystal clear thinking. And you eat them all. Year after year, you keep eating them all. What do you think will happen, eh, big guy?"

"Well," said Mr Squirrel "I suppose I'd be nice and full, and a lot less frustrated, and I'd be much more operationally optimized too — think of the efficiency savings! I could start studying again for my Master of Business Administration with the Open University. I'd have more time for my family too..."

"And there'd be no more squirrels in the woodland." interrupted the wood mouse, in a monotone that cut across his bows. "Take a look for yourself; it's all on the screen, this forest, in one hundred years time, with your perfect recollection and kernel collection."

They both stared at the screen, which flickered into life. It was terrible. The trees were all dead, as were almost all of the animals. There was no bird-song, no chirruping of the grasshopper, no buzzing of the bees and no rustling of the squirrels. There were no squirrels.

"What...happened?" stammered the squirrel.

You and your sort ate all the nuts, that's what happened. The trees were unable to reproduce because you ate all their babies. So the forest died, and you lot starved to death."

There was silence. The screen flickered and went blank.

"Of course, you could have forgotten where *all* of the nuts were hidden..." and the screen flickered back into life. The forest looked relatively healthy, although there were a lot of birds around... too many birds. The place was covered in birds. And there were no squirrels.

"What's with all the birds" Mr Squirrel asked, honestly puzzled by this *Hitchcockian* scene. "And where are all the squirrels?" he added, more tentatively.

"Well you couldn't remember where any of the nuts were, so you all starved to death. Remember in the spring, you eat bird eggs? Lots of them. Without your predation, the bird populations spiralled out of control. They'll all starve eventually. A population explosion. And then, a population crash –Malthusian Mayhem, they call it!"

The wood mouse made the screen disappear, and started to walk off into the forest. Turning to look at the stunned squirrel, he said "You see, the optimal way for nature to operate is with each of its components acting sub-optimally. If you try to strive for efficiency, the whole house will come tumbling down."

Chapter Eighty-Eight
The Fig Wasp

And nature's heart does beat with a sub-optimal rhythm. The examples are manifold. Take the fig wasp. This little insect, less than a millimetre long, has a most fascinating life. It all starts with a pregnant female, covered in fig pollen, landing on a fig and entering through a small hole at the opposite side to the stalk that attaches it to the fig plant (often a tree or a shrub). This entrance hole is partly covered in scales. The fig is basically an inside-out flower ball, with all of its little flowers inside the fig. The fig wasp is attracted to the entrance hole by chemical signals from the ripening fig (yes, diffusion in action again!).

There are three types of flowers in a fig, though some species don't have all three types in every fig. There are male flowers, which produce pollen, and two types of female flowers, one with long stalks and one with short stalks. The female flowers always mature first.

Once inside, the female wasp, which is carrying her own fertilized eggs, lays her eggs in the base of the short-stalked fig flowers, inside the ovaries, and adds a chemical that causes the flower base to undergo rapid cell division (forming what is called a *gall*). So now her babies have a nice supply of plant cells to eat. She then fertilizes the top of the long-stalked flowers with the fig pollen that she is also carrying. By doing this, she ensures that the figs' own seeds will form in these flowers.

While the wasp is doing all of this, the fig entrance hole closes over, and carbon dioxide levels begin to rise, up to ten percent (Galil *et al.*, 1973). Remember that atmospheric CO_2 has a concentration of only 0.035 percent, so the level inside the fig is some three hundred times higher than this!

If she fertilized all the flowers of the fig with pollen and eggs, then there would be no seeds that would survive, because her babies would eat all the seed. If she didn't pollinate the fig flowers, there would also be no seed. But the female fig wasp doesn't do any of these things. She pollinates all the long-stalked fig flowers, but doesn't lay her eggs in any of these.

And so each fig will contain new fig wasps and new fig seeds, allowing both fig and wasp to continue on for another generation. In other words, she doesn't maximize, or optimize, her egg laying. From the fig wasp's perspective, it might seem like a better idea to try to lay as many eggs as possible. But this would not be optimal for the greater system, just like rapacious rodent recall would not lead to a sustainable forest ecosystem. After laying her eggs, she dies (awh!).

The rest of the story is interesting too. As the babies develop inside the fig seeds, males and females look different. Males have cutting devices on their heads, but no wings. Females have wings, but no cutting devices. So the females are trapped in the seed until the males cut themselves free, and then release the females. As soon as the females emerge, the males mate with them. However at this stage the CO_2 is at a very high level. Males are unaffected by this, but females remain very lethargic.

The males then dig a tunnel out of the fig, and fresh air comes rushing in. This revives the females who collect pollen from the male fig flowers, which have now opened. It spells the end for the wingless males, who die beside their mother. The females can escape and fly away to another fig, together with their fertilized eggs and the pollen – all that is needed to continue both plant and insect lineages. And these lineages have survived together for a very long time. A recent paper reports on a 35 million-year-old fig wasp fossil, found on the Isle of Wight, off the South coast of England, basically identical to those found today (Compton *et al.*, 2010). Obviously, sub-optimality is the way to go!

Chapter Eighty-Nine
Protein Stability and Mutations

Researchers, looking at the structures of proteins, built eight thousand different types of a bacterial protein called an *arc repressor*, all identical except for changing just three of the amino acids (there are twenty different amino acids possible at each position, so 20 x 20 x 20 = 8000 types). Although they failed to improve the function of the protein, six of the new proteins with similar function were more stable (Waldburger *et al.*, 1995). Surely this was an improvement. After all, when you design something, you want it to last. The cynical among you might actually think the opposite is true – if it lasted too long, then the consumer wouldn't need to replace it. Hence less profit for the company! However in biology, such marketing ploys within an organism can have no foundation.

My point is that the protein that actually occurs in the bacteria appears to be sub-optimal compared to what it could be. However this instability turns out to be very important. Most proteins are like builders. You want them around when you are having a new conservatory constructed, but once the job is finished, you wouldn't want them moving into your spare room and staying!

Each of our cells can make a vast number of proteins, but we don't need or want them all at the same time. It is important that proteins that are not needed can be broken down and recycled. If these proteins were very stable, they would be more difficult to break down. And so instead, proteins are sub-optimal in terms of stability, but this works best for the cell. We'll see the relevance of this for design studios shortly.

Imagine if we had a system that could identify every mutation in our DNA and correct it. It would reduce the occurrence of cancer massively, eradicating many forms of it. Surely this can only be a good thing? However if there were no mutations, there would be no variation. No variation would mean no evolution, no exploration of protein-space, population space, species space or ecospace. We'd all be exactly the same. There would have been no discovery of photosynthesis, no multicellularity and no expansion of life onto dry land. No arms, hair, toes nor eyes. All of these innovations start with a mutation. Therefore what might be optimal for the individual organism would not work at other levels. The Biosphere would be unable to move towards greater entropy output if it was not for the sub-optimality in mutation correction.

Chapter Ninety
Life as Sub-optimal Information Transfer

Perhaps the most telling example of sub-optimality is life itself. To understand this, I need to mention the often forgotten Third Law of Thermodynamics. It is not as well known as its two senior partners because initially it seems extremely obscure. It states that *"the entropy of a perfect crystal approaches zero as temperature approaches zero."*

The zero temperature referred to here is what we call *absolute zero*, which is -273.15 °C. So at absolute zero, there is no further increase in chaos (entropy). This is because we have reached our destination – equilibrium, where perfect disorder becomes perfect order. Temperature actually is a measure of motion, and the temperature of an object represents the average kinetic energy of the molecules, i.e. how much they are bouncing around. At absolute zero, all motion stops. Heating something up from this stillness means causing it to become increasingly disorganized, as the molecules begin to jostle about more and more.

Imagine taking a fly and freezing it to absolute zero. Here, the genetic sequence is the same as a living fly, but there is no chaos. The information content is at a maximum. It is also not alive. As we heat it up, we introduce increasing chaos to it and so information transfer gradually decreases in quality. At a certain point, we reach the temperature range within which the fly can live. Heating beyond this becomes too chaotic for life to exist. And so life represents a window of intermediate disturbance. More or less chaos means death. So sub-optimality, in terms of reduced information content, is the signature of life itself!

As we saw in the last section, and indeed in many earlier examples, what might appear perfect for one level of organization is not perfect for another. In fact, the Biosphere only really makes sense when considered as a whole. Our consumption with efficiency, our pre-occupation with self, and our focus on the individual as the key unit of the Biosphere (though some of us have become pre-occupied with even lower levels of organization, even imbuing them with human-like identities, like those imaginary friends of childhood, and calling them things such as *the selfish gene*) distinguishes our species from all others.

And if anything exemplifies the fatal flaw within humankind, it is our view of sub-optimality. The recent history of our species is one of increasing efficiency. Combine harvesters suck every last grain from the fields, leaving nothing for the granivores of the former grasslands that we have taken as our own. Roads divide important natural habitats, in order to transfer us from A to B most quickly. Plants are genetically altered to *'improve'* agricultural efficiency.

Indeed, the progress of the Enlightenment could be re-written as our pursuit of optimization. Industrialization equates to improved profitability, productivity, and competitiveness. Yet, as we have seen, optimality can only be judged at the level of the Biosphere. For it is at this level that each of the other levels finds its balance. And it is at the level of the Biosphere alone that sustainability can be achieved.

In engineering, it is a well recognized fact that multi-task designs (i.e. designs that must respond to numerous challenges at the same time) are less efficient at any one of these tasks than they would be if designed only for that task (Farnsworth and Niklas, 1995). Also, the more design challenges there are, the greater number of increasingly sub-optimal solutions are possible

(Meredith *et al.*, 1973). And so sub-optimality at any one level is a consequence of these multiple challenges. However I would go further. The challenges at one level are compounded by challenges acting at other levels, hence the multi-armed see-saw. It is the balance of this see-saw that produces sub-optimality.

Balance means compromise. Compromise is realized in sub-optimality. Therefore, the lesson of this chapter is that to build a sustainable future, we need to find the level of sub-optimality appropriate for each of our actions. At a lecture where I was sharing these thoughts, a young student spoke up and remarked *"I guess you won't be teaching on the Harvard Business School's MBA [Master of Business Administration] programme!"*

I'd actually hope that these ideas would be part of any MBA. Because there won't be anything left to administer if we don't take heed of them. Although the thinking seems to go in the opposite direction of the modern world, it is actually in tune with almost everything else: from fig wasp to mutation and from squirrel to protein. In fact, as we have seen, it sits at the centre of life itself. By forcing our planet to be more efficient, be it through genetically engineering species or improving the soil, we destroy the balance of nature.

Central to this failure to recognize the importance of sub-optimality is the Scientific Method, which reduces systems down to bite size chunks. This is to allow experiments to be done, but it means we are not looking at the real world, but rather some strangely disconnected *Bubbleworld*, bearing little if any relevance to reality. These isolated experiments cannot possible include any balance.

And so the decisions to genetically engineer crops with additional proteins, or to make a new product out of a material that does not recycle easily, or to pollute the environment with chemicals such as the CFCs of refrigeration heaven and melanoma hell, all make sense within the experimental reductionism of a greenhouse or a test tube. By reducing our world down to selfish genes and the progressive, rational human being, we are in denial of the existence of the greater scheme of things within which lies are only hope. And if we remain inside our bubbles, we will never understand sub-optimality.

The bedfellow of reductionism is form. Our consumption with form, rather than function, again distracts us from our place in the Biosphere. The conversations that run throughout the planet are energetic in nature. The relationships we have been examining in this book are all impossible to see with reductionist, formist spectacles. But when we swap these spectacles for those that focus on energy, function and integration, a very different picture of our world, and our place in that world, emerges.

We turn now to the process of product design, which undoubtedly holds the key to our futures. Is there such a thing as sustainable design, and if so, what is it?

Chapter Ninety-One
Birth, Life and Afterlife in Design

We have already come across the form-function debate in design and architecture. Design really does lie at the heart of our future, because it is what determines how we live, and how this lifestyle impacts upon the Biosphere. Ultimately, we interface with our environment mainly through designed processes and objects. Indeed, the design of products has huge significance throughout the lifetime of the product. I like to divide this lifetime into three parts: the birth, the life and the afterlife.

The birth of a product involves the acquisition of the resources needed for this product and the assembly of these resources with all of its implications. Mining, chemical engineering and energy input all impact on our planet in many different ways. Resources, people, individual species, ecosystems, the hydrosphere and the atmosphere can all be significantly impacted upon. For example a car requires plastics, metals, paints, oil and fuel. Large manufacturing units and vast distribution networks, using trains and ships, are needed, as are sales areas (car dealerships).

The life of a product involves implications for the Biosphere in terms of what the product does, how it impacts on the Biosphere, what associated activities accompany this use and what infrastructure is required. For example, a car requires roads, bridges and parking areas, fuel stations and repair centres. It produces emissions and noise. Road run off from rain caries heavy metals from brake linings, rust, worn engine parts and tyres into neighbouring aquatic ecosystems (Pagotto *et al.*, 2001). Salt, placed on roads to counteract ice, has disastrous impacts on wildlife, resulting in fish kills (Hawkins and Judd, 1972) and amphibian deaths (Sanzo and Hecnar, 2006).

Cars lead to the deaths of many organisms as road-kill (Szerlag and McRobert, 2006). Polycyclic aromatic hydrocarbons also pose significant problems for waterways (Krein and Schorer, 2000). It has been estimated that some twenty percent of the United States of America is ecologically damaged by roads (Forman and Alexander, 1998).

Cars impact in other ways. For example, they facilitate travel, therefore allowing large developments such as shopping centres and entertainment complexes. This, in turn, encourages large-scale intensive exploitation of specific resources by allowing the development of a large market for these products. Cars also lead to the creation of *commuter villages* and *bedroom communities*, where community spirit is eroded because people only sleep in their homes rather than live in them. All of these areas, both sociological and environmental, need to be considered, in terms of the life of the product.

Finally, the afterlife of a product must be considered. How easily recycled is it? Does its breakdown produce any toxic materials? How much energy is needed to recycle it? How long does it take to recycle? How does this afterlife impact on the Biosphere? Here I would advocate the attitude of the Ancient Egyptian pharaohs, who started to plan for what came after death almost as soon as they were born. In fact, in design terms, considerations of product afterlife should begin before birth if possible. What happens to a product is extremely important to the Biosphere. We seem to view recycling as something that has to deal with the outcome of design and production, rather than something that should inform these processes. To address recycling issues, you need to begin with them.

Chapter Ninety-Two
The Importance of Flow in Sustainable Design

The key word here is *flow*. Why is flow so important? Figure VIII.2 summarises its centrality in terms of sustainable design. As we have seen in this book, the Biosphere functions to produce the maximum amount of entropy that is sustainable. Succession undergoes continuous change up to this maximum level of chaos (Fig. IV.1). Entropy is generated when energy flows through the system. Accompanying this energetic flow is the flow of nutrients, water and essential elements that are needed for life to continue. Resources must be recycled constantly.

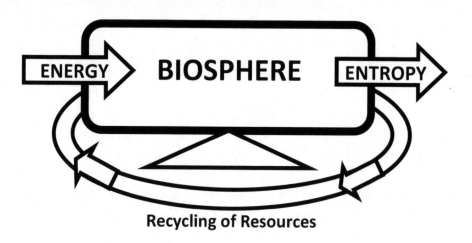

Recycling of Resources

Figure VIII.2 Energy and resources flow through the Biosphere. Energy is converted to entropy, and balance is maintained within the Biosphere. Any disturbance to the flow of energy or resources de-stabilises the system.

Natural systems are, fundamentally, structured to recycle, with the organisms involved in the care of the dead being the guardians of the gold vault. The wealth of an ecosystem lies in its raw materials. Take a tropical rainforest as an example. The vast majority of the resources are in the trees. Anything that dies on the forest floor is quickly recycled and absorbed back into the forest by a myriad of organisms from ants to fungi and bacteria.

Rainforest soil itself is relatively shallow, and acts as a waiting room through which the nutrients enter and exit quickly. This is important, as heavy rains can leach these nutrients out of the soil. Many organisms never even touch the ground in their lives or deaths, with recycling being completed high in the canopy above. So if we go into the forest and cut down the trees, driving them away in lorries, we will have raided the gold vault, and the soil that is left will not be able to sustain agriculture for long. Soon fertilizers will be needed. Of course fertilizers will always be needed for any intensive agricultural process, because each year, we remove the crops, and the nutrients along with them, and distribute them around the globe, draining the field of this raw material.

Flow is important in quality and quantity. Too much flow upsets the balance. Flow of the wrong kinds of materials, at the wrong kinds of concentrations, will be devastating. This has been documented by the devastating effects of fertilizers upon natural ecosystems. The Biosphere works through a *dynamic balance.* By this I mean that it is not a matter of just putting fixed weights on the see-saw and leaving it. Everything is continually being replaced. Material is flowing through the system. This makes it susceptible to perturbation if something or someone changes something.

Thus we see, in Figure VIII-2, that sustainable design must take into account the importance of flow and balance. Diversity is also important here, as this is a natural outcome of a diffusive exploration of energetic space. From diversity stems sub-optimality. For as we increase in complexity, we automatically experience increased sub-optimality.

Another important aspect is what I call the *Levels of Context Test*. How does each of these stages of the lifecycle of a product impact on organisms, populations and ecosystems? What is their meaning within these different levels of organization? We must look at ourselves as well as everything else here. What impact will the design have on each of us and our population? All design impacts through us, directly and indirectly. If a design permits a higher population density for humans, this has a consequence on everything else.

Chapter Ninety-Three
The Three Steps to Sustainable Design and the Triangle of Solution Space

How then should we design for a sustainable future? Well, firstly we must recognize that sustainability is only to be found within the Biosphere. In other words we need to break out of *Bubbleworld* here. We must also understand that the Biosphere is not a linear flowchart, but rather a multi-branched see-saw (Figure IV.3). Thus we are dealing with a transduction, where energy transcends and transits through all levels of organization, and where the overall outcome, an entropic Biosphere, emerges from conversations that are energetic in nature.

We have seen that sustainability must encompass flow, balance, diversity and sub-optimality, and that these are the requirements for a system to maximize its generation of chaos. How then do we set about designing our interface with the rest of the Biosphere? I suggest that this is best done in three stages.

Stage I: Fundamental Design: the *Why*.
At the outset of any design process, we must challenge ourselves in terms of the philosophy of the design. Why are we designing this particular product? The philosophy of design hinges on one criterion. Is this product essential to our *survival* or is it a *lifestyle* choice? In other words, if we do not have this product, will we die or increase our risk of death? This allows us to categorize all that we design and do. Do we really need it? Take a look around at your lifestyle at the moment. What is essential for your survival?

As we noted earlier, energy use, not including food, increased ninety-three fold from 1860 to 1991, whereas population increased only fourfold (Cohen, 1995). That means, on average, we are each now using over twenty-three times the amount of lifestyle energy than we were one hundred and fifty years ago. Indeed, given that many people have not seen anything like this profligate inflation of their lifestyles, those of us in the "West" have probably seen closer to a fifty-fold increase. This is another example of the scale of the problem facing us.

So as serious as population increase is, it is the spiralling energy consumption that ultimately translates into environmental degradation. And most if not all of this is lifestyle energy, not survival energy. Survival energy does increase slightly more than arithmetically. By this I mean that the burden of ten people upon the environment does not represent the sum of ten individual burdens. This is because as numbers increase, and habitats degrade, we need to use more energy to squeeze the system into supporting us. Our artificially raised carrying capacity not only needs the basic energy-per-person, but also must support those four old elephants upon which we are increasingly precariously perched. And this is represented by decreasing resilience.

Why, then, are we designing a particular product? Once we identify this motivation, as either survival *or* lifestyle, we can then attempt to justify its impact upon the Biosphere. If we look at nature, we note that part of its sub-optimality emerges from inefficient use of energy. And so there is some room for lifestyle activities. Play, for example is important for many animals, particularly in infancy. However there are not many examples of organisms expending energy in producing things that they do not need.

For cells continually alter which proteins they make. Forms evolve by diffusing within energetic space. Natural populations follow a trail towards carrying capacity. Ecosystems follow the path of succession as laid out by the laws of thermodynamics. And, as these examples show, the direction that each level takes is driven by the same set of laws and counterbalanced by every other level. And so the rest of the Biosphere gains its design philosophy from each of these levels. Ultimately, the design emerges from these interactions. So must it be for human design.

Lifestyle energy tends to be selfish energy, a classic symptom of *Bubbleworld*, and the reason that the human race can be seen as being so different from the rest of life is fundamentally due to our focus on lifestyle design.

Stage II. Functional design – the *what*.

Having embraced fundamental design, at least in terms of recognizing which of the two design purposes, survival or lifestyle, it is that we are engaging in, the next stage is *functionality*. What is the design meant to do? Can we re-phrase the design target? For example if it is a car, then the function is movement in space. What is the purpose of this movement? Here we are identifying the possible design space available, within which we can seek a solution, remembering that design space is, ultimately, energetic space.

Do we need to move, or can something move to us? We should consider the energetics of movement, and understand the costs related to this movement. The role that this function plays within the Biosphere is also important. It is at this stage that we carry out the Levels of Context Test, examining the repercussions of this function for all levels of the Biosphere, and applying it to our own species. How can this function be tied to the balance of nature? Does it promote diversity? Does it enhance flow? Does it include sub-optimality? Is it in conversation with the other levels?

We need to recognize its function as dynamic, and therefore wired into a feedback system that allows it to be moderated by all the other functions. And we need to understand what intermediate disturbance represents in terms of this function.

Function lies at the heart of the Biosphere, and so it is the consideration of function that represents our search for balance. Indeed, if the function is part of a sustainable future, then it will find a place within the Biosphere, for we have emerged as an expression of this Biosphere, and so we must have a functional role to play. We just need to re-discover it. This discovery can be found in how we impact upon the living planet.

That which produces a balanced sustainable outcome will reflect the role that we were originally doing. Sustainability symbolizes our original state, because species are the outcome of diffusion into solution space. So if we are contributing to the sustainability of the Biosphere positively, we are celebrating our place in that solution space. It is within the relationships that are represented by these seven curves, that we see our functional identity emerging.

Stage III. Fine Design – the *who*.
Having identified the appropriate function for our design, we finally come to the more traditional aspect of design - what form should the product take. This involves material, decorative and production aspects, but it should primarily be concerned with material flow, as discussed above. It is in the fine design that we move into the material world, and so the primary focus must be the flow of materials into and out of the product.

Recycling should consume us here. The design studio should resemble Tutankhamun's burial chamber, consumed with the afterlife! How will material move into the production of this design, and how will it leave? Form must be subservient to this above all else.

The *'who'* or personality of design is comparable to the personality of an organism. It drives the interactions with all around it. We need to design product personalities that will integrate into the Biosphere, and will contribute to the sustainable whole. The characteristics of a good design personality would include: gregarious, open, communicative, sharing and flexible.

The designer must enable the product, and its user, to converse with the Biosphere. The material expression of the function is important. Fine design should also include impact of resource acquisition and synthesis. It is the most potentially invasive aspect of design, though also the least restrained. There are multiple forms possible for any particular design, and diversity within fine design is an important element here too, offering functional redundancy.

Figure VIII.3 shows the three stages of design. Alongside these is what I call the *Triangle of Solution Space*. The area within which solutions can emerge increases as we go through the three stages. If we take the Biosphere for comparison, as shown to the right of the triangle, we can follow this pattern.

The Fundamental design of the Biosphere, as driven by the Second Law of Thermodynamics (the *ink-in-the-jar* law), is to maximally produce entropy.

The functional design of the Biosphere embraces the key energy and material transfer processes, such as from Sun to plant, from plant to herbivore, from herbivore to carnivore and from carnivore to detritivore. Energetic transfer flows from the Sun, through life, to the Universe. Material flow should be as cyclical as possible, recycling being crucial to sustainability.

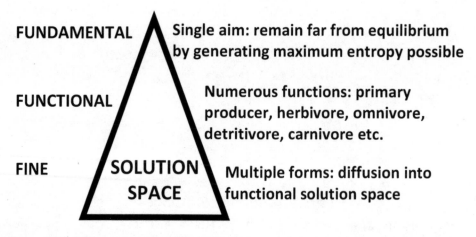

Figure VIII.3 *The Triangle of Solution Space*, showing increasing solution area from fundamental to functional to fine design. Here we use the Biosphere as an example.

Finally we come to fine design, at the base of the triangle. This is a diffusive process, and is represented in the Biosphere by millions of different forms, each expressing functional and fundamental design, and each the outcome of exploration of energetic space. This level is a consequence of the other levels, and a celebration of the laws of the universe in matter. Material moves through these forms, and provided that the design allows flow to continue and balance to be maintained, then all is well with the Biosphere.

And so the designer who sits down to design must recognize their participation in this entropic Universe, and the importance of their role in defining how humankind embraces and re-discovers their place within the Biosphere. For it is the designer who holds this responsibility and it is the designer who must combine the skills of the philosopher, the physiologist and the sculptor. Yet the answers lie within us, and the answers defines us. We do have a role; otherwise we would never have existed in this solution space. It is the rediscovery of this role that is the challenge of our age. Yet the rewards are huge: a sustainable future within a balance biosphere.

REFERENCES

Cohen, J.E. (1995) Population growth and Earth's human carrying capacity. *Science* 269: 341-346.

Compton, S.G., Ball, A.D., Collinson, M.E., Hayes, P., Rasnitsyn, A.P., and Ross, A.J. (2010) Ancient fig wasps indicate at least 34 Myr of stasis in their mutualism with fig trees. *Biology Letters* 6: 838-842.

Farnsworth, K.D. and Niklas, K.J. (1995) Theories of optimization, form and function in branching architecture in plants. *Functional Ecology* 9: 355-363.

Forman, R.T.T. and Alexander, L.E. (1998) Roads and their major ecological effects. *Annual Review of Ecology and Systematics* 29: 207-231.

Gailil, J., Zeroni, M. and Bar-Shalom, D. (1973) Carbon dioxide and ethylene effects in the coordination between the pollinator *Blastophaga quadraticeps* and the syconium in *Ficus religiosa*. *New Phytologist* 72: 1113-1127.

Hawkins, R.H. and Judd, J.H. (1972) Water pollution as affected by street salting. *Journal of the American Water Resources Association* 8: 1246-1252.

Krein, A. and Schorer, M. (2000) Road runoff pollution by polycyclic aromatic hydrocarbons and its contribution to river sediments. *Water Research* 34: 4110-4115.

Meredith, D.D., Wong, K.W., Woodhead, R.W. and Wortman, R.H. (1973) *Design and Planning of Engineering Systems.* Prentice-Hall, Inc. Englewood Cliffs, New Jersey, USA.

Pagotto, C. Rémy, N., Legret, M. and Le Cloirec, P. (2001) Heavy metal pollution of road dust and roadside soil near a major rural highway. *Environmental Technology* 22: 307-319.

Sanzo, D. and Hecnar, S.J. (2006) Effects of road de-icing salt (NaCl) on larval wood frogs (*Rana sylvatica*). *Environmental Pollution* 140: 247-256.

Szerlag, S. and McRobert, S.P. (2006) Road occurrence and mortality of the northern diamondback terrapin. *Applied Herpetology* 3: 27-37.

Waldburger, C.D., Schildbach, J.F. and Sauer, R.T. (1995) Are buried salt bridges important for protein stability and conformational specificity? *Nature Structural Biology* 2: 122-128.

SECTION IX
THE END OF THE BEGINNING

Seven curves to save the Earth? What have we learnt from these relationships that exist on our planet?

Curve One: Population-time
The hockey stick curve tells us a number of important things. Firstly, that our population growth is not natural, and has nothing to do with carrying capacity. Secondly, that our current population is not and never will be sustainable. We are living on borrowed time and borrowed resources in our attempt to maintain the number of people presently on the planet. We discovered a new set of horsemen of the apocalypse (climate change, habitat destruction and eutrophication), which have replaced the Malthusian famine, disease and war as the major threats to the Biosphere.

The history of demography also brings into focus the current philosophical framework under which the majority of governments operate, in terms of politics, economics, science and culture, and its foundation, the Enlightenment. We discovered that the Enlightenment spelt disaster for our prospects of a sustainable future, as it focused on progress, through reason and technology, and led to us entering *Bubbleworld*.

And so our first curve tells us that we must escape from *Bubbleworld*, rejoin the Biosphere, and think in a completely different way. Progress is not to be found in technology and reason, but by re-discovering our place within the greater whole.

Curve two: Selection pressure-variation
We explored the claims of Darwinism as an explanation for the evolution of life on Earth. Significant problems emerged, and there is clear evidence, from leading scientific journals, that undermines its claims as a valid explanation. We examined how it was based on an erroneous extrapolation squared, applying Malthusian modelling and domestic breeding to the natural world. Neither of these extrapolations can be justified.

We recognized that competition actually acts to reduce variation and, therefore, evolutionary potential, and that natural selection is at its weakest after mass extinctions and on oceanic islands, where evolutionary rates are highest. We then explored the concept of *survival of the fittest*, and found that in real, field-based experiments, as opposed to artificially simplistic laboratory experiments, the balance of nature is such that the apparently less fit (e.g. small crickets and dull-coloured guppies) males actually did just as well reproductively as their apparently fitter (larger, more brightly coloured) superior challengers.

All of this undermines Darwinian Theory, and instead points clearly towards a very different understanding of how the Biosphere operates. This has important repercussions for areas of thought where Darwinian thinking has had significant influence, and therefore demands that we re-evaluate these areas too, particularly the relevance of competition and reductionist thinking to such subjects as macro- and micro- economics, scientific research, industry and government. Furthermore, the exclusive teaching of Darwinian Theory in schools must be questioned.

Curve three: Entropy-time
This curve, examining the production of entropy by an ecosystem as it develops, is a very exciting one. It points to how the Biosphere works, and presents us with a completely new way of

understanding evolution, economics and ecology. We found that diversity and balance lie at the heart of a sustainable planet, replacing competition and progress. And then we encountered the multi-armed see-saw (Fig. IV.3). This, fundamentally, gives us a model upon which to build an understanding of our place in the world.

The laws of thermodynamics, that explain why perfume spreads in a room and why ink disperses in a jar of water, apply to every level of organization, from atom to biome. Reaching in and across the complex interactions between these different levels, energy is the subject of the conversations that bind the whole thing together, and we realized that only by participating in these conversations can we truly find our place in the world.

We also discovered that diffusion lies at the centre of diversification, and that the drive to diversify comes from the Second Law of Thermodynamics. Finally we reflected on our attempts at conservation, and discovered that natural succession is the best way, not the King Canute School of Conservation that dominates modern green movements. We reflected on gardens – those places where humans wage war against the laws of the Cosmos, battling to hold nature back. Leave it alone and it will do just fine. Forest glades don't need weeding!

Curve four: Diversity-energy

This curve exposes one of the greatest errors in modern environmental thinking: that carbon should form the main focus of our efforts. There is another more silent, more deadly horseman out there and it is called eutrophication. We explored the devastating consequences of fertilizing the planet, and the destruction of the Biosphere that has resulted. We discovered that this recent killing differs from all the great mass extinctions of the past, and why it places the planet at greater risk than ever before.

This raises the important issue of how we view our world. We discussed the form/function debate, seeing how modern biology is based on form, from taxonomy to phylogeny to evolution to reductionism. Instead, we look at the Biosphere from a functional perspective, and note that this gives a very different understanding. Ultimately, it is our relationship with energy that will determine our futures, and those of the rest of the living world.

Curve five: Diversity-disturbance

A common pattern emerges in many relationships on the planet: the intermediate disturbance curve. All activity disturbs something. We all leave footprints, no matter how small. Yet we find that the Biosphere needs disturbance to work properly. So how much disturbance should we input? How noisy should we be? This is important, both in terms of conservation biology, and in terms of re-discovering our roles in a system that we exiled ourselves from so long ago. We do have roles, because our existence reflects our inclusion in the play at one stage. So we need to rediscover our true voice in the drama. Sustainability doesn't mean silence; it means the right amount of noise.

Curve six: Ultraviolet radiation-survival

Progress, complexity and multi-nationalism: all bywords for the new age of human existence – built on rational thinking and technology. Yet Curve six shatters any idea that competition, specialism and global economics will ever bring us nearer to the Utopia promised by the fathers of the Enlightenment. Instead we observed that the bacterial model actually works best, especially when faced with stress. Resilience is borne out of diversity, information sharing and quorum sensing.

Isolationism, in the sense of sexual reproduction, is inferior to the gene-sharing syndicates that are the microbes. Eukaryotes are accommodated rather than representing any sort of superiority. It is the microbial world that manages the Biosphere, not the eukaryotic world. We recognize that what we perceive as progress is in fact taking us further from our goal of a sustainable Biosphere, with us as part of it. We find ourselves as the most vulnerable members of the living world, in terms of our evolution, physiology, ecology and philosophy.

If we do not begin to recognize this, and act in a more grateful way to the rest of the caste that permit us an existence at the luxury end of the market, then we may find ourselves excluded from the party. This curve also gives us significant advice on how to run our economies, both macro- and micro-, in a much more resilient way.

Curve seven: Squirrel amnesia-oak tree success.
The final curve showed us that sub-optimality is the rule in nature. We explored why this is the case, and recognized that any attempt to optimise was a step in the wrong direction. No single level of organization within the Biosphere should ever be optimised. We examined numerous examples of this, from squirrels to life itself.

We re-visited the importance of balance and flow, and set out a new concept of sustainable design, founded upon philosophy, explored in functionality and transposed into the physical world as form. The birth, life and afterlife of products were explored, with the need to place the flow of material as the primary design focus, returning to nature what was taken.

The Key Themes

From these seven curves, ten key themes emerge.

1. Sustainability is at the level of the Biosphere

Too often I have heard the mantra that marries progress to sustainability. Terms like sustainable consumption, carbon-trading, green energy, conservation strategy and economic growth all blend together, as we try to fashion a future to maintain our lifestyles and bring others into these lifestyles. It all stinks of *Bubbleworld* – the delusional place where the human race exists, cut off from natural counselling and following a path of so-called Enlightenment.

This whole tragedy is summed up in the *Weak* vs *Strong Sustainability* debate, a discussion that shouldn't even be happening. Only in *Bubbleworld*! If we go down the main street in *Bubbleworld* into the local pub, we can pull up a chair and listen in.

Weak sustainability puts forward the idea that as long as we can replace the natural world with some technological device that does the same thing, then we will be fine. Fish farms can replace the ocean ecosystem. Fertilizers can replace the natural soil, carbon storage can replace the forests, and giant tanks of algae can feed the world. Basically, we can turn the planet into a life-support system for *Homo sapiens sapiens*, one giant machine to keep the *Vulnerable Ones* alive.

Strong Sustainability argues that natural capital cannot be duplicated (Neumayer, 2010). Here, nature is viewed as irreplaceable and so must be protected in order to maintain the unique services it provides. Neither argument will save the Biosphere, provide resilience nor produce sustainability, because both models are focused on *us*. It is not until we disengage with the need for continued growth, disentangle income from wellbeing, and recognize the futility of *The Enlightenment* that we can hope to understand how the bigger picture works.

Indeed, the very term *ecosystem services* emphasises a *Bubbleworld* mentality. Our ecosystems are not service providers and the decision as to whether to replace them with technology is absurd as a result. For we are participants, not customers. We are part of the hospitality service team, not the guests in the penthouse suite. Nature is not about serving us. We need to work with the rest of the Biosphere and get our hands dirty, outside the aseptic bubble.

You may feel lost and unsure where to go, yet the signs are all around us, as we have seen. The relationships that report on the way the Biosphere works are sketched out wherever we look: from the Galapagos Islands to the perfumed gardens, from the stable forest ecosystem to the frugal coral reef and from the necessary noise within nature to the birdman of Easter Island.

And yet some of the leading human organizations, charged with leading humankind forward, are unable to see these simple things. The *Human Development Index* (HDI) is used by the United Nations, among others, to calculate how "*well*" a country is doing. Income, longevity and education are each given a score out of one. The following equation is then used:

HDI = (Income + Longevity + Education)/3

While income remains a part of this calculation, there is no hope for any policy welded to the HDI. This is because central to its calculation sits economic growth as a measure of human development. If human development is to embrace sustainability, then a spiral of deeper, more damaging exploitation of diminishing resources that is inherent in economic growth cannot be a positive contributor. Economic growth takes us further away from sustainability, not closer too it, and is part of the old-school measure of progress.

Any one of these three values can ameliorate failure in any other. So if income is high, then even though education was low, the overall Index would be high, or *vice versa*. Recently, there has been a move to include a sustainability component as part of the calculation. Again, high income can then *"make up for"* low sustainability (Desai, 1995; de la Vega *et al.*, 2001).

It is all nonsense. What we end up with is the requirement for weak sustainability for poor countries, allowing them to exchange their natural resources for cash, in order to drive human development, including improved incomes, while we practice strong sustainability in rich countries (rich, because they have already cashed in their natural resources for cash), who have the resources to attempt to replace natural ecosystem services with technological ones. We end up with a two-tiered system whichever way we go, yet there is only one planet and one sustainable outcome for all aboard it.

The point of reference is wrong. Sustainability is at the level of the Biosphere, and only if we are fundamentally integrated into the Biosphere can we hope to part of this. Furthermore, economic decline should be celebrated, not bemoaned, as we need to reverse the spiral of resource exploitation and environmental degradation. Only by economic decline can we hope to get off the backs of the elephants and return to a sustainable level of entropic generation. Equality can be found for all humans, economically and ecologically, by reclaiming our place in the greater scheme of things. For in the Biosphere, we all sit on the same see-saw.

2. Diversity is diffusion

Diversification is a natural response to space. By creating space we allow diversification. It is a natural process, and is thermodynamically driven. This applies to evolution, culture, language and ink in a jar. Therefore there is no mystery to promoting diversity. The drive is a cosmic one, entropy, and it is only by restraint that diversity is curtailed. However, we also learnt that diversity is part of a greater balance, and therefore there is an appropriate level of diversity for a system to function properly.

3. The erroneous extrapolation squared and its terrible consequences: why the theory of evolution that you choose to follow really matters

You may still be wondering why evolution has played such a significant role in this book, with a number of sections referring to it. The reason for this is because how we view evolution has significant repercussions on how we understand sustainability. The Darwinian approach, which, the evidence from a broad spectrum of scientific research argues, is wrong, dictates a much larger world view, one focussed on form, reductionism and competition. The survival-of-the-fittest is a tired mantra, based around laboratory science with little relevance to the real world.

When we look at real biology, such as those crickets in Northern Spain, we encounter a completely different biology. I have presented a huge volume of evidence in this book, taken from the leading scientific journals in the scientific community, which clearly demonstrates that competition is not a significant factor in evolution.

In fact, these papers show that the opposite is true. I have built on these observations and presented a completely different theory of evolution, based on diffusion of form driven by increasingly entropic coding. This theory accounts for the patterns we see in the fossil record and in field biology better than Darwinian Theory.

And it really does matter. Our attitudes towards what some would called *"disabled"* individuals, our embrace of selective breeding, of genetic engineering, of selective education testing, our celebration of competition in every walk of life, of the fitness and progress of the human race all find support because Darwinian Theory is accepted as representing a natural phenomenon. Life in all of its diversity should be celebrated, but natural selection is a force that reduces variation, in all of its applications, both in nature and society.

All who exist are part of a great dance between energy and matter, not the participants in some competitive fight to the death. Our context is not our neighbour but, rather, the cosmos. For nature is about the contribution of all not the selection of the fittest. Sub-optimality, not optimality, rules in this club, and strength emerges from compromise and balance, not selfishness. Because, ultimately, selfishness cannot lie at the heart of a multi-armed see-saw! And it has no place under the auspices of the laws of thermodynamics.

There is nothing natural about natural selection. If we want spaniels whose brains are too big for their skulls, then it works just fine! It is a warped, human-centric misrepresentation of the natural world. And, most importantly, it denies the existence of a multi-level, conversant, balanced interactive Biosphere, whose truth lies in its totality, not in its reduced pieces. By embracing such a twisted theory, we remain in darkness. For Darwinian Theory defines *Bubbleworld* to a tee: isolated, erroneously extrapolated and reductionist. The danger is that it detracts from our very survival. It stands in the way of our return to the Biosphere, and to sustainability. That's why it matters.

4. The multi-armed see-saw: balance in the Biosphere

Balance means sub-optimality at each level, with all levels impacting on any single level. So we observe intermediate disturbance leading to maximum diversity, and no single level operates at maximum efficiency. This is because the point of reference is the Biosphere, not the individual, and balance is achieved at this overall level. We should be prepared for noise, and should shun any idea of progress driven by optimization. Such approaches are from *Bubbleworld*. It is only if we burst the bubble, climb on board the see-saw and find our place that we can hope to leave a sustainable planet for future generations.

5. The importance of flow

A functional view of the Biosphere focuses on flow: the flow of energy through the system and the cycling of materials within the system. Thus, recycling must be the pre-eminent design criterion, driving all other decisions. The recycling van that pulls up at your door should represent *Kharon*, the ferryman of Hades, who carries the material of our existence across the Styx to the *Afterworld*. For the *Afterworld* is our tomorrow-world.

And designers, ultimately, hold the key for the future. I would urge the formation of design schools at the centre of any global programme of human re-integration. These design schools need to incorporate the best ecologists, social scientists, artists, philosophers and practitioners, working together under one roof. Design needs to embrace the broadest possible array of expertise, and needs to be guided by the principles set out in Section VIII. Design operates at the interface between the Biosphere and ourselves, and so it must be the focal point for us.

6. Integration

Once we stop thinking about ourselves and, instead, focus on the greater whole of which we were a part at one time, then we can learn how to re-integrate back into our roles. We came from the Biosphere, and were part of it. Our existence means that we still have a membership card from some stage in the past. We used to know how to behave inside the club.

As we reflected in Section I, when times become challenging, we often find ourselves returning to a more biosphere-centric focus. A still, small voice still lies deep within us, reminding us of how it used to be, and chiding us for our ignorance, isolation and self-promotion. Re-integration need not be the painful process that it may have to be, but we will either learn to live as part of the rest of it, or we will lose our membership forever.

7. Conversation

We have seen the curves that sketch out the conversations of our world. We can learn from these and partake in them, or we can continue to embrace the *omertá*, the criminal code of silence, ""*Non vedo, non sento, non parlo*" (I see nothing, I hear nothing, I say nothing). We need to be in conversation with all that is around us, listening, participating and listening some more.

8. Do less, be more

Particularly in terms of conservation, we need to stop doing things. Most of what we do at present, because it is based on such flawed thinking, married to reductionist science, is likely to be wrong, however well intentioned it is. Nature really does know best. If we leave the recovery to nature, removing our interference, then we will have sustainable recovery.

We need to stop being the gardeners of the world, meddling and weeding and clipping. Instead, let natural succession occur, and enjoy the stress-free woodland that will result. It may take several generations, but it will last. It also means that we focus our conservation efforts on facing up to the bad things that we are doing and removing these, rather than in planting inappropriate trees, and sawing down the ones that should be left to grow.

9. Energy: The Biosphere is colour-blind

There is one term that particularly irritates me, and that is "*green energy*" (a.k.a. *green fuel*). Ultimately, it doesn't really matter where the energy comes from. It is what we do with it that is the problem. The hugely increased flux of energy through our agro-ecosystems will not change if we switched to wind power this evening. We would still be set on a path of economic growth, of progress, of increased resource use and of fertilizer production (which keeps around forty percent of us alive (Smil, 2001)).

The problem is not the colour of the energy, and the problem isn't carbon. Carbon resources are dwindling anyway, and so there will be a decrease in carbon emissions. But the elephants supporting the hugely inflated human population will still need fed. The carbon argument, and its disgusting little offspring, carbon trading and green fuel, are disastrously side-tracking us from the big issues out there.

We are still turning to technology in an attempt to answer these relatively un-important questions, attempting to dig our way out of a hole. Instead we should question the rationale that underpins the technological *"miracle"*, whose wreckage lies around us in the shape of decimated ecosystems and an unbalanced Biosphere.

10. The natural order

The challenge is not to mimic how nature works in order to *'achieve'* sustainability, but rather to re-discover our place in the scheme of things, and start participating in the Biosphere. It's not a matter of grabbing some ideas and doing them better, of training the Earth to cope with its errant child, of weak or strong sustainability. No, it's about something much more fundamental than this. It's about admitting we got it very wrong.

It is about accepting that the destruction of fifty percent of the ozone layer, a massive increase in skin cancer, a huge rise in extinction rates, a population almost half of which are reliant on industrial fertilizers for our food, a toxified hydrosphere and atmosphere, and a corrupt economic and philosophical ideology of progress and enlightenment are not the signs of a successful species. And it's about admitting that, actually, given our comparative records, nature does know better than we do. So we would do well to wake up and find our place within the natural order, from whence we came.

It's really about a new attitude. I want to escape from *Bubbleworld*, but I need you all to come along. However, liberation begins within the hearts and minds of each of us. For bubbles are, ultimately, person-sized, and before we can change the world, we need to emancipate ourselves.

The invisible hand that reaches into all of what we are is not merely some economic driver, but the master designer of the Universe, thermodynamics. A global, energetic *zeitgeist*, the collective consciousness embracing the entire Biosphere, already exists, much grander than Georg Hagel ever imagined. We just need to plug ourselves back in to it.

It is not a dark, grim outlook. In Section I, we encountered Arthur Shopenhauer's (1969) pessimistic image of the human intellect as a crippled man, carried by a blind giant that represents his will. Schopenhauer's giant could not see the light. But the giant has no control over the greater Biosphere, and cannot alter the relationships that we have explored. Indeed, we have seen that the relationships of the seven curves lie far beyond the reach of such a giant as the human will. For we are merely the *Vulnerable Ones,* whose only hope of succour lies in the bosom of a forgiving Biosphere.

The answers are all there already, waiting for us. For the light is not something we strive towards, but rather it flows through all and unifies all. In a sustainable planet, *we are all the light*. So let's reconnect and shine.

REFERENCES

Constantini, V. and Monni, S. (2005) Sustainable human development for European countries. *Journal of Human Development* 6: 329-351.

Desai, M. (1995) Greening of the HDI? In: McGillivray, A. (Ed.), *Accounting for Change*. The New Economics Foundation, London, pp. 21–36.

Lasso de la Vega, C. and Urrutia, A.M. (2001) HDPI: A framework for pollution-sensitive Human Development Indicators. *Environment, Development and Sustainability*, 3: 199-215.

Neumayer, E. (2010) *Weak versus Strong Sustainability. Exploring the Limits of Two Opposing Paradigms*. Edward Elgar Publishing, Cheltenham, UK. Third Edition.

Smil, V. (2001) *Enriching the Earth: Fritz Haber, Carl Bosch and the Transformation of World Food Production.* The MIT Press, Cambridge, Massachusetts.

Schopenhauer, A. (1969) *The World as Will and Representation.* Peter Smith Publisher, Gloucester, Massachusetts.

APPENDIX I

Of Models and Curves

The Geometric Curve

I am going to teach you how to become a population modeller. With this new power, you will be able to impress your friends, dazzle your employer and run circles around your partner. You will become all powerful, at least in your own mind, and feel like taking over the world! I will show you how to look into the future, without the need of a crystal ball, and without the requirement of a long purple gown and pointy hat. No, this incredible power only needs you to be able to add, subtract, multiply and divide. By the end of this chapter, you will have the power to answer the following question. If we know the annual death and birth rates and immigration and emigration rates of India, and we start with one thousand two hundred million people in it (the current population in 2011), how many people will be in the country in fifty years time?

There are no tricks to this. It is just a straightforward question.

To work this out we need to imagine the country as a room. At the start of the day, there are a number of people in the room, the initial population (N_0). When we come back in the evening, there are only four things that could have happened (ignoring abduction by aliens, or beaming down, like Captain Kirk, from the USS Enterprise) to change the number of people in the room: births, deaths, people walking into the room (immigration) and people walking out of the room (emigration). If we know these numbers we can work out how many living people remain in the room at the end of the day without counting them. Two of these things add people (births and immigration) and two remove people (deaths and emigration). Of course, if the total arrivals (births and immigrants) equal the total departures (deaths and emigrants) then there will be no change in the number.

So far so good! Let's get some numbers sorted out. The birth (b), death (d), immigration (i) and emigration (e) rates are given *per capita* (literally, per head). In other words, it's the number per person. The reason we do it like this is because we can then take any starting population and work out the number of births we expect more easily. So if there were 250 people, and the *per capita* birth rate was 0.1 there would be 25 new births (simply calculated by multiplying the original population (250) by the per capita birth rate, (0.1)). This is written as bN_0 (births *per capita* x the starting population).

The annual *per capita* birth rate (b) for India is 0.021 (CIA World Factbook)

The annual *per capita* death rate (d) for India is 0.007 (CIA World Factbook)

The annual *per capita* immigration rate (i) for India is 0.0045 (World Bank's Migration and Remittances Factbook 2011)

The annual *per capita* emigration rate (e) for India is 0.0095 (World Bank's Migration and Remittances Factbook 2011)

Now comes the clever bit, converting these numbers into a total change in population.

We start with a population (N_0) of 1200 million, and use the rates for India. What would the population be at the end of the first year (N_1)?

All we need to do is take the departures away from the arrivals and add on the starting population to get the final number. We will convert the *per capita* rates to actual numbers, by multiplying them by the starting population (N_0).

Arrivals = births + immigrants
Departures = deaths + emigrants

So N_1, the population at the end of the first year = N_0 + the arrivals $(bN_0 + iN_0)$ – the departures $(dN_0 + eN_0)$.

$N_1 = N_0 + [(bN_0 + iN_0) - (dN_0 + eN_0)]$

i.e. the new population total will equal the old one, plus the arrivals, minus the departures.

Now for a bit of mathematical magic to simplify our equation. If you look at the equation, you can see that N_0 occurs lots of times on the right hand side. In fact it is part of every single number. So we can take N_0 and put it outside a set of brackets, meaning we multiply everything by N_0.

So $N_0 + [(bN_0 + iN_0) - (dN_0 + eN_0)]$ becomes $N_0 [1 + (b + i) - (d + e)]$

In other words, to get the population one year on, we just multiply the present population by $[1 + (b + i) - (d + e)]$, that is, 1 (to represent the starting population) plus the arrivals, minus the departures.

The term $[1 + (b + i) - (d + e)]$ is called the intrinsic capacity to increase, or the *Malthusian Parameter*. In other words it is a property of this population, and will determine if the population gets bigger, stays the same or gets smaller. Let's calculate the intrinsic capacity to increase of the human population in India.

It is: $1 + (0.021 + 0.0045) - (0.007 + 0.0095)$
$= 1 + 0.0255 - 0.0165$
$= 1.009$

This number is greater than one, so the population will increase. If it had been exactly one, there would be no change (since $N_0 \times 1 = N_0$). If it had been less than one then there would be a decrease in population. So the new population will equal the old population x 1.009. We had a 1200 million people at the start of the year, and now we have 1210.8 million people, a rise 10.8 million, roughly the population of Belgium. How about in 50 years time?

To simplify the equation, we will assume that the rates of deaths, births, emigration and immigration remain fairly similar through this time. So $[1 + (b + i) - (d + e)]$, the intrinsic capacity to increase, will also be constant. In modelling, this whole term is shortened to the letter **R**.

So $N_1 = N_0(R)$

At the end of the second year, the population (N_2) will equal the population at the start of the second year, N_1, times R.

So $N_2 = N_1(R)$

Now we know $N_1 = N_0(R)$, so if we replace the N_1 in the second year calculation with $N_0(r)$, we get $N_2 = N_0(r)(r)$, which is $N_0(R)^2$

Year three we do the same. $N_3 = N_2(R) = N_0(R)^2.(R) = N_0(R)^3$

Do you see a pattern here? Whatever year we are measuring, r is raised to the power of that year. So for ten years, the population will be the population in year zero multiplied by r to the power of 10 that is, $N_0 \times (R \times R \times R \times R \times R \times R \times R \times R \times R \times R)$.

In 50 years time, we can estimate the population of India as 1200 million x 1.009^{50}

= 1200 million x 1.56 = 1872 million people!

In fact we can work it out for any number of years to come, and all we need is the starting population and the arrivals and departures. In modelling we sum this up by writing:

$$N_t = N_0(r)^t$$

In other words to get the population *t* years in the future, we multiply the starting population by r raised to the power of that number of years. We can work out the population centuries ahead!!! See, I told you we would become all-powerful modellers!

Let's look at the curve that this equation will sketch out. If we use our equation to estimate the population over the next 500 years, we get the following graph (Figure AI:1):

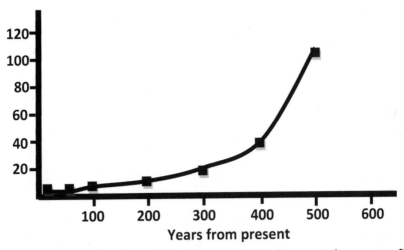

Figure AI: 1: Population of India, modelled over the next five hundred years.

This is a classic geometric curve. The rate of increase of the population increases with time. This makes sense, because as there are more people born, they can each have children, and so the population spirals upwards.

The Logistic Curve

However there is a problem here. If population growth was really geometric, then there would be terrible numbers of everything. As we discuss in Section II, this is not the case. Populations tend to level off over time. This is called the Logistic curve, and was developed by Verhulst, Pearl and Read. They realized that as a population increases, it impacts upon its environment, which in turn impacts on the population. This is called density-dependent feedback, i.e. the population receives feedback, which is a result of the density of the population. This feedback slows the population growth.

So how does density impact on population growth? We need a factor that gradually has a greater and greater impact on the rate of increase, slowing it. To do this, we imagine a maximum number of organisms that could live in a particular location. This is called the carrying capacity, (the number of organisms that the population can carry). It envisions a habitat like a basket, which you can fill up until it is full. At the start, population growth is geometric. We can look at the rate of increase of the population by expressing the change through time as dN/dt. dN/dt represents the change in population, dN (or N_2-N_1) divided by the change in time (or t_2-t_1). Here we are not calculating the change once each year, but instantaneously. dt can be as small as we want.

We can then write the geometric model as an instantaneous rate, by using r instead of R. r represents the proportion of the exponential rate of increase that would be expected at its optimum. In other words, it is an adjustment, inherent to the character of the population, that converts the universal rate of growth, or exponential growth (*e*), to the growth of this particular population. So $R=e^r$.

Re-arranging, $r=lnR$ (where *lnR* is the power that e would have to be raised to equal *R*)

So the logistic equation is:

$$\frac{dN}{dt} = rN \left(\frac{(K-N)}{K} \right)$$

That is, the rate of change of a population equals the population (N) times its intrinsic capacity to increase (r), corrected by how far that population is from the carrying capacity ((K-N)/K).

So as N increases, it has the effect of gradually feeding back to slow the rate of increase. This is what density-dependent feedback actually is.

At the carrying capacity, the population will not increase, because this is the maximum number that the population can reach.

In other words when N = K, then dN/dt (the rate of population increase) = 0

So the key thing here is the relationship of N to K. As N approaches K, growth slows down. This can by calculated by multiplying the geometric growth equation by (K-N)/K.

When N=0, (K-N)/K = K/K = 1.

In other words there is no effect. However, as N increases, K-N becomes less than K, so (K-N)/K becomes increasingly less than 1. As a result, when you multiply rN by this smaller and smaller number, the population rate of increase will decrease. And eventually, it will reach zero, when N=K (i.e. the population will not increase in size anymore).

What would happen if the population was larger than the carrying capacity? N would then be greater than K, so (K-N)/K would be a negative number. Here, the rate of increase would now be a negative number. This means that the population would decline, and keep declining until reaching K again (i.e. back to a value equal to the carrying capacity).

So the population is a bit like a ball dropped into a curved bowl. If it is too far to one side, it rolls to the centre, and if it is too far to the other side, it will again roll back to the centre. After oscillating back and forward, it will come to rest at the lowest point in the bowl. So populations are drawn towards the carrying capacity. In this book, I suggest that carrying capacity is actually thermodynamically determined (Appendix II). So what does a logistic curve look like? Well. It starts off like a geometric curve, but then changes, levelling off. This is shown in Figure AI: 2, below.

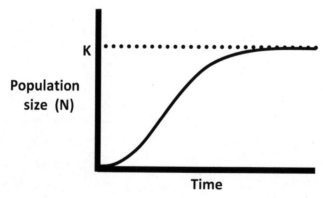

Figure AI: 2: The logistic curve, plotting population size against time. K, carrying capacity

Note that the population initially grows slowly. This is called the lag phase, and growth is limited by the number of individuals present. Later, growth becomes geometric, but then begins to slow down as it approaches the carrying capacity, K. It is also important to note that a critical assumption has been made, that r remains constant. However we have to ask if this really is the case, and we will think about this in Section II.

The Frequency Curve
The final curve is the normal distribution, or the normal curve of error. This is a fascinating curve, and was developed by Abraham de Moivre (1667-1754) the French mathematician. Having fled France to escape the protestant repression following the revocation of the Edict of Nantes, he lived in poverty for most of his life, working as a maths tutor, and later playing chess for money. In spite of being elected to the Royal Society, and being a close friend of Edmond Halley, Isaac Newton and James Stirling, leading academics of his time, he failed to secure a position in an English University, most likely because of anti-French groundswell at the time.

His work straddled trigonometry, algebra and probability. He discovered the equation for factorials, later made famous by James Stirling, but his most significant contribution was in his book, *Doctrine of Chances, or Method of Calculating the Probabilities of Events at Play*, which contained major advances in probability theory. Probability theory lies at the heart of modern statistics and the scientific method. It allows one to determine if a relationship is significant or otherwise. He developed the basis of the normal distribution, and it was Carl Gauss who formulated it. It's equation is quite complicated:

$$f(x) = \frac{e^{-(x-\mu)^2/2\sigma^2}}{\sigma\sqrt{2\pi}}$$

Where μ = mean and σ = standard deviation. This sketches out the following curve:

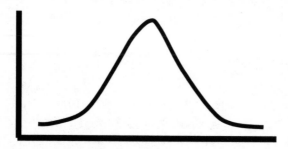

The mean is where the peak of the curve occurs, and the standard deviation is a measure of the average deviation from the mean. So a population that has a wide spread of values around a mean will have a large standard deviation, whereas one where all the members are exactly the same value will have no deviation at all. Deviation is actually a useful measure of heterogeneity within a population. A curve with high standard deviation will be a gentle low curve, whereas a curve with low standard deviation will be a much narrower, pointed curve.

Basically what it shows is the probability of a given value occurring within an infinitely large population. What we find is that the most likely value is the mean, and so the peak of the curve is the mean. Either side of the mean, the line descends, showing that there is a lower and lower probability of getting values further from the mean in either direction. The fact that the curve never reaches the x axis means "never say never", but it also means that it gets less and less likely for a value to be found the further you are from the mean.

The curve itself resembles a graceful bell, floating above the x-axis. The "tails" reach the x-axis at infinity. The curve is symmetrical about a central peak, and has an area beneath it equal to 1. This makes it incredibly useful. It can be described knowing only two values, the mean and the standard deviation. It obeys the empirical rule or the *68, 95,99.7 rule* which states that 68% of the data will fall within one standard deviation of the mean, 95% of the data will fall within two standard deviations and 99,7% of the data will fall within three standard deviations.

This characteristic is very important. It means that whatever we are measuring, we always know that if we draw a vertical line the same number of standard deviations away from the mean, and at the centre of the graph, the area under the curve between these two lines will always be the same proportion of the total area.

Put another way, if we take two values on the x-axis, and draw lines straight up from them to touch the curve, the area between these two lines, divided by the total area under the curve represents the proportion of values that lie between these two limits. This can be very useful. Say we were making silly hats for a big national celebration. We want to know what proportion of the population had head circumferences between 55 and 60 cm. We would carry out a survey of, say, 1000 individuals. From this we could use the mean and standard deviation to construct a normal curve, and then find out the proportion of the population that had head sizes between 55 and 60 cm. We could repeat this for different head size ranges, and then work out how many hats of each size to make. The point is that the area beneath the curve represents *all* members of a population, so any part of that area represents a proportion of that whole.

The normal distribution has become central to all of science and social science, because it forms the basis of parametric statistical analysis. Populations are considered to be normally distributed unless shown otherwise, and are compared with each other using mathematical approaches derived from the normal distribution. For example, in science and the social sciences, a scientific hypothesis is tested to see if there is a significant difference or relationship between two sets of data. Furthermore, two samples can be tested against each other to determine the probability that they come from a single, normally distributed population, or from two different ones.

So when you read that there was a statistically significant difference or similarity or relationship, then it is likely that the normal distribution lay at the heart of the mathematics. That's why this curve is so interesting, and it is why it appears in this book so often. Of course, not all data is normally distributed, and this requires a different approach, called non-parametric analysis.

REFERENCES

Population Division of the Department of Economic and Social Affairs of the United Nations Secretariat, *World Population Prospects: The 2008 Revision* http://esa.un.org/unpp

Verhulst, P.-F. (1845) Recherches mathématiques sur la loi d'accroissement de la population. *Nouvelle mémoire de l'Academie Royale* de Sciences et *Belle-Lettres de Bruxelles* 18: 1-41.

CIA World Factbook: https://www.cia.gov/library/publications/the-world-factbook/fields/2066.html

APPENDIX II
A LOGISTIC MODEL OF ENTROPY OUTPUT

We have seen how the logistic model works in Appendix I. In Figure IV.1, we discovered the relationship between the development of a forest ecosystem and the entropy it produced. This was taken from Holdaway *et al.* (2010). It's an amazing pattern. All ecosystems gradually develop from a very basic, barren habitat, through a series of stages, to a final, stable community. It's called ecological succession. An excellent example is the sand dune system, which develops into a forest. One of the great mysteries has been what drives a succession in the direction it takes. Why does it go through relatively rapid change and then stop? In this way it resembles a number of other things. We grow, from a single fertilized cell to an adult, and then stop growing. Populations grow for a period, and then stop growing, at what is called their carrying capacity. And the logistic curve that we met in Appendix I, describes all of these growth patterns.

So we can model the change in entropy during succession.

If we take the logistic model for growth:

Growth rate = rN[(K-N)/K] {eqn 1}

Where r = intrinsic capacity for increase, N = population size and K = carrying capacity.

For entropy generation, we can re-write this as:

$$\frac{dS}{dt} = r_S S(1-S/S_{max}) \qquad \{eqn\ 2\}$$

Where S = entropy generated, r_s is the intrinsic capacity for entropic output and S_{max} = maximum entropy output.

Now if we divide both sides of eqn 2 by S_{max}, then:

$$\frac{d}{dt}\frac{S}{S_{max}} = r_s\frac{S}{S_{max}}\left(1 - \frac{S}{Smax}\right) \qquad \{eqn\ 3\}$$

If x = S/S_{max}, then

$$\frac{dx}{dt} = rx\,(1-x)$$

Thus, solving for S(t):

$$S(t) = \frac{S_{max}S_0 e^{rst}}{S_{max}+S_0(e^{rst}-1)} \qquad \{eqn\ 4\}$$

$$\lim_{t\to\infty} S\,(t) = S_{max}$$

Where S(t) = entropic production at time t,
and S_o = entropic production at t=0

Basically, there is a maximum entropic output which can be achieved by the system, which is determined by the intrinsic capacity to produce entropy. This capacity is determined by the components within the system, and limited by stability. This equation applies to population growth, body growth and ecosystem succession.

Therefore, I propose that S_{max} is the key value that accounts for all of these growth patterns. So, for example, carrying capacity is actually a measure of the population size that maximally produces entropy. Thermodynamics applies to every level of organization, and it is the balance of the system which accounts for how any particular level behaves.

If you go to a sand dune succession, and walk from the shore, inland, you are basically walking along a time line. Each step takes you to a slightly older part of the ecosystem. This is called a *chronosequence*. Species change along the way until you reach the forest, which is the stable community.

As you walk along the chronosequence, entropy generation increases as shown in Holdaway *et al.* (2010), until you reach the forest, where there is no further change. Here, you have reached S_{max}, the maximum entropy output. At each stage of the ecosystem's development, the species present each contribute to the overall entropy output. Their interactions lead to the final total.

Thus, the species present fit into this thermodynamic function, and their individual evolution has been governed by this overall entropic context. Thus thermodynamics links each level of organization, and the evolution of these levels (a process of diffusion, restoring energetic function and maximum entropic output). All follow the same pattern. This is why entropy unifies biology.

REFERENCES

Holdaway, R.J., Sparrow, A.D. and Coomes, D.A. (2010) Trends in entropy production during ecosystem development in the Amazon Basin. *Philosophical Transactions of the Royal Society B* 365: 1437-1447.

APPENDIX III
SUMMARY OF THE ENERGETIC THEORY OF EVOLUTION
Based on Skene (2009).

A theory that explains how evolution works must account for two things: structural and functional evolution. The first question that we must ask is: do we really need a new theory of evolution? Surely, Darwinian Theory explains it all. Let's have a look at the areas where Darwin's theory falls short, in terms of form and function.

Form

1. Evolutionary tempo. Darwinian Theory cannot account for evolutionary tempo. Evolution doesn't occur at an even rate throughout time, indeed it is anything but even, as we saw in Figure III.4. Although mutation rate has been relatively constant, speciation changes dramatically. This has forced some leading evolutionary thinkers, such as Gould, Lewontin, Vrba and Eldridge, to suggest a move away from adaptation and gradualism to exaptation and punctuated equilibrium (Eldridge and Gould, 1972; Gould and Lewontin, 1979; Gould and Vrba, 1982).

2. Island biogeography. On oceanic islands, such as the Galapagos Islands, speciation occurs rapidly compared to the mainland, in conditions of reduced competition and selection.

3. Competition. It has been noted by many researchers that competition is unlikely to have played a significant role in evolution, even though it is a central tenet of Darwinian Theory. Rather than *displacement* resulting from a species outcompeting another species, what we observe is

replacement, where opportunities opened up by extinction lead to the ecological space being filled.

4. Mass extinctions. The fastest rate of evolution occurs after a mass extinction. Here, competition is at its lowest, resources are plentiful and opportunity is maximal. Evolutionary rates then gradually slow down as competition increases, the opposite to what we would expect under Darwinian Theory.

5. Lack of fitness. Research in the field, rather than in artificial laboratory experiments, shows that there is no difference in reproductive output between what would appear to be dominant and what would appear to be weaker individuals (see Section III). Furthermore, individuals that have characteristics that have been interpreted as indicators of fitness, such as bright markings in guppies, have weaker sperm, whereas dull-coloured individuals have stronger sperm. This undermines sexual selection as a driver in evolution, and makes the concept of fitness obsolete.

Function

1. Functional continuity. Although mass extinctions lead to great changes in morphologies, with every post-extinction period being dominated by different types of organisms, yet functionally, we return to the same Biosphere. Food webs are re-established, population ecology is constant and biomes are always the same. And so, functionally, there is no change. In an earlier book (Skene, 2009) I compare this to a snow globe, where form represents the snowflakes, whereas function represents the little plastic trees and houses. Functionality is constant, and forms come and go, shaped by this functional "structure". Darwinian theory, and particularly the more recent modern synthesis, neo-Darwinism, can make no comment on these higher levels of organization, since they fail to recognize

them, instead insisting that the selfish gene is the unit of currency, from which all else stems. Punctuated equilibrium also cannot comment on functional consistency. The reliance on contingency finds no relevance here, as, functionally, there is conservative restoration, not random wanderings. Evolution is directed by the laws of thermodynamics, and returns to a determined functional state, that of maximum entropic output (see section IV for details of the Maximum Entropy Principle).

2. Succession. Probably the most important process with regards to evolution, it explains how ecosystems develop and mature. After a mass extinction, the entire planet goes through this process in the restoration of the Biosphere. Darwinian Theory can make no comment on this process, as it occurs at a level which it fails to recognize. Any theory of evolution must explain succession. Again, punctuated equilibrium theory does not have the capacity to understand succession. Succession is predictable and constant, with rules that determine its direction. This is not a contingent process, yet it lies at the heart of post-extinction recovery and island biogeography.

We can summarize the failures of Darwin's theory to properly describe what we observe in the table below:

SUMMARY TABLE

Darwinian Theory	Issue
Malthusian foundation	Not applicable to the rest of the Biosphere
Domestic breeding foundation	Not applicable to the rest of the Biosphere

Competition as driver	Not recognized as significant
Competitive Exclusion Principle	Functional redundancy suggests otherwise
Species displacement	Species replacement is what we observe
Interspecific competition drives character displacement	Not observed
Stabilizing selection	Reduces population variation
Directional selection	Organisms move rather than evolve
Disruptive selection	Rare and difficult to envisage within a stabilizing context
Survival of the fittest	Survival relies on the variants, not the fittest;

(See Section III for a wide range of references, and detailed evidence on these points).

The Energetic theory of the evolution of life

The foundation of this theory, as explained in Skene (2009), begins with a definition of life, as a process of energetic flux, maintaining itself far from energetic equilibrium, and generating entropy, as any biophysicist will tell you.

The theory of energetic evolution goes further. It states that life exists in a state of intermediate entropy. Entropy increases with increasing temperature. In fact, that is what temperature represents. Too little chaos and the genetic information does not result in life, while with too much chaos and again it ceases to produce life. At this intermediate level of information disruption, life can maintain itself far from equilibrium, by the flow of energy through it, generating entropy. And so there is an intermediate level of disturbance of information flow that accompanies what we know as life. In other words, Life is a sub-optimal information processing system (see Section VIII for details).

The energetic theory of evolution states that the structure and function of life are determined by the interaction of energy and matter, and the generation of entropy, while being maintained in an intermediate state of entropy. Central to this is the process of diffusion. Forms results from increasing chaos in the genetic information content, resulting in an expansion (diffusion) in protein structures into energetic space.

Life is organized in a series of levels, and each of these levels is structured by the laws of thermodynamics. These levels are all part of the Biosphere, which is the combined outcome of all living processes. Each level is understood as an energetic state, with free energy flowing through, and entropy within the system being balanced by entropy output. These levels are structured differently, and so respond differently to the laws of thermodynamics.

Their interactions result in a balance being achieved. The perturbation of this balance by, for example, an increase in available nutrients, or dramatic reduction in energy levels during an impact winter, lead to the system re-establishing a new balance over time. This is evolution.

The Biosphere acts to produce as much entropy as possible, under the Maximum Entropy Principle. This maximum amount, as we observed in Appendix II, is determined by the interactions of all of the levels of organization. Each level poses limits, depending on how stable they are, and how entropic they can be without breaking down. We see, for example, that individual populations must fit within a food web, so that sufficient energy can pass through the system. These populations form part of an ecosystem, which changes through time, eventually reaching maximum entropic output. And within each population, individual organisms must maintain a flow of energy through them to replace that lost. Every level operates sub-optimally (Section VIII) and in such a way as to contribute to the overall balance of the Biosphere.

So how does this theory answer the questions that Darwinian Theory fails to account for?

Form

All the issues of form are resolved when evolution is understood as a *diffusional* process.

1. Evolutionary tempo. This represents the expansion and contraction of diffusional space available for life to expand into. The myriad of forms represent the diffusion of life. Reduce the space, and we get a reduction in diffusion, increase the space and we get an expansion. Entropy drives

all diffusional processes, from perfume in a room to diversification of form. It is the diffusion of protein structure, driven by increasing entropy within the genetic code and operating within an intermediate level of chaos within the information processing system that drives evolution.

2. Island biogeography.   On an island, there is diffusional space. The tanagers of the Galapagos Islands came from a limited space for diffusion on the mainland, to one where energetic space was available, and so their forms could diffuse.

3. Competition. Competition really only represents increasing diffusion, and so signifies a limit to further diffusion. Thus, competition does not lead to evolution, but rather slows it down, the opposite to Darwinian Theory.

4. Mass extinctions.   We see the most rapid evolutionary rates after a mass extinction, because the disruption of energy flow causes a collapse of life. Once energy flow is restored, then life diffuses into the space available. Later, the evolutionary rate slows down, as the space becomes filled, and the walls prevent further diffusion.

5. Lack of fitness. The idea that the guppies that put much of their energy into bright coloration also experience weaker sperm supports the energy balance concept. There is only so much energy that can stably flow through an organism, and so it cannot produce a strong output in every area. Different emphases can occur and co-exist. Nature is a balance, and so we find a balanced outcome. This also promotes variation, preventing stabilizing selection from removing variation. The survival of the fittest concept only exists in laboratory studies, where the other levels of organization do not exist. In the real world, we find instead a very different situation, with the see-saw in operation. Laboratory studies are irrelevant to evolutionary biology, as

the level of organization being studied is not within the energetic context of maximum entropic output.

Function

Function is fundamentally different than form. It represents the energetic conversations of the Biosphere, and is tightly regulated by the laws of thermodynamics. Thus we find function being restored after disruption, because the balance is restored. Function represents energy flow and entropy generation, and because this is cosmic in scale, function is fundamentally highly structured. No matter what form an organism takes, its function is conservatively determined. Function is also directed by the arrow of the Second Law of Thermodynamics, which drives the Biosphere to maximum entropic output as a system. Each level within the Biosphere is also directed similarly. So there is, fundamentally, a direction to evolution, the restoration of maximum entropic output (See Section IV for evidence and references).

1. Functional continuity. The energetic theory gives us an understanding of why ecological function is restored after disruption. The flow of energy through a system determines function, and so any disruption to energy flow effects function. However, once energy is flowing again, we get the same functionality restored every time, with a myriad of forms taking up the roles. It is like a play, with new actors but the same script. This is a much better explanation of what we observe than Darwinian Theory or Contingency Theory. Finally, function operates at all levels of organization in different ways, and functional redundancy represents the use of form to maintain function.

2. Succession. Succession is a process of increasing entropic output, up to a maximum level, wherein no further change occurs unless disrupted. Appendix II shows how there is a maximum level of entropy, S_{max}, that shapes the direction of

the transition. So succession, which lies at the heart of post-extinction recovery, is a thermodynamic process.

I would predict, based on the Energetic theory of Evolution, that:

1. Energetic space is opened up by a significant energetic disturbance (local or global), or movement to an island, such as Galapagos, with free energetic space
2. This space allows an increase in population entropy, displayed as genetic variation
3. Increase in diversification as variation becomes isolated in sexually incompatible groups
4. Increasing ecosystem entropic output following disturbance, as succession continues
5. Subsequent decrease in population entropy (variation) as increasing complexity brings greater resilience, and balance requirements of system see-saw demand changes in entropy production
6. Eventual slowing down of ecosystem entropic output as it approaches maximum entropic output
7. Concomitant decrease in diversification and stabilization of Earth system, until next perturbation.

We already have clear evidence for points 1, 3, 4, 5, 6 and 7. Therefore Step 2 remains to be tested. However we would expect our prediction to hold, as it is supported by all of the other confirmed steps.

And so we see that the Energetic Theory of Evolution is far superior to Darwinian theory in terms of explaining the fossil evidence. It also provides a functional explanation of evolution that cannot be appreciated by the form-based thinking of other theories. It is physics that we must turn to, and the selfish gene has no place within this understanding, failing as it does to take account of the role of entropic diffusion in evolution. Forms are like perfume, and, as pleasant as it is, perfume itself is not the explanation of diffusion, but rather the subject of it.

REFERENCES

Eldridge, N. and Gould, S.J. (1972) Punctuated equilibria: an alternative to phyletic gradualism. In: Schopft, J.M. (ed) *Models in Palaeobiology.* Freeman Cooper, San Francisco.

Gould, S.J. and Lewontin, R.C. (1979) The spandrels of San Marco and the Panglossian paradigm: a critique of the adaptationist programme. *Proceedings of the Royal Society of London B* 205: 581-598.

Gould, S.J. and Vrba, E.S. (1982) Exaptation – a missing term in the science of form. *Palaeobiology* 8: 4-15.

INDEX